INTERNATIONAL SCHOOL OF NEUROSCIENCE

Proceedings of the Course on
Developmental
Neurobiology

INTERNATIONAL SCHOOL OF NEUROSCIENCE

Proceedings of the Course on
Developmental
Neurobiology

Volume 1

Fidia Research Foundation

1991
Thieme Medical Publishers, Inc. NEW YORK
Georg Thieme Verlag STUTTGART • NEW YORK

Thieme Medical Publishers, Inc.
381 Park Avenue South
New York, New York 10016

Library of Congress Cataloging-in-Publication Data

International School of Neuroscience (2nd : 1990 : Praglia Abbey)
    Proceedings of the course on developmental neurobiology / Fidia
Research Foundation ; International School of Neuroscience.
        p.   cm.
    "Held at Praglia Abbey from September 30 to October 10, 1990"-
-Pref.
    "Volume 1."
    Includes bibliographical references and index.
    ISBN 0-86577-408-0. — ISBN 3-13-773701-X
    1. Developmental neurology—Congresses. I. Title. II. Title:
Fidia Research Foundation.
    [DNLM: 1. Brain—growth & development.   2. Nervous System—growth
& development.   WL 102 I651p 1990.]
QP363.5.I565   1990
591.3'33—dc20
DNLM/DLC
for Library of Congress   91-831
                                                                  CIP

Important Note: Medicine is an ever-changing science. Research and clinical experience are continually broadening our knowledge, in particular our knowledge of proper treatment and drug therapy. Insofar as this book mentions any dosage or application, readers may rest assured that the authors, editor and publishers have made every effort to ensure that such references are strictly in accordance with the state of knowledge at the time of production of the book. Nevertheless, every user is requested to examine carefully the manufacturers' leaflets accompanying each drug to check on his or her own responsibility whether the dosage schedules recommended therein or the contraindications stated by the manufacturers differ from the statements made in the present book. Such examination is particularly important with drugs that are either rarely used or have been newly released on the market.
    Some of the product names, patents and registered designs referred to in this book are in fact registered trademarks or proprietary names even though specific reference to this fact is not always made in the text. Therefore, the appearance of a name without designation as proprietary is not to be construed as a representation by the publisher that it is in the public domain.

Printed in the United States of America

5 4 3 2 1

TMP ISBN 0-86577-408-0
GTV ISBN 3-13-773701-X

Contents

Preface

As never before, science is generating new information and opening new areas of inquiry at such a rate that one wonders how to channel all these newly acclaimed intellectual riches for the benefit of mankind.

It is now essential to integrate individual perceptions of scientific information into a unified vision for a journey of discovery, striving for the time when the dream of understanding how the human brain functions may become a reality. To accomplish this integration, we must improve communication among scientists and provide better training for young investigators. This is best accomplished in an atmosphere of quiet and contemplation. The International School of Neuroscience is dedicated to providing the atmosphere and guidance required to transform new questions and information into scientific knowledge.

Fidia Research Foundation launched the school at Praglia Abbey, Padua, Italy, with inaugural classes in April 1989. The foundation continues to foster the creation of a world-class neurosciences teaching center by planning and promoting this major educational venture. This volume of proceedings is reported from the International School of Neuroscience Second Course, on Developmental Neurobiology, which was held at Praglia Abbey from September 30 to October 10, 1990.

Advanced courses are taught by an international teaching staff of highly respected researchers with expertise in the various fields of neuro-

science. The courses are attended by 50 applicants (selected on their scientific merit)—only graduate students working on their theses and young
postdoctoral fellows apply.

Each course lasts two weeks and focuses on the frontiers of neuroscience, encompassing its various specialties. In addition to the lectures,
the teaching staff is available for tutorial training geared to foster ex-
changes that may lead to future research collaborations.

Acknowledgments

W̲e are grateful to all who participated in the second course of the International School of Neuroscience that was held September 30 to October 10, 1990, and to those whose lectures are reported herein. We are especially indebted to Keith W. Brocklehurst, Ph.D., Washington, D.C., for editing this volume and thus making an invaluable contribution to Fidia Research Foundation and to the School of Neuroscience.

We also would like to thank those who reported on the lectures: Drs. David Armstrong, Mariella Bertolino, Stefano Casalotti and Dennis Grayson from the Fidia-Georgetown Institute for the Neurosciences, Washington, D.C.; Roberto Dal Toso and Marco Favaron (Fidia Research Laboratories, Abano Terme, Italy); Maria Luisa Barbaccia (II University of Rome, Italy); Maurizio Memo (University of Brescia, Italy); and Ferdinando Nicoletti (University of Catania, Italy).

Contributors

Jean-Pierre Changeux, Ph.D.
Molecular Neurobiology Laboratory
Pasteur Institute
75724 Paris, France

Martha Constantine-Paton, Ph.D.
Department of Biology
Yale University
New Haven, Connecticut 06511

Gerald M. Edelman, M.D., Ph.D.
Department of Developmental and
  Molecular Biology
Rockefeller University
New York, New York 10021

Corey S. Goodman, Ph.D.
Department of Molecular and Cell
  Biology
University of California
Berkeley, California 94720

Giorgio M. Innocenti, M.D.
Institut d'Anatomie
Faculté de Médecine
Université de Lausanne
CH-1005 Lausanne, Switzerland

Jacques Mallet, Ph.D.
Laboratory of Cellular and Molecular
  Neurobiology
CNRS
91198 Gif-sur-Yvette, France

Bruce S. McEwen, Ph.D.
Department of Neurobiology
Rockefeller University
New York, New York 10021

Mortimer Mishkin, Ph.D.
Laboratory of Neuropsychology
National Institute of Mental Health
Bethesda, Maryland 20892

John G. Nicholls, M.D., Ph.D.
Department of Pharmacology
Biocenter
University of Basel
CH-4056 Basel, Switzerland

Alain Prochiantz, Ph.D.
Développement et Évolution du
  Système Nerveux
École Normale Supérieure
CNRS URA 1414
75005 Paris, France

Pasco Rakic, M.D.
Section of Neuroanatomy
Yale University School of Medicine
New Haven, Connecticut 06510

Carla J. Shatz, Ph.D.
Department of Neurobiology
Stanford University School of
  Medicine
Stanford, California 94305

Gunther S. Stent, Ph.D.
Department of Molecular and Cell
  Biology
University of California
Berkeley, California 94720

Kathryn W. Tosney, Ph.D.
Department of Biology
University of Michigan
Ann Arbor, Michigan 48109

Colwyn Trevarthen, Ph.D.
Department of Psychology
University of Edinburgh
Edinburgh EH8 9JZ, Scotland

**Hendrik Van der Loos, M.D.,
  Ph.D.**
Institut d'Anatomie
Faculté de Médecine
Université de Lausanne
CH-1005 Lausanne, Switzerland

Semir Zeki, Ph.D.
Department of Anatomy and
  Developmental Biology
University College
London WC1E 6BT, England

Board of Directors

Erminio Costa, M.D.

Director
Fidia-Georgetown Institute for
   the Neurosciences
Washington, D.C.

Gerald M. Edelman, M.D., Ph.D.

Vincent Astor Professor
Department of Developmental and
   Molecular Biology
Rockefeller University
New York

Rita Levi Montalcini, M.D.

Director
Cellular Biology Laboratories
Italian National Research Council
Rome, Italy

International School of Neuroscience

Under the patronage of:

Georgetown University, Washington, D.C.
University of Bologna, Italy
University of Brescia, Italy
University of Milan, Italy
University of Padua, Italy
II University of Rome, Italy
Italian Society for Neuroscience, Catania, Italy

Patrons' Council

President: R. Levi Montalcini, *Director, Cellular Biology Laboratories,
Italian National Research Council, Rome, Italy*
M. Bonsembiante, *Rector, University of Padua, Italy*
E. Garaci, *Rector, II University of Rome, Italy*
J. F. Griffith, *Executive Vice-President for Health Sciences,
Georgetown University, Washington, D.C.*
G. Levi, *President, Italian Society for Neuroscience, Cagliari, Italy*
P. Mantegazza, *Rector, University of Milan, Italy*
A. Preti, *Rector, University of Brescia, Italy*
F. Roversi Monaco, *Rector, University of Bologna, Italy*

General Secretaries

P. F. Spano, *Dean, Faculty of Medicine, University of Brescia, Italy*
M. Trabucchi, *Professor, Department of Experimental Medicine and
Biochemical Sciences, II University of Rome, Italy*

Executive Director

D. L. Cheney, *President, Fidia Research Foundation, Washington, D.C.*

Permanent Teaching Staff

Y. Agid, *INSERM U 289, Paris, France*
L. Amaducci, *University of Florence, Italy*
E. A. Barnard, *MRC Molecular Neurobiology Unit, Cambridge, U.K.*
F. E. Bloom, *Scripps Clinic, La Jolla, California*
P. Calissano, *Istituto di Neurobiologia, Rome, Italy*
D. W. Choi, *Stanford University Medical School, Stanford, California*
A. C. Cuello, *McGill University, Montreal, Quebec, Canada*
G. D. Fischbach, *Harvard University School of Medicine, Cambridge
Massachusetts*

H. M. Gerschenfeld, *École Normale Supérieure, Paris, France*
P. Greengard, *Rockefeller University, New York*
H. Hippius, *University of Munich, Germany*
T. Hökfelt, *Karolinska Institute, Stockholm, Sweden*
E. R. Kandel, *Howard Hughes Medical Institute, Columbia University, New York*
R. R. Llinás, *New York University School of Medicine, New York*
D. Marsden, *The National Hospital, London, U.K.*
J. B. Martin, *University of California School of Medicine, San Francisco, California*
J. Meldolesi, *University of Milan, Italy*
L. P. Rowland, *Columbia University, New York*
B. Sakmann, *Max-Planck Institute, Göttingen, Germany*
G. Sedvall, *Karolinska Institute, Stockholm, Sweden*
P. Seeburg, *University of Heidelberg, Germany*
E. M. Shooter, *Stanford University School of Medicine, Stanford, California*
C. F. Stevens, *The Salk Institute, San Diego, California*
R. F. Thompson, *University of Southern California, Los Angeles, California*
H. Van der Loos, *Université de Lausanne, Switzerland*

Scientific Advisory Council

L. Battistin, *University of Padua, Italy*
G. Biggio, *University of Cagliari, Italy*
C. Cazzullo, *University of Milan, Italy*
G. Crepaldi, *University of Padua, Italy*
G. L. Gessa, *University of Cagliari, Italy*
E. Ferrari, *University of Bari, Italy*
C. Fieschi, *University of Rome "La Sapienza," Italy*
W. Haefely, *Hoffmann-La Roche Ltd., Basel, Switzerland*
J. Hughes, *Parke-Davis Research Unit, Cambridge, U.K.*
M. Karobath, *Sandoz Ltd., Basel, Switzerland*
S. Langer, *Synthélabo Recherche, Paris, France*
H. Niall, *Genentech Inc., South San Francisco, California*
R. Paoletti, *University of Milan, Italy*
P. Strata, *University of Turin, Italy*
G. Toffano, *Fidia Research Laboratories, Abano Terme, Italy*
G. Woodruff, *Parke-Davis Research Unit, Cambridge, U.K.*

Organizing Secretary

L. Linzi, *Fidia Research Laboratories, Abano Terme, Italy*

Topobiology

Gerald M. Edelman

Gerald M. Edelman is Vincent Astor professor at Rockefeller University, director of the Neurosciences Institute, and scientific chairman of the Neurosciences Research Program. After receiving an M.D. in 1954 from the University of Pennsylvania, Edelman spent a year at the Johnson Foundation for Medical Physics, and, following a medical house officership at the Massachusetts General Hospital, served as a captain in the Army Medical Corps. He received his Ph.D. in 1960 from Rockefeller (then known as the Rockefeller Institute), where he has remained throughout his distinguished career.

Edelman has made significant contributions in biophysics, protein chemistry, immunology, cell biology, and neurobiology. His early studies on the structure and diversity of antibodies led to the Nobel Prize in physiology or medicine in 1972. He then turned his attention to mechanisms involved in the regulation of primary cellular processes, particularly the control of cell growth and the development of multicellular organisms. He has focused on cell-cell interactions in early embryonic development and in the formation and function of the nervous system. These interests led to the discovery of cell adhesion molecules (CAMs), the functions of which are significant for the development and morphology of brain structures. Edelman also has theorized the process of neural group selection to explain the development and organization of higher brain functions. At present he is testing this theory by constructing automata capable of carrying out pattern recognition and motor control tasks.

Topobiology

LECTURER:

Gerald M. Edelman

The word topobiology refers to "place-dependent" interactions, which appear most strikingly in the developing embryo. Surprisingly, their study has provided a major clue to the origins of the immune system.

One of the most gratifying things about science is that it is impossible to predict just where a particular trail of research will lead. Indeed, an extended investigation may wind up shedding light on a long-standing puzzle in a field that initially appeared to be quite distant. Just such an unexpected connection has recently appeared between the two areas of biology on which I have spent most of my scientific career working. The first of these areas was the structure of antibodies, the immune system molecules that recognize invaders and trigger their destruction. That work reached its culmination in the late 1960s with the elucidation of the complex structure of antibodies.

Then, in the early 1970s, it became apparent that antibodies belong with certain other immune system molecules in a single evolutionary entity called the immunoglobulin superfamily. Although that was a striking finding, I was perhaps not quite as intrigued as I might have been a few years before, because by that time my interest had turned to another problem: how cells interact in a developing embryo to yield an organism. The new work led to the discovery of cell-adhesion molecules, or CAMs, which are proteins that mediate interactions between cells in the embryo. More recently insights derived from the analysis of CAMs and related molecules have begun to lay the groundwork for a molecular embryology, which links the form and function of embryonic tissues to evolution and genetics. Most of this article will be devoted to describing those recent investigations.

Yet before the article ends I shall return to the subject of my earlier work. The reason for the recursion is that, ironically, the discovery and analysis of CAMs have resolved the long-outstanding problem of the evolutionary origin of the immunoglobulin superfamily. Recently it has been shown that the genes for CAMs and those for immunoglobulins have so many similar DNA and protein sequences that they must be related in evolution. Moreover, CAMs are widespread in the animal kingdom, whereas the adaptive immune system is limited to vertebrates. Therefore, it seems likely that the immune system molecules arose from the genes of the cell-adhesion system in a remarkable piece of evolutionary opportunism.

Both antibodies and cell-adhesion molecules have their main effects at the surfaces of cells. Surface interactions between cells can lead to changes in gene expression and in cell shape, movement and function. Just which reactions will take place when cells interact depends in part on the history of the cells: on what interactions they have had with other cells in the past. What is more, because these interactions depend on what cells surround any given cell, cells react differently at different places. Such "place-dependent" interactions do occur in the immune system, but they are particularly important in embryonic development. Indeed, the fates of cells—what they will become in the mature organism—are crucially dependent on the place or neighborhood of the cells in the embryo.

Although embryologists have long been aware in general of the possibility that place is a critical element in determining cell fate, it seemed necessary to refocus the subject by giving a name to the study of those place-dependent interactions at the cell surface that lead to cell regulation. About two years ago I coined the term topobiology (from the Greek word *topos,* meaning "place") to describe this dynamic, interactive process.

As the discovery of CAMs made clear, one of the key factors determining the place of an embryonic cell (and ultimately the form and pattern of the tissues) is the presence of cell-adhesion molecules. In the past few years several families of molecules have been shown to mediate such adhesions and the related intercellular transactions (see Edelman, 1984). Aside from the CAMs themselves, the most important of these are substrate-adhesion molecules, or SAMs, and cell-junctional molecules, or CJMs. Whereas CAMs are always on the cell surface and mediate cell-to-cell interaction, SAMs are thrown out by cells into the environment, forming part of the complex extracellular matrix to which cells sometimes attach. CJMs serve in the formation of the complex structures (including the so-called tight junctions, gap junctions and adherens junctions) that join cells together in tissues.

All of the known CAMs, SAMs and CJMs are complex proteins, and the structures of some of them are becoming reasonably well understood.

Attention is now focusing on how each of these adhesion molecules functions in the embryo and whether the functions of different molecules are interrelated. It has been established that almost all known CAMs bind to one another by a mechanism that is homophilic: a CAM on one cell joins a CAM of the same type on an apposing cell. Yet there are differences among CAMs; they show different binding specificities and varying dependence on ions, for example the calcium ion.

One of the recurrent motifs of embryonic development is the transition from epithelium to mesenchyme and back. A mesenchyme is a group of loose or migrating cells that are not firmly organized in a geometric sense. An epithelium, on the other hand, is a sheet of cells that is highly organized geometrically and often joined at its base to the extracellular matrix. The joining of the epithelium to the matrix is accomplished by SAMs, and the epithelial cells are often linked by junctions composed of various CJMs. Because the transition from one collective form to another is an underlying theme of development, it would be valuable to know which of these molecules is responsible for the initial conversion of mesenchyme to epithelial sheet.

Recent experiments in my laboratory suggest that the initial role in linking epithelial cells is played by CAMs and that the formation of junctions such as gap junctions and adherens junctions depends on CAM linkage. That result was obtained by inserting CAM DNA, by means of the process called transfection, into cultured cells that ordinarily lack it. The CAMs that were chosen were of two types—neural CAM (N-CAM) and liver CAM (L-CAM). These were the first CAMs to be discovered, and they were named for the tissues in which they were first found. They are now known to be much more widely distributed in the embryo.

Before transfection of L-CAM the cells were separate and resembled a mesenchyme. After transfection of the L-CAM gene the cells were linked in a sheet that had some of the characteristics of an epithelium. After the sheet formed, gap junctions and adherens junctions appeared between its cells. It seems likely that the action of CAM genes caused existing CJMs to assemble into junctions, and so it seems that this process is CAM-dependent. Moreover, adding fragments of antibodies against L-CAM, which block the typical homophilic binding of that molecule, led to dissolution of the sheets and a marked decrease of junctions between cells.

Such results give a hint of the significance of CAMs in the development of the embryo. As I noted above, the transition from epithelium to mesenchyme and back is one of the fundamental motifs of embryonic development. But it is not the only one. Among the others are certain precise

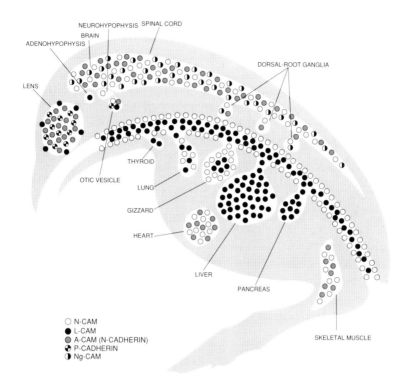

Fig. 1. Distribution of five known CAMs (cell-adhesion molecules) is shown for a chick embryo just before hatching. The distribution of CAMs (each with a different binding specificity) suggests they are involved in the generation of form in the embryo. Their spatial distribution changes over time: earlier, the areas overlap and cover most of the depicted area. [George V. Kelvin, all rights reserved.]

tissue movements and the formation of new boundaries between tissues. These processes are part of the overall pattern of morphogenesis: the appearance of distinct, specialized organs and tissues in the animal. The significant role of CAMs in these spatial processes is shown by the fact that CAMs with different specificities are distributed differently, each one in a characteristic pattern that emerges in time and space in the developing embryo.

An excellent example of all of these topobiological processes is provided by the formation of feathers, a crucial part of the development of the chick embryo. Feathers are formed by a series of coordinated processes that include cells moving, dividing, dying in patterned ways, adhering to each other and differentiating. In its early stage much of this coordinated

G. M. Edelman

development depends on interactions between two types of embryonic tissue, known as mesoderm and ectoderm. From mesoderm most bones and muscles arise; from ectoderm come the skin and nervous system.

Now, in some parts of the developing chick embryo, a layer of a specialized ectodermal tissue—the epidermis—lies above mesodermal tissues. The first step in feather formation is the induction in the epidermis of structures called feather germs that later give rise to the feather. The appearance of the feather germs requires passage of an intricate pattern of chemical signals between mesoderm and ectoderm—a process called embryonic induction. The efficacy of that signaling in turn depends on the action of CAMs, which can be studied by transferring embryonic skin tissues into laboratory culture.

Recent experiments carried out in my laboratory shed light on the relations between CAM linkage and the signaling that leads to feather-germ patterning. Simply put, the thrust of the experiments was to disturb the CAM linkage and observe the effect on the intricate normal geometry of the feather germs. In the normally developing embryo the induced feather germs begin at the embryonic midline and form a hexagonal array as they spread laterally. That pattern is seen both in the placodes, the precursors of the feather germs that will form the structures of the mature feather, and in the dermal condensations, the underlying mesodermal cells that give the inducing signal needed for the formation of the placodes in the overlying epidermis.

The rationale of the experiment was that the cells of the epidermal placodes were linked by L-CAM but had no N-CAM. Conversely the dermal condensations were linked by N-CAM and had no L-CAM. We proposed that a signaling loop, set up by the CAMs, was needed for proper pattern formation. In such a loop, signals would move not merely from mesoderm to epidermis but also from epidermis to mesoderm. Therefore, we placed antibodies against L-CAM in the culture. These antibodies could only affect epidermal linkages, not those of the dermal condensations. Nonetheless, the pattern of the dermal condensations was also changed after the introduction of the antibodies into the culture (Fig. 5).

These results indicated that changing the CAM linkages in one layer of cells can alter the signaling loop on which patterning depends. Either the response of epidermal cells to signals from below may be altered, or their own downward messages may be changed, but in either case the result is the same: normal pattern formation is interrupted. What is more, the effect is long-lasting. When the antibodies were washed out and the perturbed cells cultured for 10 days, the normal pattern of feather development was severely disturbed. As these experiments indicate, correct

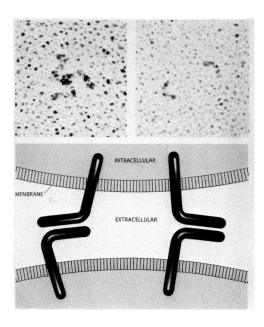

Fig. 2. CAMs bind cells to each other by a homophilic mechanism: a CAM on one cell binds to the same type of CAM on an apposing cell (**lower panel**). The images in the **upper panel** were made by shadowing CAMs with platinum and viewing them in the electron microscope. One (**left**) shows three neural cell-adhesion molecules (N-CAMs) linked by a "hub" made up of the areas that would have protruded through the cell's outer membrane. The other (**right**) shows a single liver cell-adhesion molecule (L-CAM). CAMs appear to be hinged linear molecules. The lower panel depicts two hypothetical binding mechanisms based on the hinged structure of N-CAM. [George V. Kelvin, all rights reserved.]

formation of patterns depends on the correlation between CAM linkages and cellular responses to inducing signals.

That correlation retains its significance as the feather develops. The mature feather is a complex structure with a central spine, or rachis, from which smaller spines called barbs diverge. The barbs are held together by even smaller filaments that project from them called barbules. All these structures are made up of a fibrous protein called keratin, which is deposited by the cells of the feather as they die at the end of the process of maturation. The barbs and barbules are formed in so-called feather filaments from folds called barb ridges (Fig. 4). After swelling out from the inner surface of the filament, the folds ultimately pinch off to yield cylindrical structures that interconnect; these cylinders are the barbs, ultimately linked by barbules.

The cells of the barb ridge arise from precursors that originally express both L-CAM and N-CAM. As the ridges develop, however, an intriguing specialization occurs that distinguishes the ridges from the valleys between them. As the ridges mature they come to express only L-CAM. At a certain point the cells in the valleys lose L-CAM, express only N-CAM and proliferate, which leads to the formation of regions bordering each ridge called marginal plates. Soon afterward all the cells expressing L-CAM begin synthesizing keratin and all those expressing N-CAM die. As a result, the borders between N-CAM and L-CAM expression are converted to the edges of new structures: the barbs and barbules.

Thus, the expression of specific CAMs, coupled with cell differentiation and with cell death, can lead to morphogenesis. It would be misleading, however, to imply that CAMs are the only morphoregulatory molecules. An example based on recent experiments in my laboratory shows how SAMs can also influence patterning events in the embryo. The example concerns a group of cells that give rise to the dorsal-root ganglia: bundles of nerves inserted into each vertebra in the mature organism. The vertebrae themselves develop from mesodermal tissue that is grouped into segments called somites, each somite corresponding to a single vertebra. Somites give rise to a number of other tissues as well; the mesodermal condensations of the feather, for example, come from a mesenchyme arising in somites. The dorsal-root ganglia originate in ectodermal cells that migrate as a mesenchyme from a structure called the neural crest.

In order for the correct ganglionic pattern to be made, the neural-crest cells must enter only the mesenchymal portion of the somite (the sclero-

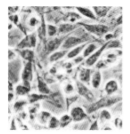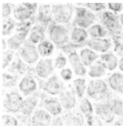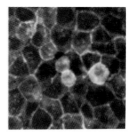

Fig. 3. CAMs change the form of groups of cells, as shown in micrographs made in the author's laboratory. Cultured cells lacking the L-CAM gene assume a loose form similar to one known in the embryo as a mesenchyme (**left**). When the L-CAM gene is inserted into the cells and activated to make L-CAM, the cells form a more regular arrangement resembling the one known as an epithelium (**middle**). Fluorescent techniques show that L-CAM is on the cell's surface (**lighted regions in right panel**). [Courtesy Gerald M. Edelman, Rockefeller University.]

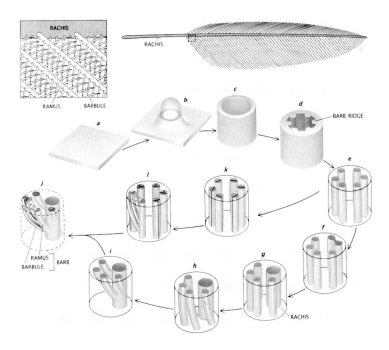

Fig. 4. Feather forms from a precursor called a placode. Mesenchymal cells of a type called mesodermal migrate beneath a simple epidermal sheet (*a*) and form a collective that sends signals upward to induce formation of the placode. The sheet bulges to form a bud (*b*) and then a filament consisting of a cylinder of epidermis (*c*). The cylinder develops ridges of epithelium called barb ridges (*d*), which subdivide to form the branched structure characteristic of the mature feather (*e–l*). [George V. Kelvin, all rights reserved.]

tome) in its front part. How is this entry guided? Earlier studies by Jean-Paul Thiery of the National Center for Scientific Research (CNRS) in Paris had shown that neural-crest cells migrate on pathways made of fibronectin (among other molecules); fibronectin is a SAM. In addition, my colleagues and I had found that another SAM, cytotactin, is distributed in distinct patterns during the formation of the embryo. Cytotactin is capable of binding to fibronectin as well as to a third SAM known as cytotactin-binding proteoglycan, or CTBP. It seemed worthwhile to find out whether the periodic pattern produced by the neural-crest cells as they migrate into the sclerotome was correlated with the pattern of the three SAMs in the somites.

A tantalizing clue was provided by examination of the distribution of the SAMs during the invasion of the somites by the neural-crest cells. At early stages of embryogenesis cytotactin, fibronectin and CTBP were distributed evenly over the entire extent of the somite, but as development proceeded, a periodic pattern appeared: although fibronectin was still spread more or less evenly throughout the somite, cytotactin was concentrated in the front part, and later CTBP became concentrated in the rear portion. This alternating distribution of SAMs, which emerged just as the migrating cells entered the sclerotome, resulted from molecules synthesized by the cells of the somite and not by the arriving cells of the neural crest.

Separate experiments were conducted in an attempt to tease out the effects of the SAMs on cell shape and movement. Work in tissue culture showed that cytotactin and CTBP cause neural cells to assume the somewhat rounder shape characteristic of cells that are not migrating. What is more, such rounded cells would not migrate into regions of tissue containing the SAMs. In contrast, on a mesh of fibronectin alone, crest cells were flatter and migrated readily; they showed intermediate behavior on mixtures of fibronectin and either of the other two SAMs. Although the details remain to be sorted out, the general conclusion of this work is that various admixtures of different SAMs, linked to one another, form networks that can have different effects on cell behavior and movement in the embryo.

It is striking that such SAM-mediated events are topobiologically coordinated with the expression of CAMs: migrating neural-crest cells lose

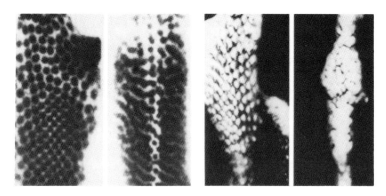

Fig. 5. Perturbation experiment shows CAM links are required in feather formation. As the placode develops, the mesodermal cells beneath it take on a symmetric arrangement of "blobs" (*1*) and later undergo further changes (*3*). If the tissue is cultured in the presence of antibodies against L-CAM, the "blob" geometry is perturbed to yield "stripes" (*2*); later the overall form is disrupted (*4*). The antibodies affect only L-CAM links (between epidermal cells), not N-CAM links (between mesodermal cells). Yet the mesodermal pattern is disrupted, implying a signaling loop between these tissues. [Courtesy Gerald M. Edelman, Rockefeller University.]

N-CAM at their surfaces as they move, but as they interact in the somite to form dorsal-root ganglia, N-CAM again appears on their surfaces. (Indeed, N-CAM is present on most neural cells in their fully mature, differentiated state.) Clearly CAMs and SAMs are regulated in a coordinated manner during development; both kinds of molecules can affect tissue patterning. I have already mentioned that cells probably must be bound by CAMs before CJMs can form junctions between them; it therefore seems that in general intricate dependencies come into play among these three classes of morphoregulatory molecules as an organism develops.

Yet these interactions, complex as they are, are not sufficient to account for how the embryo develops. The differentiation of embryonic tissues into mature tissues requires that they produce tissue-specific proteins: liver proteins in liver cells, muscle proteins in muscles and so on. The genes that code for such proteins are separate from the genes for cell-adhesion molecules. Yet the actions of these two classes of genes are not independent, and I have proposed the so-called morphoregulator hypothesis to account for the cycle that connects them.

In the morphoregulator hypothesis cells are controlled mechanochemically by cycles of CAM expression and by SAM networks. A good example of such control is provided by the changes in shape and movement of neural-crest cells caused by their binding to particular SAMs. The expression of CAM and SAM genes alters their shape and response to signaling

Fig. 6. Alternating pattern of L-CAM and N-CAM is seen as the barb ridges develop. Each panel shows a cross section through a developing feather follicle stained with fluorescent antibodies against a specific CAM. L-CAM (**left**) links ridge cells, whereas N-CAM (**right**) links the cells in the valleys between the ridges. Shortly after this stage cells with L-CAM make a fibrous protein called keratin while cells with N-CAM die. [Courtesy Gerald M. Edelman, Rockefeller University.]

patterns by controlling the formation of cell collectives that exchange signals at a given place. By these means expression of CAM and SAM genes affects the expression of other genes, including historegulatory genes that code for tissue-specific proteins. In topobiology the interaction of cell surfaces controls the mechanochemical driving forces, creating collectives of cells whose signaling is thereby altered, along with their state of differentiation. Such modulation of cell state by CAMs and SAMs must play a major role in the evolution of animal form and in the development of tissue pattern.

The morphoregulator hypothesis focused the attention of my colleagues and me on the genes that code for the morphoregulatory molecules, CAMs in particular. Bruce A. Cunningham and I worked out the structure of the genes for N-CAM and L-CAM by determining the DNA sequences that code for these CAMs. Our work showed that N-CAM and L-CAM are each specified by a single gene and that the genes differ substantially in their detailed structure, which suggests that the two molecules are not closely related in evolutionary terms.

The differences between the L-CAM and N-CAM genes lie partly in how they are processed to yield the ultimate message specifying a protein. Almost all mammalian genes contain coding regions called exons and noncoding regions called introns. After RNA has been transcribed from the gene, the noncoding portions are removed and the coding portions are spliced together to yield the finished messenger RNA (mRNA) molecule. In some instances alternative splicing of the mRNA can yield different proteins. That is the case for N-CAM: its 19 (or more) exons can be spliced in a variety of ways, some of which can give rise to CAMs that differ somewhat in the region that attaches the molecule to the cell membrane. Changes in that region may alter the strength of the binding of N-CAMs to each other and to the cytoskeleton, the cell's internal skeleton. The L-CAM gene, on the other hand, although it comprises a number of exons, gives no evidence of alternative splicing.

It should be emphasized that the alternative forms of splicing seen in the case of the N-CAM gene do not alter the specificity of the homophilic binding of the CAM: N-CAM molecules bind to each other no matter how their genes have been spliced. Only the collective strength of the attachment is affected by the alternative splicing of the genetic message. This is so because the number and arrangement of CAM molecules, and therefore the total binding efficacy, would be changed by altering the way these molecules attach to the cell membrane. This arrangement fits nicely with the notion that there are perhaps only a few dozen or so CAMs of different binding specificities, whose dynamic regulation at the cell sur-

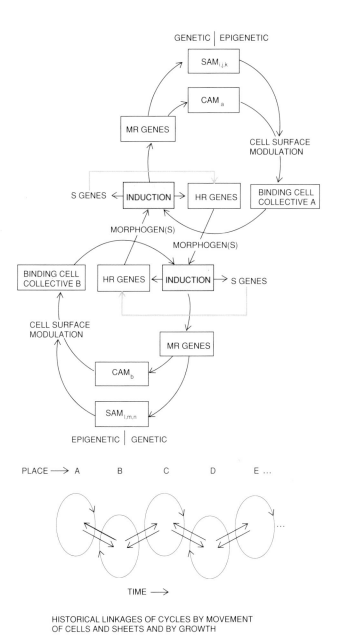

Fig. 7. Morphoregulator hypothesis seeks to explain how CAMs and substrate-adhesion molecules, or SAMs, create cell collectives and interact with them to determine the shape of an animal's body. In CAM cycles (**top**) collectives of cells linked by CAMs make molecules called morphogens that induce cells linked by different CAMs to alter the activity of their morphoregulatory (MR) genes: genes encoding CAMs and SAMs. The morphogens also affect historegulatory (HR) genes: genes encoding tissue-specific proteins. In some cells the HR genes are regulated in turn by selector (S) genes. As the cell collectives interact they alter their environment; new CAM cycles (**bottom**) come into play, signaling to each other (double arrows). [George V. Kelvin, all rights reserved.]

face by a variety of means can result in a very wide range of nuances of binding.

Some additional members of this small molecular family have already emerged from the laboratory. Not long after Cunningham and I reported our results, several studies indicated that N-CAM resembles another protein found in tissues of the nervous system. It is now suspected that this molecule, myelin-associated glycoprotein, or MAG, is also a CAM. Subsequent DNA work by Masotoshi Takeichi and his colleagues at the University of Kyoto showed that several other CAMs, called cadherins, exist, similar to L-CAM in DNA sequence and structure but with a different distribution in the embryonic tissues.

All these findings on the genetic structure of CAMs were very interesting, but perhaps the most striking was the discovery that N-CAM shares structural homologies with the antibody molecule. When my colleagues and I first completed the analysis of the amino acid sequence of the entire antibody molecule in 1969, a number of very beautiful structural, genetic and evolutionary relations became apparent (see Edelman, 1970). These relations were embedded in the "domain hypothesis," which held that immunoglobulins are made up of two types of structural and functional subunits, each about 100 amino acids long. These are the variable, or V, domains, which differ from molecule to molecule within a functional class, and the constant, or C, regions, which do not.

The characteristic T shape of the antibody molecule arises from a specific assemblage of V and C domains. Each antibody includes a pair of what are known as light chains, consisting of one variable and one constant region, and a pair of heavy chains, consisting of one variable and as many as three constant domains. Within this assembly the V regions are responsible for binding to the antigen, whereas the C regions carry out various "effector" functions, such as promoting the ingestion of a bound foreign protein antigen by immune system cells called macrophages. Intriguingly, all the domains, both C and V, of the antibody molecules share certain homologies of amino acid sequence, and it was proposed that they arose in evolution as the result of repeated duplication of a precursor gene that specified a region no longer than one domain.

Since its formulation in 1969 the domain hypothesis has been amply confirmed. Indeed, the evolutionary family so defined has been broadened to include other molecules; among them are growth-factor receptors and the histocompatibility antigens that mediate certain crucial interactions among cells of the immune system. This evolutionary clan has been called the immunoglobulin superfamily. As its members emerged one question remained: How did this diverse group arise in evolution?

The finding that N-CAM is homologous to these molecules suggested a possible answer to that question. I have proposed that the entire adaptive immune system, which is characterized by the presence of the immuno-globulin superfamily, arose from a more ancient cell-adhesion system. The reasoning underlying this hypothesis rests on the fact that the adaptive immune system is found only in vertebrates, implying that it arose late in evolution, whereas the system of CAMs appears to be much more wide-spread.

Some recent observations strongly support this notion. Thomas C. Kaufman and Mark Seeger of Indiana University have found a DNA se-quence in the *antennapedia* gene complex of the fruit fly *Drosophila me-lanogaster* that is homologous to approximately two and one-half domains of the N-CAM gene sequence; this sequence specifies a protein called amalgam. Later Corey S. Goodman and his colleagues at the University of California at Berkeley showed that the sequence of a suspected CAM called fasciclin II, found on nerve cells of *Drosophila*, is also homologous to N-CAM. Fruit flies have nothing that resembles a system of adaptive immunity. Because insects have N-CAM–like molecules and only verte-brates have an antibody-based immune system, it appears likely that CAM genes, present in some early precursor of both insects and vertebrates, provided the basis for the emergence of the molecules of the adaptive im-mune system.

Several additional facts help to provide a scheme for the evolution of the cell-adhesion molecules and their descendants that is a satisfying ex-tension of the domain hypothesis. Unlike the CAMs, each immunoglobu-

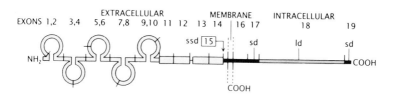

Fig. 8. Structure of N-CAM has been deduced from protein chemistry and determination of the DNA sequence in the N-CAM gene. N-CAM comes in several variants that differ according to how many exons (coding regions) of the N-CAM gene they incorporate. Nineteen exons are shown here; more have recently been discovered. All known variants include five loops that are linked by disulfide bonds (**left**). The illustration shows three variants: ssd stops at exon 15 and has no transmembrane region; sd includes exons 17 and 19 but lacks 15; and ld includes exon 18 but lacks 15. [George V. Kelvin, all rights reserved.]

lin is specified by multiple genes for V and C regions that have arisen by duplication of an original precursor during evolution, and these families of duplicated genes show homologies from species to species of vertebrate. Yet it would seem that unless special mechanisms are operating, independent mutations accumulating in different genes of such a duplicated family would destroy the homology among species. What might the mechanism be?

In 1969 my colleague Joseph A. Gally and I proposed that if such genes underwent a process called "democratic gene conversion" then the families they belonged to could evolve in parallel between species. The details of the process are somewhat beyond the scope of this article, but its essence is that the genes of the family recombine with one another in a particular way that makes the coevolution possible. What is more, the families may actually serve as "mutation nets" that spread favorable mutations among their members. Since a mutation favorable for one species' adaptive immune system may well be favorable for another's, these nets, combined with selective pressure, might also help preserve the homologies in the families of immunoglobulin genes. This idea, important as it is for antibodies, is a general one and applies to the evolution of all multigene families.

The functional collaboration of CAMs and antibodies has now been shown in the immune system in the revelation that various lymphocytes, which are among the most important effector cells of the immune system, require adhesion to carry out their functions. Recently Timothy A. Springer of the Harvard Medical School discovered a molecule called I-CAM on a variety of cells. I-CAM is homologous to N-CAM, and Springer has shown that it binds to a molecule called LFA-1, which is found on lymphocytes. LFA-1 resembles cell-surface molecules called integrins, which serve as receptors for SAMs.

If all of this information is combined into a general scheme, a magnificent example of evolutionary opportunism emerges. Its starting point is a stretch of DNA about half the size of an N-CAM domain. Analysis of the structure of the N-CAM gene reveals that this half-size precursor was duplicated to give rise to N-CAM–like genes in the ancestors of insects and vertebrates. Then, through the genetic shuffling of exons, DNA regions resembling SAMs such as fibronectin were introduced. The single gene for N-CAM–like adhesion molecules was then itself duplicated, giving rise to all the other related CAMs, including those in the central nervous system such as MAG.

All of these molecules were employed topobiologically in morphogenesis. But in some early vertebrate (or an immediate precursor), a gene in this family was turned to a different purpose altogether. By duplication

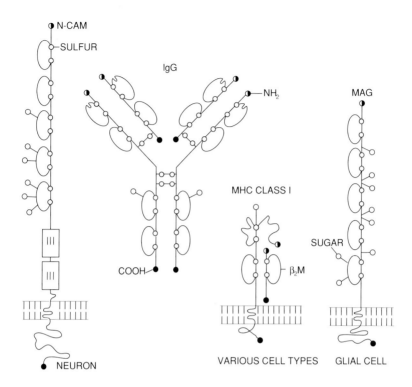

Fig. 9. Immunoglobulin superfamily, now known to include CAMs, is made up of molecules that are structurally and functionally diverse. Each of these molecules includes several domains. IgG, the antibody molecule, circulates in body fluids and binds to foreign substances. MHC class I proteins, components of almost all animal cells, associate with processed antigens; they are required for effective presentation of antigen to the white blood cells called T lymphocytes. The small chain of the MHC class I proteins is a single domain, β_2-microglobulin. MAG is a suspected cell-adhesion molecule found in membranes of glial cells, nonexcitable nervous system cells. Glial cells (and MAG) play a role in the myelination of certain neurons. [George V. Kelvin, all rights reserved.]

from a CAM-like piece of DNA, there arose the V and C regions of immunoglobulin genes, receptors on certain lymphocytes and histocompatibility antigens. Thereafter, genes for the V regions duplicated frequently to yield families that were kept similar by democratic gene conversion. Similar conversion events took place in the histocompatibility family. CAMs such as I-CAM arose to serve as attachment points for LFA-1, the independently evolved receptor on the surface of the lymphocyte.

Thus, the key functions of the adaptive immune system arose from an early cell-adhesion system that operated topobiologically to regulate the cell movements and tissue patterns that give rise to animal form. Although lymphocytes are not dedicated to establishing form, their functions do rely

G. M. Edelman

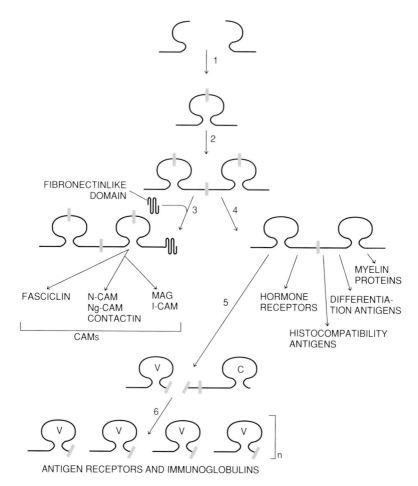

FIBRONECTINLIKE
DOMAIN

FASCICLIN   N-CAM   MAG
           Ng-CAM   I-CAM
        CONTACTIN

CAMs

MYELIN
PROTEINS

HORMONE   DIFFERENTIA-
RECEPTORS   TION ANTIGENS

HISTOCOMPATIBILITY
ANTIGENS

ANTIGEN RECEPTORS AND IMMUNOGLOBULINS

Fig. 10. Evolutionary scheme shows how the adaptive immune system arose from early CAMs. Exons encoding two "half-domains" combined to yield the gene for a single domain: a functional unit of a protein (**1**). Gene duplication produced the gene for a multidomain protein, an early N-CAM (**2**). "Exon shuffling" joined a fibronectinlike domain to those for the N-CAM family (**3**). Gene duplication and divergence gave rise to a variety of CAMs. Other genes lost the introns (stretches of noncoding DNA) within the domains but not the ones between domains (**4**). Subsequent divergence in that group gave rise to other members of the immunoglobulin superfamily. Insertion of a genetic element (possibly from a virus) created the potential for protein diversification in different lymphocytes (**5**). Along with this change went an increase in the number of variable (V) regions, providing the basis for generation of a vast population of antigen receptors and antibodies during the life of an individual (**6**). [George V. Kelvin, all rights reserved.]

on intricately regulated interactions between cells. That regulation in turn depends on specific binding mechanisms that may hail back to the cell-adhesion origins of the adaptive immune system. A specific type of protein folding is seen at all of the binding sites of immunoglobulins—and probably all those of CAMs as well. This type of folding is called the beta-pleated sheet; two such sheets form a special sandwich in the immunoglobulin domain. The beta-pleated sheet may be part of an ancient "language" of binding and cell regulation that the adaptive immune system has inherited from its CAM-like forebears.

The interaction between antibody and antigen, which can take place in the test tube in a fluid medium without respect to position, is frequently thought of as emblematic of the entire immune system. It must not be forgotten, however, that the immune system has solid tissues (such as the lymph nodes) as well as fluid ones (such as the blood). Even among free, circulating lymphocytes there are populations that "home" to particular bodily tissues. Although immune responses of single cells can occur in the test tube, it is likely that position is as critical in the overall immune response as it is in morphogenesis. Indeed, analysis of the morphoregulatory molecules and the immunoglobulins shows that these two systems are deeply linked both in genetics and in evolution.

It may not be amiss to add a final word about paths of research. The line of thought that links immune system molecules and CAMs would not have been possible within any one area of scientific specialization. It required following a vague surmise through a long trail of research (on CAMs) to the solution of a problem (the origins of immunoglobulins) posed at the end of a previous, apparently unrelated trail of research. This line of thought would have been much impoverished if it had been conceived within the limits of a specialty such as immunology or embryology. Only by seeing biology in its broadest evolutionary, genetic and developmental perspectives while pursuing specialized research can one connect what may first appear to be unrelated matters into a whole that is both organic and intellectually satisfying.

Additional Reading

1. G. M. Edelman, "The structure and function of antibodies," *Sci. Am.* **223,** 34 (1970).
2. G. M. Edelman and J. A. Gally, "Arrangement and evolution of eukaryotic genes," in *The Neurosciences,* F. O. Schmitt, Ed. (Rockefeller University Press, New York, 1970), Second Study Program, pp. 962–972.
3. G. M. Edelman, "Cell-adhesion molecules: A molecular basis for animal form," *Sci. Am.* **250,** 118 (1984).

4. G. M. Edelman, "CAMs and IGs: Cell adhesion and the evolutionary origins of immunity," *Immunol. Rev.* **100,** 11 (1987).
5. S.-S. Tan, K. L. Crossin, S. Hoffman, G. M. Edelman, "Asymmetric expression in somites of cytotactin and its proteoglycan ligand is correlated with neural crest cell distribution," *Proc. Natl. Acad. Sci. U.S.A.* **84,** 7977 (1987).
6. G. M. Edelman, "Topobiology: An introduction to molecular embryology" (Basic Books, New York, 1988).

The Acetylcholine Receptor: Functional Architecture and Regulation of Gene Expression During Endplate Formation

Jean-Pierre Changeux

Jean-Pierre Changeux was born in France, where he has spent most of his research career. He is presently a professor at the Collège de France and at the Pasteur Institute in Paris. He began his graduate studies at the Pasteur Institute in the laboratory of Nobel Laureate Jacques Monod. As a student, Changeux made seminal discoveries about the properties of bacterial regulatory enzymes, which led to the theory of allosteric interactions of proteins.

In 1964, Changeux earned his Ph.D. in molecular biology. He then achieved the isolation, characterization, and purification of the acetylcholine receptor—the first neuro-transmitter receptor to be identified—to which he successfully applied his concepts of allosteric regulation. With his colleagues, he developed in vitro systems for measuring ionic fluxes and rapid kinetics in order to dissect the activity of this receptor. His recent work has continued to analyze the functional organization of the acetylcholine receptor and he has begun to study both the genetic development of synapse formation and mechanisms of learning at synaptic and neuronal network levels.

The Acetylcholine Receptor: Functional Architecture and Regulation of Gene Expression During Endplate Formation

LECTURER:

Jean-Pierre Changeux

The main topic of this presentation concerns a mechanism of intercellular communication between nerve cells and between nerve and muscle cells. Synapses constitute the bottleneck of information transfer between cells in the nervous system, and a large fraction of them use a chemical substance, or neurotransmitter, as an intercellular communication signal. It thus appears critical to understand how such chemical synapses work and how they develop. Three main ideas have been central to this area of research: (i) The mechanism by which the chemical signal is transduced into an electrical signal involves a postsynaptic, membrane-bound, allosteric protein. This protein recognizes the neurotransmitter and contains an ion channel and all the structural elements that account for the transduction of the chemical signal into electrical activity. Such a protein must possess several topographically distinct sites that are coupled by conformational transitions. (ii) The synapse is a highly specialized organelle and its morphogenesis is under the control of an ensemble of regulatory mechanisms of gene expression. (iii) Mechanisms of selection take place during synaptic development.

The neuromuscular junction is composed of the motor nerve ending—which contains synaptic vesicles filled with acetylcholine (ACh)—a highly folded postsynaptic membrane, and a basal lamina that is located between the nerve ending and the postsynaptic membrane. A structurally elaborate cytoskeleton underlies the folds of the postsynaptic membrane, and it is at the tip of these folds that the ACh receptor (AChR) molecules are clustered. Physiological studies have revealed that on arrival of the nerve impulse, ACh is released into the synaptic cleft, most likely as a result of the entry of Ca^{2+} into the nerve ending. The local concentration of ACh in the synaptic cleft increases from 10^{-9} M to approximately 10^{-4} to 10^{-3} M, and thereafter declines rapidly. Therefore, the chemical signal consists of a transient, high concentration pulse of ACh. The binding of

---

This chapter was edited by Keith W. Brocklehurst, and was originally reported by Stefano Casalotti.

22

ACh to the AChR causes a change in the conductance of the postsynaptic membrane, which results in a change in electrical potential. Because the effect of ACh takes place under transient conditions, the synapse operates under a nonequilibrium regime on a time scale of milliseconds to seconds. The postsynaptic response caused by ACh is an increase in conductance for Na^+, K^+, and Ca^{2+} that can be viewed as the sum of elementary openings and closings of ion channels. The initial recordings of Katz and Miledi in 1970 revealed these microscopic fluctuations in conductance within background "noise." Later recordings made with the patch clamp technique resolved these fluctuations into square openings of single channels.

A slower type of regulation of the AChR takes place at the neuromuscular junction and also in the brain. This type of regulation is generally referred to as desensitization, because it is usually a negative regulation. However, in some systems, a slow positive regulation is observed and is more aptly termed sensitization. When ACh is applied at the endplate for an extended period, the amplitude of the response first increases and then slowly declines with a time course of several seconds. This desensitization can be viewed as a mechanism for regulating synaptic efficacy in the short term.

The initial purification of the AChR was achieved with the use of snake venom α-toxin and by solubilization with mild detergents of the receptor from membranes prepared from fish electric organ. Reconstitution of the purified receptor, which has a molecular mass of approximately 300 kilodaltons, into lipid bilayers has shown that this protein complex not only contains the ACh and the α-toxin binding sites but also the ion channel. By measuring fluxes of radioactive ions, it has been demonstrated that the reconstituted receptor displays activation and desensitization properties that are almost identical to those of the native receptor. Thus, nearly all of the physiological properties of the postsynaptic response to ACh are determined by a single molecular complex.

The AChR is a pentamer of four different subunits with a stoichiometry of $\alpha_2\beta\gamma\delta$. The exact geometrical order of the subunits is still controversial, but it appears that the two α subunits are separated by one other subunit. Interestingly, positive cooperative interactions occur between the ACh binding sites that are present on the two α subunits. Because the two α subunits are not adjacent, their interaction must be indirect—which is consistent with the definition of an allosteric interaction.

Purification of the AChR has allowed work to proceed on the identification of the amino acids that contribute to the ACh binding site in the α subunit and those that form the ion channel. The identification of the ion channel has been aided by the availability of noncompetitive blockers of the permeability response that bind to specific sites on the purified protein. One of these sites is a high-affinity site to which all subunits contribute and which has been postulated to lie on the axis of pseudosymmetry of the receptor protein. The distance between this high-affinity site and the ACh binding sites is approximately 30 to 50 angstroms, which is larger than the distance between the heme groups in hemoglobin. Thus, the interactions between these distant sites of the AChR macromolecule must be allosteric.

Progress in the identification of the several categories of binding sites carried by the AChR protein was facilitated by the cloning and sequencing of cDNAs for the four AChR subunits. The amino acid sequences of the four subunits are approximately 40% identical, with some regions more homologous than others. This homology supports the ideas that the AChR molecule possesses properties of symmetry and that the genes for the various subunits are derived from a common ancestral gene. Hydrophobicity plots of the amino acid sequences of the four subunits reveal another level of homology. All subunits contain highly hydrophilic domains in the amino- and carboxyl-terminal regions, and four highly hydrophobic regions, each of about 20 amino acids, which have been interpreted as corresponding to transmembrane α helices. The hydropathy profiles of the AChR subunits are also similar to those of subunits of the type A receptor for γ-aminobutyric acid (GABA$_A$ receptor), which is a ligand-gated Cl$^-$ channel. The extent of amino acid identity between the subunits of these two receptors is only on the order of 25%. Yet, it appears plausible that these various receptor subunits belong to a superfamily of proteins that have a similar backbone organization—the differences in the specificity of the binding sites and the ion channels would then result from the variability in the amino acid side chains.

The amino acids that contribute to the ACh binding site are located in the amino-terminal hydrophilic domain, which must therefore be exposed to the synaptic cleft. Three distinct loops from this domain contain amino acids labeled by photoaffinity analogues of competitive blockers of ACh binding. These amino acids are conserved in nicotinic AChRs not only from *Torpedo* to man, but also from muscle to brain. The central loop also seems to be conserved in other ligand-gated ion channels. The structure of the ion channel has been probed by affinity labeling studies with the noncompetitive blocker chlorpromazine, which binds to the single high-affinity site on the axis of pseudosymmetry mentioned above and covalently labels the homologous serine residues at positions 262, 254, 248, and 257, on the δ, β, α, and γ subunits, respectively. These amino acid residues are situated in the MII hydrophobic segment of each subunit, and both affinity labeling experiments with an additional channel blocker and in situ mutagenesis support the notion that the MII segments contribute to the ion channel structure. In addition to the ring of serine residues in the putative walls of the channel, there is a ring of serine or threonine residues and a ring of leucine residues, both of which are highly conserved. The labeling data are consistent with an α-helical structure of MII with the labeled residues facing the inside of the ion channel. These rings may act as a "catalytic" site to facilitate ion translocation. Furthermore, rings of acidic amino acid residues at each end of the MII segments may determine the selectivity of ion transfer through the channel.

An important feature of the AChR is that it can undergo fast (in the millisecond time range) conformational transitions between open and closed states and that it can also slowly interconvert to a high-affinity desensitized state or states. At the neuromuscular junction, under resting conditions, the AChR is present mainly in a low-affinity, readily activatable state. In brain, a substantial portion of neurotransmitter receptors, including AChRs, may exist in an inactive state. Such receptor populations may thus be activated by endogenous allosteric modulators—such as glycine in the case of the N-methyl-D-aspartate (NMDA)–sensitive glutamate receptor, or endogenous benzodiazepines in the case of the $GABA_A$ receptor.

The changes in AChR distribution and properties that take place at the neuromuscular junction during development are essential for the efficient transmission of nerve signals to the muscle. At the adult motor endplate, the AChR is exclusively localized under the nerve ending, and this anisotropic distribution arises progressively from a more "symmetrical" distribution that encompasses the entire muscle fiber. Thus, in the chick embryo, the AChR both accumulates at the level of the motor nerve ending and becomes gradually removed from the extrajunctional membrane. In addition, in some species (for example, rat, mouse, and frog), there is a change in conductance of the AChR that takes place during postnatal development. The adult conductance state is associated with an additional receptor subunit, the ε subunit, which replaces the γ subunit present in the embryonic protein.

The chick embryo undergoes spontaneous movements that are elicited by oscillator neurons present in the spinal cord. These movements can be blocked by curare, and it has been shown that the electrical activity of the muscle fibers is necessary for the elimination of the extrajunctional receptors. In situ hybridization with an α subunit probe shows that in the 11-day-old embryo, the α subunit mRNA is distributed throughout the muscle fiber. After embryonic day 14, clusters of α subunit mRNA start to disappear, so that by 19 days, only one cluster per muscle fiber persists and this cluster coincides with the endplate. The same pattern of RNA expression is observed with an α subunit intronic probe, which suggests that regulation of expression is at the transcriptional level. (An intronic probe will hybridize only to unprocessed mRNA, which is very short-lived. Thus, an increase in the amount of unprocessed mRNA is generally ascribed to an increase in de novo transcription, whereas an increase in mature mRNA can also result from reduced mRNA degradation.) Denervation causes a reactivation of the expression of the α subunit gene in extrajunctional areas, thus demonstrating that electrical activity represses gene expression in areas away from the neuromuscular junction. There is a privileged expression of several AChR subunit genes in the nuclei at the endplate; nuclei present in the same cytoplasm, but away from the endplate, do not express these genes. Furthermore, the endplate nuclei display a morphology different from that of the extrajunctional nuclei—for example, the endplate nuclei contain a large nucleolus—and were already termed "fundamental" by Ranvier at the end of the 19th century.

Chick myoblasts in primary culture can fuse and form myotubes, which contract and show spontaneous electrical activity. These cultures thus provide an in vitro model for the study of AChR gene regulation in the developing muscle cell. Addition of the Na^+ channel blocker tetrodotoxin (TTX) to these cultures causes an increase of up to 20-fold in the steady-state concentration of α subunit mRNA. A similar increase is apparent with an α subunit intronic probe, but some myotube nuclei are stained whereas others are not, suggesting that an all-or-none switch regulates α subunit gene expression at the level of individual nuclei in the muscle fiber.

With regard to the second messengers responsible for regulation of gene expression, it has been shown that the entry of Ca^{2+} into myotubes is required for repression of α subunit mRNA synthesis: the Ca^{2+} channel blocker verapamil gives rise to the same phenotype as TTX; and the effect of TTX can be reversed by the Ca^{2+} ionophore, A23187. Thus, Ca^{2+} enters the myotubes through voltage-dependent Ca^{2+} channels, which open in response to the depolarization mediated by Na^+ entry through voltage-sensitive Na^+ channels. One of the subsequent steps appears to be the activation of protein kinase C (PKC), as has been demonstrated with the use of the PKC inhibitor, staurosporine. Staurosporine causes a fivefold increase in the concentration of the α subunit mRNA, and this increase is antagonized by the PKC activator 12-O-tetradecanoyl phorbol-

13-acetate (TPA). The link between Ca^{2+} entry and PKC activation has not yet been elucidated.

It is clear that there must be a factor of neural origin that prevents the electrical activity–induced repression of AChR gene expression at the endplate. Several factors have been proposed for this role, including ARIA (AChR-inducing activity) and CGRP (calcitonin gene–related peptide). CGRP is a neuropeptide synthesized by the motor neuron and coexists with ACh. In cultured myotubes, CGRP induces a 50% increase in the number of AChRs and a threefold increase in the concentration of α subunit mRNA. These effects of CGRP are additive with those of TTX, thus showing that the effects of electrical activity and CGRP operate in parallel. Moreover, CGRP causes an increase in adenosine $3',5'$-monophosphate (cyclic AMP) accumulation.

These data thus suggest that whereas electrical activity—acting through Ca^{2+} and PKC—represses AChR gene expression at the level of nuclei located throughout most of the muscle cell, CGRP (or a similar compound), acting through cyclic AMP (or an antagonist of PKC), maintains expression at the endplate. This model has been investigated further by studying the promoter organization of the α subunit gene. By linking 850 base pairs (bp) of the α subunit gene promoter to the reporter gene chloramphenicol acetyltransferase (CAT), it has been shown that the promoter sequence can direct the expression of the CAT gene in a muscle-specific and developmentally regulated manner. Furthermore, an enhancer element has been identified between nucleotide positions -110 and -50.

Transgenic mice have been constructed that have the α subunit gene promoter region linked to both a nuclear localization sequence and the β-galactosidase gene. The pattern of β-galactosidase activity within muscle fibers was found to correlate with that of α subunit mRNA levels—as revealed by in situ hybridization—in the embryos of these transgenic mice. Furthermore, with the use of confocal microscopy and immunocytochemistry, it was shown that the amount of β-galactosidase was higher in the nuclei near the nerve ending than in extrajunctional nuclei. These results indicate that this 850-bp promoter region of the α subunit gene is sufficient to cause compartmentalized expression of the reporter gene at the endplate.

Within the promoter region of the α subunit gene are two consensus binding sites for proteins of the MyoD family. Transfection of mesenchyme cells with genes that encode MyoD proteins induces the differentiation of these cells into myoblasts. Three lines of evidence indicate that

MyoD proteins are important in AChR gene regulation: (i) MyoD proteins bind to the enhancer region of the α subunit gene promoter. (ii) Cotransfection of fibroblasts or mesenchyme cells with a MyoD cDNA and the α subunit gene promoter–CAT construct results in trans-activation of the reporter gene. (iii) Site-directed mutagenesis of either of the two MyoD recognition sites leads to a 50% decrease in CAT activity in cotransfected cells; mutagenesis of both sites results in a 90% decrease.

Denervation of mouse muscle causes not only an increase in α subunit gene expression but also an increase in the synthesis of proteins of the MyoD family. It has also been shown that the regulation of α subunit gene expression by electrical activity requires protein synthesis, and it is thus possible that this is a reflection of a requirement for the MyoD proteins. The effect of electrical activity on α subunit gene expression may therefore be mediated indirectly through the MyoD proteins, which may regulate their own expression in an autocatalytic manner—as has been shown to occur for genes of this family and for various oncogenes. Such an autocatalytic switch could result in either a negative or a positive regulation of α subunit gene expression. Therefore, this all-or-none switch could preset nuclei into an unstable configuration, so that α subunit gene expression is activated in nuclei at the synaptic region and repressed in extrasynaptic nuclei. This model is consistent with the notion that two components are required for morphogenesis: long-range inhibition (electrical activity) and local autocatalysis (the MyoD autocatalytic switch).

Posttranscriptional regulatory processes are also important for morphogenesis of the neuromuscular junction, and in particular for the targeting, clustering, and stabilization of the AChR at the level of the postsynaptic membrane. With the use of monoclonal antibodies, the Golgi apparatus can be shown to be localized near the endplate in adult muscle; however, after denervation, this organelle spreads from the endplate and shows a more diffuse distribution similar to that found in the embryo. Cytoskeletal elements—in particular, tubulin—and the basal lamina may also play important roles in these posttranscriptional events.

In summary, evidence suggests that the transfer of information from the motor nerve ending to the postsynaptic target cell is mediated by an allosteric protein, the AChR (final proof of this proposal awaits determination of the x-ray crystal structure of the protein). The clustering of the receptor at the neuromuscular junction is a developmental process that is critical for the synapse to function and which involves a complex regulation of gene expression. The role of trans-activating proteins, such as the MyoD proteins, has been emphasized in this control of gene expression. These proteins are also allosteric proteins and are regulated by second messengers, either through phosphorylation or by some other means—they are thus sensitive to the second messenger composition of the cell, which in turn is determined by synaptic activity. An additional level of regulation may involve transsynaptic factors, which have been proposed to play an important role in the selection of the adult neuronal connectivity by epigenesis. Regulation by such factors may occur not only at the postsynaptic level but also at the presynaptic nerve ending. In addition to regulation of the topology of the AChR on the surface of the postsynaptic cell by transcriptional and posttranscriptional processes, the stability of the afferent nerve ending may be regulated by transsynaptic factors that are under the control of the activity of the postsynaptic cell.

Additional Reading

1. B. Fontaine and J.-P. Changeux, "Localization of nicotinic acetylcholine receptor α-subunit transcripts during myogenesis and motor endplate development in the chick," *J. Cell Biol.* **108**, 1025 (1989).
2. J. Giraudat *et al.*, "The noncompetitive blocker [^{3}H]chlorpromazine labels segment M2 but not segment M1 of the nicotinic acetylcholine receptor alpha-subunit," *FEBS Lett.* **253**, 190 (1989).
3. B. J. Jasmin, J. Cartaud, M. Bornens, J.-P. Changeux, "Golgi apparatus in chick skeletal muscle: Changes in its distribution during endplate development and after denervation," *Proc. Natl. Acad. Sci. U.S.A.* **86**, 7218 (1989).
4. J. Kirilovsky *et al.*, "Acetylcholine receptor biosynthesis in primary cultures of chick myotubes. II. Comparison between the effects of spinal cord cells and calcitonin gene-related peptide," *Neuroscience* **32**, 289 (1989).
5. A. Klarsfeld *et al.*, "Regulation of muscle AChR α subunit gene expression by electrical activity: Involvement of protein kinase C and Ca^{2+}," *Neuron* **2**, 1229 (1989).
6. E. Kordeli, J. Cartaud, H. O. Nghiêm, A. Devillers-Thiéry, J.-P. Changeux, "Asynchronous assembly of the acetylcholine receptor and of the 43-kD nul protein in the postsynaptic membrane of developing Torpedo marmorata electrocyte," *J. Cell Biol.* **108**, 127 (1989).
7. R. Laufer and J.-P. Changeux, "Activity-dependent regulation of gene expression in muscle and neuronal cells," *Mol. Neurobiol.* **3**, 1 (1989).
8. M. Österlund, B. Fontaine, A. Devillers-Thiéry, B. Geoffroy, J.-P. Changeux, "Acetylcholine receptor biosynthesis in primary cultures of embryonic chick myotubes. I. Discoordinate regulation of the α-, γ- and δ-subunit gene expression by calcitonin gene–related peptide and by muscle electrical activity," *Neuroscience* **32**, 279 (1989).
9. J. Piette, A. Klarsfeld, J.-P. Changeux, "Interaction of nuclear factors with the upstream region of the α-subunit gene of chicken muscle acetylcholine receptor: Variations with muscle differentiation and denervation," *EMBO J.* **8**, 687 (1989).
10. J.-P. Changeux, "Functional architecture and dynamics of the nicotinic acetylcholine receptor: An allosteric ligand-gated ion channel," in *Fidia Research Foundation Neuroscience Award Lectures* (Raven Press, New York, 1990), vol. 4, pp. 21–168.

11. J.-P. Changeux, "The nicotinic acetylcholine receptor: An allosteric protein proto-
type of ligand-gated ion channels," *Trends Pharmacol. Sci.* **11,** 485 (1990).
12. A. Duclert, J. Piette, J.-P. Changeux, "Induction of acetylcholine receptor α-subunit
gene expression in chicken myotubes by blocking electrical activity requires ongoing
protein synthesis," *Proc. Natl. Acad. Sci. U.S.A.* **87,** 1391 (1990).
13. J.-L. Galzi *et al.,* "Identification of a novel amino acid α-tyrosine 93 within the
cholinergic ligands-binding sites of the acetylcholine receptor by photoaffinity labeling," *J. Biol. Chem.* **265,** 10430 (1990).
14. B. J. Jasmin, J.-P. Changeux, J. Cartaud, "Compartmentalization of cold-stable and
acetylated microtubules in the subsynaptic domain of chick skeletal muscle fibre,"
Nature **344,** 673 (1990).
15. J. Piette, J.-L. Bessereau, M. Huchet, J.-P. Changeux, "Two adjacent MyoD1-
binding sites regulate expression of the acetylcholine receptor α-subunit gene," *Nature* **345,** 353 (1990).
16. F. Revah *et al.,* "The noncompetitive blocker [³H]chlorpromazine labels three amino
acids of the acetylcholine receptor γ subunit: Implications for the α-helical organization of regions MII and for the structure of the ion channel," *Proc. Natl. Acad. Sci.
U.S.A.* **87,** 4675 (1990).

Cell Adhesion and Cell Recognition During Neuronal Development: Molecular Genetic Studies in *Drosophila*

Corey S. Goodman

Corey S. Goodman conducted undergraduate studies in biology at Stanford University, where his interests first began to focus on trying to understand how nerve cells find their correct targets during development. Goodman received his Ph.D. in developmental neurobiology from the University of California, Berkeley, where he worked in neurogenetics and developmental neurobiology. From 1977 to 1979, while conducting postdoctoral research at the University of California, San Diego, he pioneered studies on growth cone guidance in the grasshopper embryo. For the next eight years, Goodman was on the faculty of the Stanford University Department of Biological Sciences. Here his laboratory switched their studies from grasshopper to *Drosophila,* and began a molecular genetic analysis of growth cone guidance.

Since 1987, Goodman has been at the University of California, Berkeley, where he is presently a professor of genetics and neurobiology in the Department of Molecular and Cell Biology. He also is an investigator with the Howard Hughes Medical Institute. His laboratory continues to focus on uncovering the molecules that impart specificity to the developing nervous system, allowing growth cones to recognize their correct pathways and targets.

Cell Adhesion and Cell Recognition During Neuronal Development: Molecular Genetic Studies in *Drosophila*

LECTURER:

Corey S. Goodman

There are certain advantages to studying organisms, such as the fruit fly, that "have" genetics. There are certain aspects of developmental biology—such as sex determination and early pattern formation—for which genetics can reveal a great deal of information about the relevant gene hierarchies. However, genetics is just one of the many tools that have been applied to the complex problem of development in the nervous system: genetic information must go hand in hand with that obtained from cell biological, molecular biological, and biochemical approaches. It would thus be an oversimplification to suggest that genetics can provide all of the answers to this problem.

One of the key issues in nervous system development is how pathways are set up, and related to this is how growth cones distinguish these pathways and ultimately distinguish their final target. An important question concerning this process is: What are the molecular signals in the environment that guide growth cones as they grow toward and ultimately reach their target?

There are both pros and cons with any organism that one chooses to study. The motivation for studying nervous system development in insects is that these organisms have relatively simple nervous systems; and yet these simple nervous systems have to deal with many of the same problems that complex nervous systems do. Most of the molecular mechanisms involved in setting up a nervous system evolved long ago—although they have continued to be elaborated on. The advantage of working with an organism such as the fruit fly is the ability to use powerful genetic techniques. However, the cells of the fruit fly are small and they interact with one another in a compact way, so that it becomes difficult to study the cell biology of nervous system development in the same organism. In contrast, the grasshopper has many advantages for cell biological studies: for example, the cells of the grasshopper are enormous compared

This chapter was edited by Keith W. Brocklehurst, and was originally reported by Dennis Grayson.

32

to embryonic cells of other species, and the embryos have a very thin and transparent neuroepithelium. However, the generation time of the grasshopper is too long for molecular genetic studies. It thus becomes advantageous to study both organisms.

The nervous system of the fruit fly contains a set of segmental neuromeres, similar to the situation with a segmented spinal cord. The ventral nerve cord is made up of a series of segmental repeats. Every segment is connected by longitudinal tracts and each has a very large anterior commissure and a posterior commissure. Most of the interneurons extend across from one side of each segment to the other: they travel across in one of the commissures and then turn either up or down into the longitudinal connectives. Finally, there is a series of nerve roots, which consist of bundles of axons both of motor neurons that exit the central nervous system (CNS) for the periphery and of neurons that carry information from the sensory cells in the periphery into the CNS; the nerve roots therefore serve as exit and entry points. Thus, there is a stereotyped pattern of pathways, and a key question is: Why do these pathways form where they do? The short answer is that there is a prepattern of nonneuronal cells—different classes of glial cells—and the interactions of these cells with one another prefigure where the pathways will form.

The longitudinal connectives, or tracts, and the anterior and posterior commissures are made up of bundles of axons, or fascicles. The associations or interactions between neurons in the bundles also prefigure synaptic connections that are made later. The particular bundle a neuron is in determines which subsequent pathway is taken by that neuron. Intrinsic to this process is the question of choice—how growth cones are able to choose one bundle from another. It has been shown, for example, that cells which differ by only one cell division can travel across the midline in one of the commissural bundles, but when they reach the other side they suddenly diverge and choose very different pathways. What has emerged from this type of analysis is that the growth cones first travel toward the midline, and once there, they begin to display their individuality.

One cell biological approach that has been applied to the study of pathway determination is to examine the effects of ablating specific cells with a laser microbeam on growth cone migration. From this kind of approach, for example, it was learned that certain glial cells are important early in development for determining where the patterns form. If these glial cells are destroyed, growth cones keep extending and do not take the pathway they would normally have taken. Overall, there are two main conclusions that have emerged from this work. The first is that there is some sort of cell recognition occurring. That is, individual neuronal growth cones are able to recognize small groups of other neurons, and it appears that what is being recognized is the surface of the neurons. If an entire group of neurons—that is, an entire affinity group—is removed, then the cells that normally grow toward, recognize, and become a part of that group grow abnormally. It appears that each cell within a particular affinity group expresses the recognition marker—even if only one cell of a particular affinity group remains, there is sufficient information for subsequent cells of that group to recognize the pathway. Furthermore, once a cell joins an affinity group, it also must express the same marker on its surface. Such a marker might consist of a single molecule or a constellation of molecules.

The second conclusion is that the affinity groups are transient and that cells must be changing in a very dynamic way—that is, the markers expressed at the growth cone must be changing. Neurons must thus be able to transport different surface molecules, such as glycoproteins or other glycoconjugates, out to the growth cone so that it can vary its surface properties. Certain events, such as migration past the midline, change the properties of the growth cone. Individual cells that at one point may have been expressing the same marker on their surface can thus diverge and suddenly express different markers. One of the mysteries that we will need to solve in the future, in addition to how the marker molecules function and what actually guides a growth cone into a single pathway, is what orchestrates these sorts of changes. How can two cells that are very similar in their development and initially express the same molecules on their surface be induced suddenly to express very different markers?

So far, then, two different concepts have been discussed. The first is that nonneuronal cells play a role in the early prepatterning, and the second is that once neuronal pathways are established, they express different cell surface markers. These two concepts will be discussed in more detail after first describing an important methodological development, which is known as the enhancer trap screen (Fig. 1).

In *Drosophila*, there is a particular transposable element called the P element, which can be used to "hop" around the genome in a random way. Furthermore, this transposon can be extensively manipulated with the use of recombinant DNA techniques. For example, P elements have been constructed that contain the *lacZ* gene—which encodes β-galactosidase—downstream of a neutral promoter that contains control elements only for directing the start of transcription; that is, there is nothing present in this promoter to control for either tissue or temporal specificity of expression. The transposon can also be manipulated to contain elements that specify eye color, an origin of replication, and genes that specify antibi-

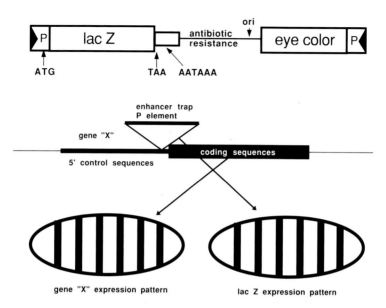

Fig. 1. Schematic representation of a P element as used in an enhancer screen assay. (**Top**) The P element contains coding sequences for β-galactosidase (lacZ) linked to a neutral promoter (P). A gene for antibiotic resistance and sequences for replication (ori) are included to facilitate cloning of the targeted genes. An eye color element is included for identification of mutants. (**Bottom**) If the P element inserts into gene "X" in such a way that it lands in the transcriptional control element, then β-galactosidase is expressed in the same temporal and spatial pattern as gene "X." [Courtesy Corey S. Goodman, University of California, Berkeley.]

otic resistance, so that it becomes easy to clone the genes in which the P element lands. When a P element containing the *lacZ* construct inserts into the 5' control region of a particular gene, *lacZ* comes under the control of the promoter into which it has inserted; that is, *lacZ* "parasitizes" the adjacent control sequences, which then direct the expression of β-galactosidase. For example, if gene "X" is normally expressed as a pattern of stripes in the embryo and the modified P element lands within the 5' flanking region of gene X, then β-galactosidase is also expressed as a pattern of stripes in the developing embryo (Fig. 1). Thus, the pattern of expression of β-galactosidase matches the pattern of expression of the neighboring gene, and so the P element construct can be used as a gene marker.

P elements can also be used to generate mutations. Although the insertion of the transposon into the genome may not necessarily cause a mutation, when it "pops out" it may take with it some of the surrounding DNA, in what is termed an imprecise excision. This can result in a deletion of several hundred to several thousand base pairs, which will usually generate a null mutation.

With this method, members of the Goodman lab have generated approximately 11,000 independent insertions, which represent about 25% of the *Drosophila* genome. The method has begun to reveal information about the different types of glia in the *Drosophila* nervous system—in terms of the prepattern of glia—and it has also allowed the identification of genes that are important for early prepatterning. The transposon has been constructed so that β-galactosidase is targeted to the cell nucleus. Thus, what is observed is not the full morphology of the glia and neurons, but the location of the nuclei. From these studies, it has become apparent that the positions of the glia are prefigured; that is, they are in position before the neuronal pathways form, and the first neuronal growth cones thus run along the surface of the glial cells. The glial cells that surround the midline serve to illustrate this point. Most interneurons, which represent the majority of the cells in the fly CNS, head across the midline, bypassing pathways on their own side that they will follow on the other side. There thus seems to be something quite important about the midline, and the six glial cells that sit along the midline probably play a key role in these decision-making events.

In vertebrates, there is a special set of cells located at the bottom of the neural tube, called the floor plate, which seems to be important for patterning in the neural tube. Similarly, in arthropods, a special set of cells located right at the midline of the developing neuroepithelium seems to be important in patterning of the neuroepithelium. A single row of cells on each side comes together at the midline to form the midline structure. These cells have been described as mesectoderm because they have a special association with the mesoderm and seem to have many mesodermal properties but are maintained within the epithelium that gives rise to the nervous system. Each individual segment is initially four cells long, and during a process called germ band elongation, these four cells from each side interdigitate to become a single row that is eight cells long. The enhancer trap screen has been used both to identify markers for each of these individual cells and to identify the different lineages of neurons and glia that they generate. It has been shown that as soon as the eight midline cells divide once, so that there are 16 cells at the midline, the first growth cones start to head toward the midline. By identifying each of the individual cell interactions, it has been shown that different cells that head toward the midline interact with different cues coming from the midline, and this process is orchestrated over time in a precise manner to give rise ultimately to the pattern of commissures. Furthermore, although the midline glia ultimately have a specific orientation, they actually start out with a very different orientation; after the pathways form on a particular focal point, the glia migrate to their final positions and separate the different commissures. Thus, the growth cones seem to be attracted at first from some distance, they grow to specific points, they fasciculate, the glia migrate into position, and various cells move, so that finally the mature pattern of commissures is produced.

By carefully examining the effects of existing mutations and by generating new mutations that alter these events, it is possible to gain insight into the molecular mechanisms involved in guiding the growth cones and in setting up the mature pattern of commissures. For example, how do we know that the midline cells are important for commissure formation? There are two mutations that selectively eliminate the midline cells: one of these mutations is called *single minded* and the other is called *slit*. In embryos with either of these mutations, the midline cells degenerate and the commissures do not form. Indeed, the whole patterning of the nervous system is affected; that is, if this single row of cells at the midline is missing, the patterning of axonal pathways is disrupted.

Three mutations in different genes have been characterized that either cause the midline glial cells to die or prevent their normal differentiation. With each of these mutations, the same phenotype results. In wild-type flies, two well-organized commissures are formed and the glia are positioned between them. However, in the mutant flies, axons travel across the midline but they are misorganized. Indeed, the entire CNS becomes misorganized and fused, with axons that wander back and forth. The fusion occurs because the glia do not properly migrate and do not wrap around the axons so as to establish the normal set of pathways.

In summary, the mutations that have been described thus far show that formation of the commissures involves a whole set of cell interactions. These include interactions between neurons and glia and between neurons and neurons, and a variety of different cues are used to set up these interactions. Mutations can be identified that either cause cells to die or to differentiate in an incorrect way, and these mutations cause specific perturbations in the way the pathways form. These mutations have thus been used to perturb development in order to determine the cellular rules: which cells and which interactions are involved. Most of the mutations are in genes that control cell fate. However, genetic screens have also been designed to help determine which signals are involved; the hypothesis being that there are a number of different signals coming from the midline. Thus, the purpose of these genetic screens is to try to identify the molecules that are either being secreted from, or are present on the surface of, these cells and which are involved in such pathfinding decisions as whether cells cross the midline or not.

A whole series of cell adhesion molecules is expressed on the surface of neurons. Many of these molecules belong to families, such as the immunoglobulin superfamily (of which N-CAM is a member) and the cadherin family. One of the goals of research on the fruit fly has been to identify the *Drosophila* homologues of these proteins and another has been to identify new molecules. Once these molecules are identified, it is possible to begin a genetic analysis of how these proteins function during neuronal development.

A number of approaches have been taken in order to facilitate the search for *Drosophila* adhesion and recognition molecules. *Drosophila* homologues of characterized vertebrate proteins can be identified by protein purification and characterization, and subsequent cloning either by low-stringency screening of *Drosophila* cDNA libraries with vertebrate probes or by the polymerase chain reaction (PCR). Once the homologues are in hand, a genetic analysis of the vertebrate molecules can be performed in the fruit fly. This approach led to the identification of the different genes that encode the different subunits of laminin and also to the identification of some of the cadherin genes in *Drosophila*.

Another approach has involved the use of monoclonal antibodies that recognize cell surface molecules. This approach allowed the cloning of a series of four surface glycoproteins that show appropriate patterns of expression; that is, the expression of these four axonal glycoproteins is consistent with their potential involvement in neuronal recognition and growth cone guidance. Three of these molecules—neuroglian, fasciclin II, and fasciclin III—have immunoglobulin domains and are members of the immunoglobulin superfamily; the fourth molecule, fasciclin I, is very different from the others and from any other protein present in the data bases (Fig. 2). Fasciclin I has its own special domain structure, with about 150 amino acids per domain.

These four proteins share a number of different features, the most important of which is that each is expressed on a particular subset of axon pathways; in some cases, they are also expressed on the glial cells that these pathways extend along. All of the axons in a particular bundle that fasciculate together express the same member of this group of proteins. None of these molecules is restricted to a single pathway; instead they are found on multiple pathways. Usually in any one location, however, they tend to be restricted to a single pathway or to mark a particular subset of pathways. On any given neuron, these molecules tend to be expressed in a regionally defined way. As mentioned above, as growth cones migrate

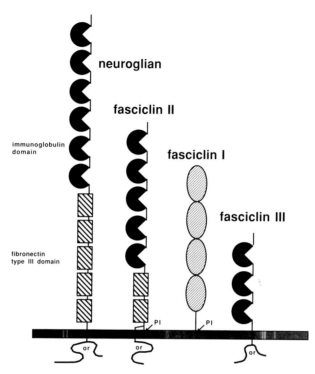

Fig. 2. Domain structure of the insect axonal glycoproteins fasciclin I, fasciclin II, fasciclin III, and neuroglian. Neuroglian and fasciclin II have multiple immunoglobulin domains followed by multiple fibronectin type III domains. Fasciclin III has more-divergent immunoglobulin domains. Fasciclin I has a unique structure composed of four tandem domains and is linked to the cell membrane by a phosphatidylinositol (PI) anchor. [Courtesy Corey S. Goodman, University of California, Berkeley.]

across the midline they change in a dynamic way and suddenly show affinity for a longitudinal pathway, suggesting that the neurons may be switching the molecules they express on their surface. That has now been shown to be the case for these four proteins. On any specific neuron, a particular protein (or group of proteins) is expressed only on the commissural process or only on the longitudinal process, and the growth cone changes its expression pattern after it crosses the midline. The expression of these proteins is thus dynamic during the period of axonal outgrowth; however, expression is drastically reduced by the time the organism becomes fully mature. These proteins are also expressed outside of the developing nervous system, at sites of invagination and of cell-cell contact in other tissues.

These four axonal glycoproteins are expressed on different but overlapping subsets of growth cones and axon fascicles. Neuroglian is the most widely distributed, with fasciclins I, II, and III being expressed on more restricted subsets of axons. It appears that neurons change the pattern of proteins they express on their surface as a result of signals they receive from adjacent cells. However, in addition to triggering a change in the expression of cell surface molecules at the growth cone, these signals must also stabilize the commissural versus longitudinal patterns of expression.

The switching in the expression of cell surface molecules that occurs when growth cones reach the midline is a phenomenon that can be seen in many different species. In the vertebrate spinal cord, projection interneurons express a molecule known as TAG-1 on their commissural processes and then express another molecule, L1, on their longitudinal processes after crossing the midline. Not only is the general phenomenon common, but the actual molecules are highly related.

It should be emphasized that pathways are not defined simply by the presence of single adhesion molecules; thus, these molecules are expressed in combinations and there is significant overlap in expression. At one stage of development, all four of the aforementioned insect glycoproteins are simultaneously expressed on one bundle of axons, and there are other pathways that do not express any of these molecules. Thus, if one can find individual pathways that express all four of these glycoproteins and other pathways that express none of them, it seems reasonable to assume that many more of these adhesion molecules exist.

The function of the insect glycoproteins has been investigated by introducing the corresponding cDNAs into cultured *Drosophila* S2 cells, which normally do not express any of these molecules on their surface and which grow as individual cells. Expression of fasciclin I, fasciclin II, fasciclin III, or neuroglian cDNAs in these cells causes them to aggregate and to form clumps. Thus, all four of these molecules act as homophilic adhesion molecules. Moreover, when cells transfected with different cDNAs are mixed, the different cell populations sort out, so that cells expressing the same adhesion molecule associate with each other but not with cells expressing a different adhesion molecule. However, although cells expressing individual adhesion molecules will sort in vitro, in the developing organism there does not appear to be a situation where any one of these molecules acts alone.

In terms of the evolutionary relations of the insect adhesion molecules, it was mentioned above that fasciclin II, fasciclin III, and neuroglian are members of the immunoglobulin superfamily. If the sequences of these proteins are aligned with some of the vertebrate adhesion molecules, various similarities become apparent. For example, fasciclin II and vertebrate N-CAM are related to the extent that they share a common ancestor; there must have been a certain molecule that existed before the arthropod-chordate split that gave rise to the molecules which eventually became fasciclin II and N-CAM. Similarly, a common ancestor gave rise to neuroglian and three molecules present in vertebrates—L1, TAG-1, and F11. Fasciclin III, however, has very divergent immunoglobulin domains, and so far no closely related molecule has been found in vertebrates.

Some of the insect molecules were initially purified and cloned from grasshopper, which is separated evolutionarily from the fruit fly by approximately 300 million years. This represents approximately the same difference in evolutionary time as that which separates fish and humans; that is, the time required for most of vertebrate evolution. When the fruit fly homologues of these molecules were isolated and sequence analyses performed, it was found that a significant amount of variation had occurred during those 300 million years. For example, the grasshopper and fly fasciclin II molecules are about 50% identical. If these molecules are compared with N-CAM, then the amino acid sequence identity is in the range of 30%. Moreover, the proteins are expressed in different ways: arthropods use fasciclin II only on certain subsets of axonal pathways, whereas in vertebrates, N-CAM is used widely during development. Also, whereas in vertebrates, L1 seems to be expressed primarily on longitudinal pathways and is used very little outside the nervous system, arthropods use neuroglian as a general cell adhesion molecule in epidermal tissues. For these reasons, it is difficult to say that, for example, fasciclin II and N-CAM, or neuroglian and L1, are true homologues. It is safer to say that they share a common ancestor.

With regard to genetic analyses of the insect adhesion molecule genes, null mutations in all four loci have been obtained. This proved to be a nontrivial task, because, with the exception of the neuroglian mutant, none of the mutations already existed. The neuroglian and fasciclin II mutations are lethal. The fact that flies with fasciclin I or fasciclin III mutations are viable does not mean that there is nothing wrong with them, it simply means that the complete loss of function of these proteins does not so completely devastate the animal that it fails to develop. With most of these mutations, there do appear to be associated behavioral phenotypes, which suggests that there are wiring defects within the nervous system. A fasciclin I mutant is most striking in this regard; the affected fly is not coordinated and walks and flies in a peculiar way. Behavioral abnormalities have also been described for fasciclin III mutants. It is interesting that the expression of the two genes that give rise to viable mutants is restricted in the wild-type fly to subsets of pathways in the nervous system; whereas expression of the neuroglian gene—mutations in which are lethal—is the most general. Furthermore, lethality of the neuroglian mutations does not seem to arise from any specific nervous system defect, but rather from a defect elsewhere, possibly in the hindgut.

The embryonic nervous system in these null mutants is not grossly disorganized, although there are subtle differences. It might have been predicted that "knocking out" any one of these molecules would eliminate particular pathways, but this does not happen. Thus, it appears that none of these molecules acts alone to specify any particular pathway. At the individual cell level, however, changes can be seen. In the wild-type fly, there is a particular group of sensory cells that adhere to each other in a specific way to form a highly organized sensory structure. However, in the neuroglian mutant, although the cells still stick together, they are not organized in their normal way: instead of being lined up as they are in the wild-type fly, the cells are clumped together and are more round, the membrane apposition is different, the dendrites are oriented in different directions, and the normal sensory structure does not form.

Fasciclin I is expressed on commissural pathways in the developing CNS. The fasciclin I mutant is uncoordinated as an adult, for reasons that are not yet clear; although the uncoordination may be related to the fact that the sensory neurons in these flies show arborization patterns that are different from those of wild-type flies. The major structures of the CNS, however, do not show any gross abnormalities. If this mutant is crossed with a fly that has a null mutation in the *abl* tyrosine kinase gene, however, major abnormalities result.

The concentration of certain tyrosine kinases—in particular, kinases of the Src family—is very high in growth cones, and this has led to the suggestion that signal transduction processes involving these enzymes may be very active in growth cones. In *Drosophila,* Abl—a member of the Src family—is expressed in the developing nervous system, with the place of highest expression being the growth cones in the CNS. However, null mutants of either *src* or *abl* show no gross abnormalities in the CNS. Abl and fasciclin I double mutants have been constructed with various allelic combinations; in one combination, the commissures begin to disappear, and in another combination they disappear altogether. If a wild-type copy of either *abl* or the fasciclin I gene is introduced into the double mutant, the phenotype is rescued. Over 80% of the growth cones in these double mutants grow out on their own side and do not cross the midline. The growth cones extend at their normal rate and at the normal time, but they are apparently unable to recognize the signal for crossing the midline.

There are probably a number of signals involved in getting growth cones across the midline. Fasciclin I is undoubtedly a participant in this process. However, because removal of fasciclin I does not completely abolish the ability of growth cones to cross the midline, there must be additional cues. Some of these other signals may be acting via the Abl tyrosine kinase. Thus, if both the fasciclin I and Abl signal transduction pathways are blocked, cells cannot cross the midline. The task now is to identify not only genes that when mutated on their own give rise to these defects, but also genes that when mutated in combinations block CNS development. If the development of any particular neuronal pathway requires a number of different cues, then simply eliminating any one gene may not be sufficient to block development of the pathway. Thus, growth cones probably make use of a number of different surface and secreted molecules and a number of different second messenger systems to navigate through pathway choice points.

Additional Reading

1. J. A. Raper, M. J. Bastiani, C. S. Goodman, "Guidance of neuronal growth cones: Selective fasciculation in the grasshopper embryo," *Cold Spring Harbor Symp. Quant. Biol.* **48,** 587 (1983).
2. C. S. Goodman *et al.*, "Cell recognition during neuronal development," *Science* **225,** 1271 (1984).
3. A. L. Harrelson and C. S. Goodman, "Growth cone guidance in insects: Fasciclin II is a member of the immunoglobulin superfamily," *Science* **242,** 700 (1988).
4. K. Zinn, L. McAllister, C. S. Goodman, "Sequence and expression of fasciclin I in grasshopper and *Drosophila,*" *Cell* **53,** 577 (1988).
5. J. R. Jacobs, Y. Hiromi, N. Patel, C. S. Goodman, "Lineage, migration, and morphogenesis of longitudinal glia in the *Drosophila* CNS as revealed by a molecular lineage marker," *Neuron* **2,** 1625 (1989).
6. P. M. Snow, A. J. Bieber, C. S. Goodman, "*Drosophila* fasciclin III: A novel homophilic adhesion molecule," *Cell* **59,** 313 (1989).
7. T. Elkins, K. Zinn, L. McAllister, F. M. Hoffmann, C. S. Goodman, "Genetic analysis of a *Drosophila* neural cell adhesion molecule: Interaction of fasciclin I and Abelson tyrosine kinase mutations," *Cell* **60,** 565 (1990).
8. M. Hortsch, A. J. Bieber, N. H. Patel, C. S. Goodman, "Differential splicing generates a nervous system-specific form of *Drosophila* neuroglian," *Neuron* **4,** 697 (1990).
9. C. Klämbt, J. R. Jacobs, C. S. Goodman, "The midline of the *Drosophila* central nervous system: A model for the genetic analysis of cell fate, cell migration, and growth cone guidance," *Cell* **64,** 801 (1991).
10. G. Grenningloh *et al.*, "Molecular genetics of neuronal recognition in *Drosophila:* Evolution and function of immunoglobulin superfamily cell adhesion molecules," *Cold Spring Harbor Symp. Quant. Biol.* **55,** 327 (1991).

Neuronal Pathfinding in the Developing Chick Embryo

Kathryn W. Tosney

Kathryn W. Tosney earned a Ph.D. in biology in 1980 from Stanford University. Her thesis research examined the control of neural crest migration and addressed the causal relationships between cytoskeletal organization and motile activity in growth cones. Her postdoctoral research at Yale University and the University of Connecticut initiated her continuing studies on the guidance of motor axons in the chick embryo. She joined the University of Michigan in 1984 and is currently an associate professor and an associate chair in the Department of Biology.

Tosney's area of expertise is embryology and her research is dedicated to elucidating guidance mechanisms during development. Her current research addresses two major types of guidance. First, what mechanisms are responsible for the development of the highly specific innervation of axial muscles? Studies in this area focus on understanding how the morphogenesis of axial muscle is controlled and how these developing axial muscles acquire and maintain the appropriate motor innervation. Second, what mechanisms control the development of a stereotyped, gross anatomical pattern of nerves? Studies in this area focus on identifying the embryonic tissues and the cellular interactions that guide the advance of both axons and neural crest cells.

Neuronal Pathfinding in the Developing Chick Embryo

LECTURER:

Kathryn W. Tosney

Neurons can extend for long distances by means of a specialized structure, the growth cone, which guides the growing axon to the correct target. Cues that the growth cone uses for guidance have been studied in the chick embryo. The spinal cord of the chick embryo contains motor neurons within the lateral-ventral areas of the cord. These motor neurons comprise subsets or pools that are destined to go to particular targets. The guidance cues for growth of these neurons fall into two main categories: (i) General cues to which all motor neurons can respond and which define the gross anatomical nerve pattern. All the motor neurons can extend into spinal nerves that occur at regular intervals along the anterior-posterior axis. At the base of the limb, the growth cones congregate in an area known as the plexus region, then enter the limb via dorsal or ventral nerve trunks, and finally project to muscles. (ii) Specific cues to which only some neurons respond. For example, some axons will grow into the ventral but not the dorsal nerve trunk in the limb.

Tissues in the embryo that provide either general or specific guidance cues have been identified by removing particular areas of the developing embryo and observing if all or only specific populations of nerves are affected. After a tissue that provides a guidance cue has been identified, the nature of the cellular interactions that are important for this guidance can be investigated; for example, these interactions could be mediated by a diffusible factor released from the guiding tissue that elicits a neuronal chemotactic response or by direct cell-to-cell contact.

Motor neurons growing out of the spinal cord have to choose, on reaching the base of the limb, between the dorsal and ventral nerve pathways. That there are specific cues somewhere between the base of the limb and the target that are essential for neuron growth was demonstrated by cutting, rotating, and replacing the limb early in development; after this operation, the neurons were still able to reach the correct targets even though the muscles were in abnormal positions. This finding also showed that the neurons are programmed to reach a specific target via these cues.

This chapter was edited by Keith W. Brocklehurst, and was originally reported by Stefano Casalotti.

46

If the limb was completely removed, the neurons still made the correct turning decision even in the absence of the target, thus showing that specific cues for neuron growth also lie somewhere between the spinal cord and the base of the limb.

The largest tissue between the base of the limb and the spinal cord is the somite, which is divided into a ventral sclerotome and a dorsal dermamyotome. Each of these somite components can be removed to answer questions such as, Does the dermamyotome provide a specific cue that is essential for the motor neurons in the limb to make any specific pathway decision? Removal of parts of the somite also allows one to search for general cues. As the motor axons emerge from the spinal cord, they do not extend into the periphery as a sheet but, instead, extend at regular intervals and form spinal nerves. This segmentation pattern is due to an interaction of the motor neurons with the somite and could theoretically arise by the motor neurons growing between adjacent somites or by the neurons growing out within a somite and bundling together. However, what actually happens is that after contacting the somite, motor neurons only grow through the anterior half. The anterior and posterior portions of the somite look alike; each has a sclerotome and dermamyotome. It was therefore of interest to determine whether it is the sclerotome or the dermamyotome that provides the general cues that are required for the segmentation of axon outgrowth.

A third question that can be addressed by removing parts of the somite concerns the epaxial muscles, which are located in the trunk. The epaxial muscle in each segment is innervated by motor neurons that grow out from the spinal nerve and immediately extend dorsally. Each epaxial muscle develops from the corresponding dermamyotome. By removing the dermamyotome, it is therefore possible to determine whether the dermamyotome provides a specific cue that is recognized by the motor neurons that normally innervate the epaxial muscle, but not by motor neurons that innervate the limb muscles. The effect of removing the dermamyotome from one side of young embryos, in which the first motor neurons have not yet developed but the somite has already started to differentiate into a dorsal-lateral dermamyotome (which will later form the epaxial muscle and the dermis) and the sclerotome (which will eventually form part of the vertebral column) has been investigated. After allowing the embryo to develop further, it was shown that on the side of the spinal cord where the dermamyotome was removed, the epaxial muscle is absent. A dye can be injected in the ventral pathway of the limb so that it will be taken up only by the axons following that pathway and label the corresponding cell bodies in the spinal cord. Despite the removal of the dermamyotome, only the set of neurons that normally go through the ventral pathway absorbed the dye. This result indicates that the dermamyotome does not provide any essential specific cues for pathfinding out to the limb targets.

The effect of removing three dermamyotomes is shown in Fig. 1. Motor neurons normally grow out in the anterior and not in the posterior part of the somite and extend through the sclerotome, and continue to do so when the dermamyotomes are deleted. Therefore, the dermamyotome does not provide any essential cues for the segmentation of motor axons. The epaxial neurons normally grow out into the spinal nerve and then grow dorsally into the developing epaxial muscle in each segment. When their prospective developing target is deleted, these neurons show target-dependent and target-directed outgrowth. For example, the epaxial neurons from segment 2 grow out into the anterior somite, then grow dorsally, and, finding no muscle, they turn to the closest anterior target. The neurons from segment 4 behave similarly but turn to the nearest posterior target. In each case, the neurons are growing into the closest available target. However, no epaxial nerve growth was observed from segment 3, which is more than one somite away from any potential target. This result is consistent with a long-distance cue being produced by the target that is essential for outgrowth of epaxial growth cones; the cue is highly specific because it does not affect the motor neurons growing toward the limb. The

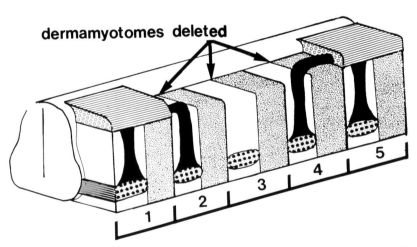

Fig. 1. The effect of dermamyotome removal on motor neuronal development. Five somitic segments are shown. Black bands, epaxial motor neuron axons; striped area, dermamyotome; stippled area, posterior sclerotome. See text for further details. [Reproduced with permission from Tosney (1991).]

possibility that some undetected neurons grew but did not find a target, and therefore retracted their axons, cannot be excluded; if this had happened, it would indicate a contact-dependent, rather than a chemotactic, mechanism. Because the neurons in the epaxial nerve grow in the anterior and not posterior part of the sclerotome, in addition to responding to specific epaxial muscle cues, they are responding simultaneously to general pathway cues; the anterior sclerotome is a pathway, whereas the posterior sclerotome is a barrier, for all classes of motoneurons.

In another experiment, several entire somites were removed from one side of the spinal cord of a young embryo. On the unmanipulated side of the spinal cord, the axons grew out to form segmented spinal nerves. Sensory ganglia (dorsal root ganglia) also formed in a segmented pattern, which is achieved through an interaction between neural crest cells and the somites. On the side where the somites were deleted, however, the pattern of axonal segmentation was completely abolished; the axons grew out in sheets rather than bundles. Furthermore, the dorsal root ganglia were fused and formed an elongated structure. Thus, the overall segmental pattern of growth had been lost. From the results of this experiment, several conclusions can be drawn: (i) Axon elongation and neural crest cell migration do not require the somites. (ii) Because the target specificity of the axons extending into the periphery from the manipulated side of the spinal cord was not changed, neither the somite nor the normal pattern of segmentation is essential for correct targeting of neurons to the limbs. (iii) Segmentation appears to coordinate the pattern of axon outgrowth with the developing anatomy of the embryo.

All the navigational cues that are important for the development of the gross anatomical nerve pattern are now believed to be part of a broader developmental process in the chick embryo. In the developing embryo, neurons appear to avoid areas that will eventually become bone. Early markers for cartilage formation may provide avoidance signals for the growth cone and thus establish the general pattern of nerve growth. In addition to the posterior sclerotome, another example of a tissue that acts as a barrier to growth is the developing pelvic girdle, which lies between the extending motor axons and the limbs. Two small holes are present in the developing pelvic girdle, through which the anterior and the posterior nerve trunk will grow. If an artificial hole is made in the pelvic girdle, the motor axons will grow through it, thus indicating that the pelvic girdle normally acts as a barrier. A third example of a tissue that acts as a barrier is the perinotochordal mesenchyme, which is derived from the ventral sclerotome. The barrier function of the perinotochordal mesenchyme was shown by surgically altering one-half of the spinal cord so that the axons from the motor column would extend directly ventrally. Such axons turned to avoid the perinotochordal mesenchyme. In an alternative approach, the notochord, which permissively induces the sclerotome to form cartilage, was removed. Under these conditions, the perinotochordal mesenchyme did not develop cartilage markers and no longer acted as a barrier.

A common feature of all tissues that act as barriers is that they express early markers for cartilage formation, which may thus provide a mechanism for neurons to avoid bones. The fact that growing neurons can recognize tissue that will turn into bone is also advantageous from an evolutionary standpoint because a change in the general morphology of an organism will not require a reprogramming of neuronal outgrowth. Markers for cartilage formation could be the molecular entities of neuronal guidance. Indeed, these markers may play a broader role because they are also found in the central nervous system.

There are no apparent physical differences between the anterior and posterior sclerotome that could explain why motor axons and neural crest cells travel through the former but not the latter; therefore, direct cellular interactions are probably responsible for the anterior sclerotome serving as a path and the posterior sclerotome as a barrier. Direct cellular interactions, such as contact-mediated avoidance responses, that are involved in neuronal outgrowth can be studied more directly by analyzing the interactions of neurons with anterior and posterior sclerotome. This type of analysis has been achieved by observing neurite outgrowth in tissue culture on dissected anterior and posterior sclerotome (Fig. 2). It was shown that (i) neurites growing on the posterior sclerotome are much shorter than those growing on the anterior sclerotome; (ii) posterior sclerotome is not a totally nonpermissive substrate for growth; (iii) neither tissue is toxic because neurons survived equally well on both anterior and posterior sclerotome; (iv) no repulsive factor diffuses out of the posterior sclerotome because neurites are not repelled at a distance; (v) neurites on anterior sclerotome turn on contacting posterior sclerotome and thereby exhibit a contact-mediated avoidance response; and (vi) neurite outgrowth is generally inhibited on the posterior sclerotome, and whatever growth does occur is directed toward the nearest anterior sclerotome, indicating the presence of a diffusible trophic factor or factors released from the anterior sclerotome.

Two contact-mediated mechanisms could account for the contact-mediated avoidance response to posterior sclerotome. The first, substrate preference, was previously considered the only possible mechanism of axon guidance. A growth cone that can grow perfectly well on a particular

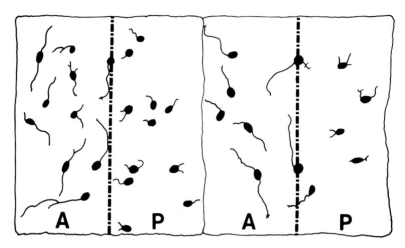

Fig. 2. Motor neurite outgrowth on anterior (A) and posterior (P) sclerotome. [Adapted with permission from Tosney (1991).]

substrate will, if given the choice, consistently extend axons on a more suitable substrate after contact with that substrate is made. A second type of contact-mediated mechanism is contact paralysis, in which the growth cone loses its motility on contact with the inhibitory substrate. According to this mechanism, the neurites grow until the growth cone encounters the barrier; at this point all the neuronal processes and the growth cone collapse. These two mechanisms can be distinguished by observing the interactions of growth cones with each cell type. Preliminary evidence suggests that a contact paralysis mechanism for the inhibition of neuronal growth by posterior sclerotome is not the major or only contact-mediated mechanism involved. Rather, it appears that neurons prefer the anterior to the posterior sclerotome for growth; in addition, the anterior sclerotome may produce a diffusible stimulatory cue.

These studies of growth cone guidance have gone "from the embryo down" rather than "from the molecule up." First, tissues have been identified that provide general and specific guidance cues for neuronal growth; then, assays have been devised for cellular mechanisms that mediate guidance. These same assays can now be used to begin to investigate the molecular basis of guidance.

Additional Reading

1. P. C. Letourneau, "Cell-to-substratum adhesion and guidance of axonal elongation," *Dev. Biol.* **44,** 92 (1975).

2. B. Ferguson, "Development of motor innervation of the chick following dorsal-ventral limb bud rotation," *J. Neurosci.* **3**, 1760 (1983).
3. J. A. Raper, M. Bastiani, C. S. Goodman, "Pathfinding by neuronal growth cones in the grasshopper embryo," *J. Neurosci.* **3**, 31 (1983).
4. K. W. Tosney and L. T. Landmesser, "Development of the major pathways for neurite outgrowth in the chick hind limb," *Dev. Biol.* **109**, 193 (1985).
5. K. W. Tosney, M. Watanabe, L. T. Landmesser, U. Rutishauser, "The distribution of N-CAM in the chick hind limb during axon outgrowth and synaptogenesis," *Dev. Biol.* **114**, 437 (1986).
6. K. W. Tosney, "Proximal tissues and patterned neurite outgrowth at the lumbosacral level of the chick embryo: Deletion of the dermamyotome," *Dev. Biol.* **122**, 540 (1987).
7. K. W. Tosney, S. Shroeter, J. A. Pokrzywinski, "Cell death delineates axon pathways in the hind limb and does so independently of neurite outgrowth," *Dev. Biol.* **130**, 558 (1988).
8. M. Grim, K. Nensa, J. H. Jacob, K. W. Tosney, "A hierarchy of determining factors controlling motor neuron innervation," *Anat. Embryol.* **180**, 179 (1989).
9. K. W. Tosney and R. A. Oakley, "The perinotochordal mesenchyme acts as a barrier to axon advance in the chick embryo: Implications for a general mechanism of axonal guidance," *Exp. Neurol.* **109**, 75 (1990).
10. K. W. Tosney, "Growth cone navigation in the proximal environment of the chick embryo," in *The Nerve Growth Cone,* S. B. Kater, P. C. Letourneau, E. R. Macagno, Eds. (Raven Press, New York, 1991).

Molecular Genetics of
Catecholamines and Serotonin

Jacques Mallet

Jacques Mallet was born in France and began his research studies in the United States at Harvard University, where he received a Ph.D. in 1972 in physical organic chemistry. He then returned to France, where he pursued studies in neurobiology at the Pasteur Institute, Paris, under the direction of Jean-Pierre Changeux. The rapidly expanding field of molecular genetics led him to create in 1980 a laboratory at the Université d'Orsay, where his studies focused on the expression of neurotransmitters. In 1984, he continued his research in France at the Centre d'Etude du Système Nerveux in Gif-sur-Yvette, creating the Department of Molecular Genetics in the CNRS Laboratory of Neurobiology. Mallet currently serves as director of research at CNRS.

Mallet's studies comparing the regulatory mechanisms and analyzing the interactions of different systems of neurotransmission—such as the cholinergic or the serotonergic system—have brought to light the diversity of those systems. At present, Mallet and colleagues' experiments grafting genetically modified cells into the brains of animal models of Parkinson's disease have led to partial functional recovery. The implications of these experiments pave the way for achieving functional recovery from a host of other degenerative diseases. Another important area of study is the molecular level of genetic components of certain psychiatric diseases such as manic depression and schizophrenia. Such studies may lead to an understanding of how environmental factors interact with gene expression in these diseases.

Molecular Genetics of Catecholamines and Serotonin

LECTURER:

Jacques Mallet

Neuronal plasticity refers to the adaptive response of a given neuron or neuronal network to environmental changes. If adaptation occurs early in the life cycle of the cell or of the organism, plasticity may be synonymous with development; alternatively, when adaptation occurs at a mature or adult stage, the phenomenon of plasticity may be related to such events as nerve regeneration or the processing, storage, and retrieval of information.

One way to change or to set to a certain level the responsiveness of neurons would be to modulate the availability of neurotransmitters in cells. This may in turn affect the plasticity of the whole system in which the cell is operative. The catecholaminergic neurons, both in the peripheral and central nervous system (CNS), constitute a suitable model system in which to investigate the molecular events that are responsible for the modulation of transmitter availability and, ultimately, the plasticity of cells in response to environmental cues.

In catecholaminergic (adrenergic, noradrenergic, and dopaminergic) neurons, the rate-limiting step in the synthesis of neurotransmitters is that catalyzed by the enzyme tyrosine hydroxylase (TH): the conversion of tyrosine to L-DOPA (L-dihydroxyphenylalanine), the direct precursor of the catecholamines. Enzymes that catalyze the synthesis or degradation of a given neurotransmitter can often be used as phenotypic markers of cells that contain the transmitter. TH, for example, is specific to neuronal tissue; L-DOPA decarboxylase (which catalyzes the conversion of L-DOPA to dopamine), however, is not, as it is present also in other tissues, such as kidney.

TH activity and expression can be regulated by several different mechanisms, both during development and in the adult. During development, the expression of TH is modulated by the continuously changing environment that surrounds the neuroblasts during their migration, by the target tissues of these cells, and by growth factors such as nerve growth factor (NGF). In the adult, TH can be regulated by synaptic activity. The

This chapter was edited by Keith W. Brocklehurst, and was originally reported by Maria Luisa Barbaccia.

54

catecholaminergic phenotype of superior cervical ganglion (SCG) neurons in the newborn rat is easily modified by a variety of external stimuli. The phenotype of these cells depends on the balance between the regulation of expression of at least two enzymes: TH and choline acetyltransferase (ChAT). Culture medium that has been conditioned by muscle cells depresses the expression of TH and activates expression of ChAT, thus changing the phenotype of SCG neurons from noradrenergic to cholinergic; on the other hand, chronic depolarization and stress accelerate the noradrenergic differentiation of these neurons.

The intracellular mechanisms that mediate these changes in the activity or expression of TH can be divided into short-term and long-term mechanisms. Phosphorylation is one of the most important and physiologically relevant short-term mechanisms for controlling TH activity. Rat TH is phosphorylated in vitro by a number of different protein kinases: protein kinase C, a Ca^{2+}/calmodulin–dependent protein kinase, and adenosine $3',5'$-monophosphate (cyclic AMP)–dependent protein kinase. In each case, phosphorylation increases enzyme activity. Very little is known about the phosphatases that mediate the reverse dephosphorylation process; however, phosphorylated TH is much less stable than the unphosphorylated enzyme, so degradation of the phosphorylated enzyme may serve the same function as dephosphorylation. Analysis of the amino acid sequence of TH (predicted from the nucleotide sequence of the gene), together with other information, indicates that the enzyme has two domains: the carboxyl-terminal region (negatively charged) contains the catalytic site, and the amino-terminal region (positively charged) acts as an inhibitory regulatory domain. The regulatory domain contains several phosphorylation sites, which have been shown to undergo phosphorylation in vivo. The addition of negatively charged phosphate groups to the regulatory domain relieves the inhibition of the enzyme and enhances the activity of the catalytic site.

With the use of molecular biological techniques, cDNAs for human (HTH) and rat (RTH) TH have been expressed in bacteria. The proteins produced in bacteria are enzymatically active; moreover, in bacteria, the enzymes do not undergo posttranslational modification and, therefore, being completely unphosphorylated, represent optimal substrates with which to evaluate the effect of various degrees of phosphorylation on catalytic activity. With this approach, it was possible to establish that phosphorylation is not required for TH activity; phosphorylation serves only to modulate activity.

Electrical activity, stress, or drugs, such as reserpine, can elicit a long-term increase in TH activity that does not result from activation of preformed molecules but, instead, is due to the synthesis of new enzyme molecules. This phenomenon, which may last for up to several weeks, is termed transsynaptic induction. The time courses of the increase in both TH activity and the amount of TH mRNA after a single injection of reserpine have been analyzed in rat brain locus coeruleus and adrenal medulla. In adrenal medulla, TH activity increases to reach a plateau by day 4 and returns to basal values approximately 1 week after reserpine injection. More strikingly, in the locus coeruleus, where the reserpine effect is much more pronounced, even after 3 weeks there is still a twofold increase in TH activity. When a phenomenon persists for such a long time, it is possible that the process may constitute the biochemical basis for information storage. These increases in TH activity reflect higher concentrations of TH mRNA, which are achieved by increased transcription of the gene.

Very little is known about the events that are responsible for neuronal activity–induced gene activation. In particular, it will be important to know which nucleotide sequences in the regulatory regions of the TH gene are responsible for long-term changes in gene expression. Analysis of the promoter of the TH gene has provided some information. Both RTH and HTH gene promoters contain (i) a POU element, which may be an important determinant of the tissue specificity of gene expression; (ii) a cyclic AMP–responsive element (cyclic AMP increases TH mRNA levels); and (iii) an AP-1 site (also known as the TPA-responsive element).

Exposure of cells to TPA (12-*O*-tetradecanoyl phorbol-13-acetate) for several minutes increases protein kinase C activity; with prolonged exposure, however, protein kinase C activity becomes down-regulated. The effect of TPA on transcription of the TH gene has been investigated in PC12 cells, which are derived from a rat pheochromocytoma. Nuclear run-on experiments show that TH gene transcription increases to a maximum within 15 min and thereafter sharply falls back to control levels. On analysis, in parallel, of TH mRNA levels, two interesting observations were made: (i) there is a lag between the increase in TH gene transcription and the increase in TH mRNA levels, as if a homeostatic mechanism regulated the maturation of the pre-mRNA so as to allow the mRNA to respond to various degrees of transcriptional activation; (ii) after the initial increase, the mRNA level falls below control values, thus suggesting that protein kinase C affects not only transcription but also the stability of TH mRNA.

The TH gene promoter contains an AP-1 site that differs from the classical site at the central base, which is a thymidine instead of the usual cytosine (TGA*T*TCA instead of TGACTCA); this difference may have functional significance. Gel-shift experiments with an oligonucleotide containing the AP-1 site of the TH gene have revealed that PC12 cells that have been exposed to TPA show an additional band that is not present in control PC12 cells. The response of the TH gene promoter to TPA has also been analyzed in trans-activation experiments, in which the TH promoter was linked to the coding sequence of the chloramphenicol acetyltransferase (CAT) gene. Transcription of the CAT gene was also increased by TPA. Furthermore, of the various nuclear proteins that bind to the AP-1 consensus site, c-Jun was found to activate CAT gene transcription, whereas c-Fos had very little effect by itself and, moreover, did not potentiate the effect of c-Jun as would have been expected for a "regular" AP-1 site.

These results suggest that the AP-1 site (in concert with or independent of the cyclic AMP–responsive element) may play a role in the control of TH gene expression. However, unequivocal proof that the AP-1 site mediates the transsynaptic induction of TH requires the demonstration that transgenic mice carrying a mutation of the AP-1 element do not show this phenomenon. Moreover, it should also be kept in mind that the relevance of the AP-1 site and the cyclic AMP–responsive element may vary depending on the particular cell type.

The cloning of an HTH cDNA from human pheochromocytoma cells showed that four different, but related, mRNA species exist: HTH-1 is homologous to the RTH cDNA; HTH-2 differs from HTH-1 by a 12-nucleotide insert; HTH-3 differs from HTH-1 by an 81-nucleotide insert; and HTH-4 contains both the 12- and 81-nucleotide inserts. These inserts are located in the coding sequence of the regulatory domain of the protein. Analysis of the exon-intron composition of RTH and HTH genes suggests that this diversity of TH mRNA species may derive from alternative splicing of the pre-mRNA. Whereas human pheochromocytoma cells express all four forms of TH mRNA, three forms are found in adrenal medulla, and only two (HTH-1 and HTH-2) have been thus far detected in the CNS.

Each of the four mRNA species, when injected in frog oocytes, yielded functional TH proteins; these proteins showed different specific activities, however, with HTH-1 the most active and HTH-2 the least active (having approximately 70% of the activity of HTH-1). These proteins have also been produced in bacteria, from which they have been purified and shown to be good substrates for phosphorylation. As is the case for RTH, phosphorylation decreased the K_m of the enzymes for the pyridine cofactor and thus increased enzyme activity. The presence of an extra arginine residue in HTH-2, which is encoded by the insert, may affect the efficiency of phosphorylation of the adjacent serine by a Ca^{2+}/calmodulin–dependent protein kinase. Thus, alternative mRNA splicing may regulate both the basal activity of the enzyme and the modulation of activity by phosphorylation.

Together, these results reveal at least three different levels at which the activity of TH can be modulated: (i) at the level of transcription of the gene; (ii) at the level of mRNA splicing; and (iii) at the level of posttranslational processing. A fine control of mRNA splicing may result in long-term changes in activity of the enzyme and, therefore, in the availability of neurotransmitter at various synapses.

In situ hybridization experiments have been performed on human substantia nigra with a probe that recognizes all four HTH mRNA isoforms. It was found that both cell somata and dendrites were labeled. More specifically, in situ hybridization with probes that selectively recognize either HTH-1 or HTH-2 mRNA showed that HTH-1 mRNA was detectable only in somata, whereas HTH-2 appeared to be present in somata and dendrites. The finding that dendrites contain TH mRNA may have functional significance because it has been shown that dopamine can be released by dendrites in rat substantia nigra.

HTH mRNA has also been visualized by in situ hybridization in postmortem brain samples from control subjects and individuals affected by Parkinson's disease. As might have been expected, a selective, significant loss of TH mRNA–containing neurons was observed in parkinsonian patients. Over the years, various approaches have been taken to compensate for the dopaminergic cell loss that occurs in the substantia nigra of Parkinson's disease patients. Recently, grafting of human fetal substantia nigra cells and of adrenal cells has been attempted, but in general the results have not been impressive—probably because the grafted cells produced only small amounts of dopamine. It may be possible to overcome this problem by infecting a particular cell type—chosen for its ability to survive the graft and to make synapses—with a retrovirus containing the HTH gene. Three types of cells have been thus far infected with a retrovirus containing the HTH-1 cDNA: (i) NS-20 cells, which originate from a neuroblastoma; (ii) NIH 3T3 cells, which originate from fibroblasts; and (iii) At-T20 cells, which originate from a pituitary tumor. After infection, NS-20 and NIH 3T3 cells produced L-DOPA, but dopamine was undetectable. At-T20 cells, however, produced both L-DOPA and dopamine; dopamine was not only produced but was also stored, and its release could be induced by depolarizing potassium concentrations in a Ca^{2+}-dependent manner. In NS-20 and NIH 3T3 cells, L-DOPA was released constitutively and was not stored.

The genetically modified At-T20 cells have been grafted into rats carrying 6-hydroxydopamine–induced lesions of the substantia nigra. Behavioral data indicate that the grafts were successful. Interestingly, grafts performed with cells that produce only L-DOPA were even more successful, and it has now been shown that the L-DOPA released from these cells can be converted to dopamine by L-DOPA decarboxylase present in neighboring cells. Currently, these experiments are being repeated with primary cells instead of tumoral cells.

There are indications that an alteration in catecholaminergic transmission may be functionally associated with psychopathological states such as schizophrenia and manic-depressive disease. Both syndromes also show a genetic component in their pathogenesis. The HTH gene is located on the short arm of chromosome 11 and the possible cosegregation of the HTH gene and genetic markers for these syndromes has been investigated. Previous studies performed with an Amish pedigree showed that markers on chromosome 11, such as H-*ras* and the insulin gene, were linked to manic-depressive disease. However, when this first pedigree was extended by including more probands, a reanalysis of the data showed a dramatic decrease in the probability of linkage between the same loci on chromosome 11 and manic depression. Furthermore, linkage could not be demonstrated in additional pedigrees. Two possible explanations for these findings are: (i) manic depression may be a heterogeneous disease and several genes may independently give rise to the condition; (ii) manic depression may have a polygenic etiology, in that mutations in several genes are necessary before the condition is manifest. In both of these cases, linkage analysis—which requires both knowledge of the mode of transmission and that penetrance be established—may not yield consistent results with different groups of individuals.

Another possible approach to this problem is to perform association studies; that is, to compare the frequency of particular alleles in unrelated individuals. This approach has the advantage of being nonparametric and knowledge of the mode of transmission is not required. In such a study, an allele detected by the restriction endonuclease Taq 1 at the $5'$ end of the TH gene and another allele detected by Bgl II at the $3'$ end of the gene were found to be associated with manic depression at a statistically significant level: the frequency of the allele detected by the Taq 1 enzyme was 12% in controls and 27% in bipolar manic-depressive patients; the frequency of the allele detected by Bgl II was 38% in controls and 22% in bipolar patients. Thus, a mutation located in the vicinity of the TH gene may confer vulnerability to the disease. The data do not imply, however, that such a mutation is the only one responsible for full expression of the disease. It is probable that expression of the symptomatology of manic depression relies on the concurrence of genetic and environmental cues.

Finally, a few words about the serotonergic system. Tryptophan hydroxylase (TPH) catalyzes the rate-limiting step in the synthesis of serotonin. TPH, TH, and phenylalanine hydroxylase (PH) constitute a family of hydroxylases and use similar cofactors. The amino acid sequences of these three enzymes show a high degree of similarity at their carboxyl termini (the location of the catalytic domain) but are different at their amino termini (the location of the regulatory domain). In the brain, TPH is present in the raphe and in the pineal gland. There appears to be only one coding sequence for TPH in the rat, but differences have been found in the 5' and 3' untranslated regions of TPH mRNAs. Three different 3' sequences corresponding to three polyadenylation sites, and two different 5' sequences corresponding to two promoters, have been detected.

Northern (RNA) blot analyses with a TPH probe have revealed the presence of two bands for the pineal gland and for the intestine, but no signal was detected for the brain stem. Consistent with these observations, in situ hybridization of TPH mRNA gave a strong signal for the pineal gland and a weak signal for the raphe. Surprisingly, although TPH immunoreactivity was abundant in the pineal, it was even more abundant in the raphe. Quantitative analysis of these data showed that each TPH mRNA molecule produces 300 times more protein in the raphe than in the pineal. Thus, TPH activity appears to be regulated at the level of translation. The contribution of an additional TPH gene, the expression of which is overwhelming in the raphe, cannot however be eliminated at this stage.

Serotonin has also been implicated in the pathogenesis of affective disorders; however, no evidence of linkage or association of these disorders with the TPH gene has yet been found.

Additional Reading

1. B. Grima, A. Lamouroux, F. Blanot, N. Faucon Biguet, J. Mallet, "Complete mRNA coding sequence of rat tyrosine hydroxylase," *Proc. Natl. Acad. Sci. U.S.A.* **82**, 616 (1985).
2. B. Grima *et al.*, "A single human gene encoding multiple tyrosine hydroxylases with different predicted functional characteristics," *Nature* **326**, 707 (1987).
3. J. Mallet *et al.*, "Molecular genetics of catecholamines as an approach to the biochemistry of manic-depression," *J. Psychiatr. Res.* **21**, 559 (1987).
4. A. Brice *et al.*, "Complete sequence of a cDNA encoding an active rat choline acetyltransferase: A tool to investigate the plasticity of cholinergic phenotype expression," *J. Neurosci. Res.* **23**, 266 (1989).
5. S. Dumas, M. C. Darmon, J. Delort, J. Mallet, "Differential control of tryptophan hydroxylase expression in Raphe and in pineal gland: Evidence for a role of translation efficiency," *J. Neurosci. Res.* **24**, 537 (1989).

6. P. Horellou, B. Guibert, V. Leviel, J. Mallet, "Retroviral transfer of a human tyrosine hydroxylase cDNA in various cell lines: Regulated release of dopamine in mouse anterior pituitary At-T20 cells," *Proc. Natl. Acad. Sci. U.S.A.* **86,** 7223 (1989).

7. S. Dumas, F. Javoy-Agid, E. Hirsh, Y. Agid, J. Mallet, "Tyrosine hydroxylase gene expression in human ventral mesencephalon: Detection of tyrosine hydroxylase messenger RNA in neurites," *J. Neurosci. Res.* **25,** 569 (1990).

8. P. Horellou, P. Brundin, P. Kalén, J. Mallet, A. Björklund, "In vivo release of DOPA and dopamine from genetically engineered cells grafted to the denervated rat striatum," *Neuron* **5,** 393 (1990).

9. P. Horellou, L. Marlier, A. Privat, J. Mallet, "Behavioural effect of engineered cells that synthesize L-DOPA or dopamine after grafting in the rat neostriatum," *Eur. J. Neurosci.* **2,** 116 (1990).

10. M. Leboyer *et al.,* "Tyrosine hydroxylase polymorphisms associated with manic-depressive illness," *Lancet* **335,** 1219 (1990).

11. S. Vyas, N. Faucon Biguet, J. Mallet, "Transcriptional and post-transcriptional regulation of tyrosine hydroxylase gene by protein kinase C," *EMBO J.* **9,** 3707 (1990).

Development of a Simple Nervous System

Gunther S. Stent

Gunther S. Stent was born in Berlin and studied physical chemistry in the United States, where he earned his Ph.D. in 1948 from the University of Illinois. As a postdoctoral fellow at the California Institute of Technology, Stent joined Max Delbrück's "Phage Group," a group that sparked the field of molecular biology. Stent joined the faculty of the University of California, Berkeley, in 1952, where he has served as a professor of molecular biology since 1959.

Stent's research has exciting implications in molecular biology and neurobiology, as well as in the history and philosophy of science. In 1948 he began studying the structure and replication of genetic material, and the regulation and mechanism of expression of genetic information. In the 1960s, he focused on the structure of, embryological development of, and control of movement by simple nervous systems. Stent's work in neurobiology set the experimental and theoretical standards for circuit analysis of neuronal rhythm generators. He also has published on the origins of molecular biology. At present his research mainly focuses on identifying the cellular components of the leech nervous system during embryonic development.

Development of a Simple Nervous System

LECTURER:

Gunther S. Stent

The study of invertebrate nervous systems has the disadvantage that these nervous systems are both organizationally and phyletically remote from the mammalian, and especially from the human, nervous system—thus, the applicability of any insights gained in invertebrate developmental neurobiology to the nervous systems of higher animals is uncertain. On the other hand, invertebrate nervous systems have the tremendous advantage of being much simpler than those of higher animals—they are two to three orders of magnitude less complex in terms of the number of component neurons, and presumably of even less complexity with regard to the number of synaptic connections. The simplicity resulting from the reduced number of neurons, however, is somewhat compensated for by the fact that invertebrate neurons are much more complex than vertebrate neurons. Thus, complexity that is achieved in mammals by circuits made up of simple neurons—each of which may be capable of performing just one or two tasks—is achieved in invertebrates by individual neurons that are in effect "little brains" and which carry out complex and integrated functions. The nervous system on which this discussion will be based is that of the leech, which is one order of magnitude simpler than that of the fruit fly.

One consequence of the reduced number of neurons in invertebrate nervous systems is that it is possible reproducibly to identify individual cells, whereas in vertebrates it is only possible to identify populations of cells. The question thus arises as to the mechanisms by which these identified cells achieve their individuality during development. The position, morphology, transmitter phenotype, connectivity, and function of a neuron are characteristics that determine its individuality. Two alternative schemes for the determination of neuronal identity have been proposed: according to one scheme, the line of descent of a cell determines its identity; according to the other scheme, the local environment of a cell determines its identity. Both schemes play a role in development, and the identity of most neurons is actually determined by elements from each scheme.

This chapter was edited by Keith W. Brocklehurst, and was originally reported by Marco Favaron.

Leeches belong to the phylum of segmented worms, the members of which show a high degree of evolutionary conservation of adult anatomy and function but show a tremendous diversity with regard to embryological development. Natural selection appears, therefore, to have both preserved the final form and, at the same time, allowed a diversification in the mechanisms by which this final form is attained—a situation that can be explained by the highly varied environments in which embryonic and postembryonic development take place. The leech body is subdivided into 32 metameric segments: the rostral four form specialized structures of the head (including the anterior sucker), the caudal seven are specialized to form the posterior sucker, and in between are the 21 abdominal segments, which are similar to each other but are also locally specialized.

All the studies that will be discussed in this article were performed on the abdominal segments. The segments can be identified externally because the epidermis is subdivided into annuli, or rings, and the number of rings per segment is fixed, although it varies between species (Fig. 1). The nervous system of the leech reflects this morphological segmentation. The basic units of the central nervous system (CNS) are the segmental ganglia, each of which contains approximately 150 sets of bilaterally paired neurons. Segmental ganglia are connected by the connective nerve, which carries axons along the longitudinal axis of the leech. The segmental ganglia and their connective nerves form the ventral nerve cord. Segmental nerves, which run orthogonal to the connective nerve and contain axons of motor and sensory neurons, connect the ganglia to the periphery. Approximately half of the neurons present in the segmental ganglion are motor and sensory, whereas the other half comprise interneurons (the axons of which do not project into the periphery but run only in the CNS). The leech nervous system is highly accessible. All the cells mentioned can be

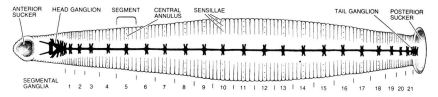

Fig. 1. Body plan of the medicinal leech *Hirudo medicinalis* showing the dorsal aspect, with the body wall cut open along the dorsal midline to expose the ventral nerve cord and its segmental ganglia. The 21 abdominal segments are numbered in rostrocaudal sequence. Circumferentially distributed small dots within the central annulus of each segment indicate the position of sensory organs, or sensillae. [Reproduced with permission from Nicholls and Van Essen (1974). ©1974 by Scientific American, Inc. All rights reserved.]

penetrated by microelectrodes, and it is possible to make simultaneous recordings from two or more cells so that the connectivity of the system can be established. Furthermore, each cell has its own characteristic electrophysiological signature. Histochemical and immunohistochemical analyses are easy to perform in the leech, so that the neurotransmitter phenotype, for example, can be identified for many cells. It is also possible to work on semi-intact preparations, in which only one segment is opened for electrophysiological recordings; such preparations have enabled the neuronal circuitry responsible for swimming, for example, to be defined.

Reproduction of the leech begins with the pairing of two hermaphrodites, one serving as the male and the other serving as the female. A few days after fertilization, large eggs are laid by the "mother," and these eggs then develop within a cocoon. Development may also proceed outside the cocoon in simple culture medium—the eggs are full of yolk, which supplies food and energy for the entire developmental process. A series of cell divisions of the fertilized egg gives rise to large blastomeres, which include five bilaterally paired teloblasts named M, N, O, P, and Q located at the future posterior end of the embryo. It is from these five paired teloblasts that mesodermal (muscle, connective tissue, genitalia, nephridia) and ectodermal (nervous system, epidermis) structures are derived: the M teloblasts produce the mesoderm and the N, O, P, and Q teloblasts produce the ectoderm. The teloblasts divide in the stem cell mode: Each teloblast undergoes a series of iterated, highly asymmetrical cleavages that give rise to much smaller daughter cells. The daughter cells are similar to each other but different from the large mother cell and are termed primary blast cells.

The primary blast cells produced by each teloblast remain attached to each other and form a bandlet; both blast cells and their bandlets are referred to by the letters m, n, o, p, and q (Fig. 2). The bandlets rise to the surface of the embryo, where the five on each side unite to form a ribbon that is termed the germinal band. The n, o, p, and q bandlets are situated next to each other in alphabetical sequence on the surface of the germinal band, with the m bandlet lying underneath. As more and more blast cells are added at the rear of the embryo, left and right germinal bands advance forward. Eventually, the left and right germinal bands meet at the site of the future head, where they coalesce along the ventral midline in a zipper-like manner from the head to the tail to form the germinal plate. It is in the germinal plate that further development of mesodermal and ectodermal tissues occurs (Fig. 2). Within the germinal plate, right and left n bandlets lie apposed across the ventral midline, with the o, p, and q bandlets situated more and more laterally, respectively, and the m bandlets lying un-

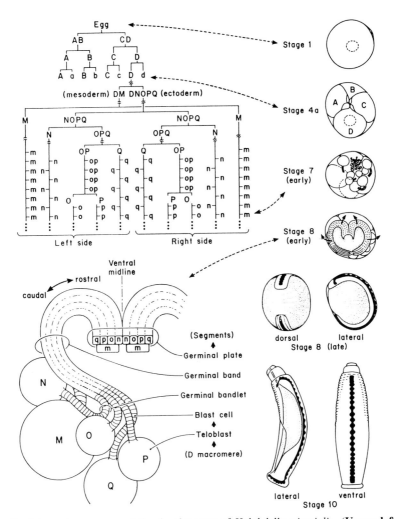

Fig. 2. Schematic summary of the development of *Helobdella triserialis*. (**Upper left**) Cell pedigree leading from the uncleaved egg to the macromeres A, B, and C; the micromeres a, b, c, and d; the teloblast pairs M, N, O, P, and Q; and the paired primary blast cell bandlets. The number of op blast cells produced prior to cleavage of proteloblast OP varies from four to seven. (**Lower left**) Hemilateral disposition of the teloblasts and their primary blast cell bandlets within the germinal band and germinal plate. (**Right margin**) Diagrammatic views of the embryo at various stages. In the stage 7 embryo, the dashed circle signifies the right M teloblast (which is invisible from the dorsal aspect), and the many small, closed contours in the upper midportion indicate the micromere cap. In the stage 8 (early) embryo, the heart-shaped germinal bands migrate over the surface of the embryo in the directions indicated by the arrows. In the stage 8 (late) embryo, the germinal plate is shown to lie on the ventral midline, with the nascent ventral nerve cord and its ganglia and ganglionic primordia indicated in black. In the stage 10 embryo shown, body closure is nearly complete. Here, the stippled areas signify the yolky remnant of the macromeres and teloblasts, now enclosed in the gut of the embryo. The chain of ganglia linked via connectives, shown in black, already closely resembles the adult nerve cord. [Reproduced with permission from Weisblat, Kim, Stent (1984).]

derneath. The cells in the germinal plate proliferate, so that the structure expands circumferentially over the surface of the embryo until the leading left and right margins finally meet at the future dorsal midline of the animal. At this point, the body tube of the leech closes. The body tube is virtually the same size as the egg, so that this developmental process represents morphogenesis and differentiation without growth.

Study of the developing leech nervous system is greatly facilitated by the presence of a rostral-caudal developmental gradient: At the front of the embryo, development of the germinal plate has progressed much further than at the rear, because the rostral structures are derived from the earliest blast cells produced. Thus, various stages of nervous system development can be examined in a single specimen, with the rostral segments more advanced than caudal segments.

Immunohistochemical studies have revealed that the musculature actually develops before the nervous system. Two types of muscles can be easily distinguished: those that course circumferentially and are termed circular muscles, and those that course longitudinally and are termed longitudinal muscles. Muscles are also segmental structures. They are individually identifiable and arise in a particular sequence. The first muscle that can be visualized in a given segment is the $c1$ circular muscle, which is situated just posterior to the anterior segmental boundary. Among the earliest longitudinal muscles to appear in each segment is the pair termed deep longitudinal, which is situated on either side of the ventral midline. Two successive $c1$ circular muscles, and the left and right deep longitudinal muscles situated between them, define a rectangle that is the domain of the future segmental ganglion.

The development of the leech CNS has been followed by means of lineage tracer methodology, which involves injecting a tracer substance into identified blastomeres and following the developmental fate of this tracer. This methodology requires that the tracer is passed only to the direct descendants of the injected cell. The most widely used tracers are adducts of the fluorescent dyes rhodamine (red) and fluorescein (green) with dextran—it is necessary to couple the dyes to dextran in order to prevent their diffusion through the gap junctions linking many of the embryonic cells. Such lineage tracing experiments have shown that the descendants of each teloblast give rise to a segmentally iterated, strictly ipsilateral pattern of differentiated cells—these patterns are termed M, N, O, P, and Q, corresponding to the teloblast of origin. Right and left patterns are symmetrical. The M pattern provides for all muscle fibers, excretory organs, and connective tissue. The N pattern consists of approximately half of the neurons of the segmental ganglia. The remainder of the ganglionic neurons is provided by the O, P, and Q patterns, which comprise also the neurons of the peripheral nervous system. In addition to producing central and peripheral neurons, the O and P patterns include the ventral epidermis, and the Q pattern the dorsal epidermis.

Each hemisegmental complement of the M pattern consists of a clone of cells that originate from a single m blast cell. The hemisegmental complements of the O and P patterns also originate from single o and p founder blast cells, respectively. However, the hemisegmental complements of the N and Q patterns are derived from two successively born founder n and q blast cells, respectively—in either case, the elder blast cell gives rise mainly to the anterior sector of the segment, and the younger gives rise to the posterior sector. Therefore, each hemisegment consists of seven cell clones: one m, one o, one p, two n, and two q.

The pattern of cell divisions that give rise to the tissues of each segment is highly stereotyped. After their birth, cells achieve their final positions by migration. For example, the q bandlets are situated at the lateral edges of the germinal plate, whereas the future domain of the hemiganglion borders the ventral midline. Thus, q cells must migrate in order to contribute to the CNS. This migration process can be visualized in a single leech preparation, in which, due to the rostrocaudal developmental gradient, the various segments have achieved progressively more advanced stages of development. Thus, in the front part of the germinal plate, the q cells may already have migrated into the CNS at a time when migration has not yet started in the rear part. Two groups of dividing cells leave the q bandlet and migrate toward the position of the future ganglion. The first group consists of three cells and the second group of two cells, and the two groups follow different migratory pathways. All five of the migratory cells in each hemisegment arise from the more anterior (elder) of the two founder q blast cells. Glia do not play a role in this migratory process because they do not develop until a later stage; instead, muscle fibers are an essential component of the guidance mechanism that leads these cells to the CNS.

The n bandlet cells arise entirely within the domain of the future ganglion, and therefore they do not have to migrate over large distances in order to make their contribution to the CNS. Nevertheless, these cells must migrate within the domain of the ganglion in order to reach their definitive positions. This migration became manifest by the results of an experiment in which the left N teloblast had been injected with a rhodamine tracer, and the right N teloblast was ablated by injection of deoxyribonuclease at a time when it had produced only a few daughter cells. Embryos were examined after development of the nervous system had been completed. Because under normal conditions, each N teloblast contributes cells only to its ipsilateral side of the germinal plate, it might have been expected that the hemiganglia on the right, N teloblast–deprived side would lack the N pattern, whereas the left hemiganglia would show the normal N pattern. In some segments, this was actually the case; the right hemiganglia were quite small because the cell contribution from the right n bandlet was missing. However, in the majority of segments, it was found that cells derived from the left n bandlet were distributed over both sides of the ganglion. Finally, in a few segments, the left hemiganglion did not contain any neurons because they had all migrated to the N teloblast–deprived, right side. These findings show that there is no intrinsic laterality to the n bandlet neuronal precursor cells. Although each of them is predestined to become a particular type of neuron, the cell can fulfill that destiny and take up its definitive position on either the right or left side of the embryo. Under normal conditions, cells migrate only on their side of birth, but, in the absence of the contralateral bandlet, they may take up their definitive positions on either side of the midline.

Migrating cells achieve their definitive positions by attending to local cues, which must be distributed symmetrically over both sides of the germinal plate. M teloblast ablation experiments have shown that these cues reside in the mesoderm: in m bandlet–deprived germinal plates, neurons are distributed randomly, although they still manifest their normal transmitter phenotype. Thus, it is not necessary for a neuron to occupy its predestined position in order to express its predestined phenotype.

As mentioned above, although they are very similar, the body segments of the leech are not identical. For example, the male and female reproductive organs are located in abdominal segments 5 and 6, respectively, where they develop in place of nephridia. How do cells know to form genitalia in abdominal segments 5 and 6 and nephridia in other segments? This kind of question was first addressed for certain ectoderm-derived structures. The axonal branching pattern of a particular serotonin-containing neuron is different in the reproductive segments 5 and 6 from that in other segments. It was found that when such neurons were transplanted into ectopic segments, the axonal branching pattern that developed was characteristic of the host segment into which the cell was transplanted rather than of the donor segment of origin. Thus, there are local, segmentally differentiated cues that influence the morphological development of these neurons. However, this is not the case for some mesoderm-derived structures. Experiments in which m blast cells were transposed to ectopic segments inappropriate for their birth ranks have shown that the differential segmental development of genitalia and nephridia from homologous founder m blast cells is determined autonomously by birth rank of the blast cells and not by local factors external to the m bandlet.

Finally, not all developmental characteristics are determined solely by line of descent. For instance, o and p blast cells normally have different fates. However, if a P teloblast is ablated, o blast cells will give rise to the P pattern. This phenomenon is termed transfating, and o blast cells are therefore pluripotent at the time of their birth.

Additional Reading

1. J. G. Nicholls and D. Van Essen, "The nervous system of the leech," *Sci. Am.* **230,** 38 (1974).
2. D. A. Weisblat, S. Y. Kim, G. S. Stent, "Embryonic origins of cells in the leech *Helobdella triserialis,*" *Dev. Biol.* **104,** 65 (1984).
3. G. S. Stent, "The role of cell lineage in development," *Philos. Trans. R. Soc. Lond. (Biol.)* **312,** 3 (1985).
4. D. K. Stuart, S. A. Torrence, M. I. Law, "Leech neurogenesis. I. Positional commitment of neural precursor cells," *Dev. Biol.* **136,** 17 (1989).
5. S. A. Torrence, M. I. Law, D. K. Stuart, "Leech neurogenesis. II. Mesodermal control of neuronal patterns," *Dev. Biol.* **136,** 40 (1989).
6. G. P. Keleher and G. S. Stent, "Cell position and developmental fate in leech embryogenesis," *Proc. Natl. Acad. Sci. U.S.A.* **87,** 8457 (1990).

Control of Neuronal Morphogenesis

Alain Prochiantz

Alain Prochiantz was born in Paris, France, where he earned his Ph.D. in 1976 from the University of Paris for research defending the structural and functional study of the 3′ terminus of the turnip yellow mosaic virus RNA. In 1976 Prochiantz joined the laboratory of J. Glowinski at the Collège de France, where they studied the development of nerve cells in culture and examined the specific interactions between dopaminergic neurons and their striatal target cells. This work led Prochiantz and his colleagues to make their first observations on the regulation of neuronal polarity.

From 1976 to 1990, Prochiantz has studied the pharmacology of the rodent brain, the cytoskeleton of different cell types in the central nervous system, and cell interactions such as neuro-neuronal interactions and interactions between neurons and astrocytes. Since 1990 he has worked at the Ecole Normale Supérieure as director of a CNRS-Ecole Normale research unit. His recent studies have focused on understanding the expression and role of genes that code for small guanosine 5′-triphosphate–binding proteins, and the modification of neuronal morphogenesis and polarity in vitro. In this context, Prochiantz and his colleagues currently are developing an in vitro model to allow one to follow the morphological consequences of interfering with the positioning of homeobox proteins on their cognate binding sites.

Control of Neuronal Morphogenesis

LECTURER:

Alain Prochiantz

Neurons are polarized cells, possessing dendrites and axons, and it is clear that the growth of these two types of neurites is regulated by different mechanisms. One important goal in the study of neuronal development is to define the cell programs that control the growth of the axon and of dendrites, and which thereby determine the specific polarity of neuronal growth. The use of specific markers that define a population of neurons may allow the visualization in tissue of both the preferential path of axonal migration and the spreading of the dendritic arborization. In E15 (embryonic day 15) rodent embryos, for example, immunofluorescent staining of mesencephalic neurons with antibodies to tyrosine hydroxylase allows one to follow the elongation of migrating axons to their final target, the caudate nucleus.

In cultured neurons, it is difficult to distinguish the axon from the dendrites on the basis of their morphology. For this reason, most studies on cultured neurons have been devoted to the search for "neurite growth factors," and these studies have focused on the gross effects of such molecules on neuronal arborization. However, the identification of specific protein markers has now made it possible for one to study the differential growth of axons and dendrites. Thus, antibodies to the highly phosphorylated 200-kilodalton (kD) component of neurofilaments selectively stain the axon. In contrast, antibodies to the type-2 microtubule-associated protein (MAP2) stain the soma and dendrites, at least during the early stages of neuronal maturation in culture.

It has been established that astrocytes are critical for the regulation of the growth and spatial orientation of dendrites. If neurons from specific brain regions, such as the striatum or the mesencephalon, are dissociated in culture and grown on a layer of astrocytes, the extent of dendritic growth depends on the anatomical origin of the underlying glial cells. If cultures are "homotopic" (that is, neurons and astrocytes originate from the same brain area), both axons and dendrites grow. In contrast, in "heterotopic" cultures (in which neurons and astrocytes originate from two different regions), dendritic growth is inhibited (Fig. 1). A similar pattern

This chapter was edited by Keith W. Brocklehurst, and was originally reported by Ferdinando Nicoletti.

74

of differential growth can be observed if neurons are grown in homotopic astrocyte-conditioned medium (medium from cultured astrocytes of the same brain region) and in heterotopic medium (derived from astrocytes of a different brain region). In the latter condition, dendritic growth is limited and most cells have long individual axons. For these experiments, neurons are plated at very low density so that they are not able to establish connections or to condition their own medium.

Taken together, these results indicate that astrocytes do not affect neurite growth nonspecifically, but, rather, they influence neuronal polarity. If this is the case, it is important to know which molecules produced by and eventually released from astrocytes participate in the regulation of dendritic growth. As an initial step taken to answer this question, astro-

		Neurons	
		Mesencephalon	Striatum
Astrocytes	Mesencephalon	Homotopic: Dendrites Axons	Heterotopic: Axons
	Striatum	Heterotopic: Axons	Homotopic: Dendrites Axons

Fig. 1. The effect of homotopic and heterotopic interactions between neurons and astrocytes on dendritic and axonal growth.

cyte-conditioned medium was separated into particulate (P100) and soluble (S100) fractions by centrifugation (100,000g for 3 hours). Neurons
cultured in medium containing the suspended P100 fraction of homotopic
astrocyte medium were mostly unipolar with a long axon. In contrast,
neurons grown in the presence of the S100 fraction were multipolar, with
a large dendritic arborization (Fig. 2). Chemical analysis of the P100 and
S100 fractions of the astrocyte-conditioned medium revealed them to have
basically identical constituents; that is, the components of the extracellular
matrix that would be expected to be secreted by astrocytes, including
laminin, fibronectin, entactin, and heparin sulfate and chondroitin sulfate
proteoglycans. The differential morphogenetic effects of the soluble and
particulate fractions may thus be attributable to the presence of soluble
and insoluble isoforms, respectively, of molecules of the extracellular matrix. This hypothesis implies that the nature of the physical interaction
with extracellular matrix components may influence the polarity of neuronal growth.

Neurons were thus grown in the presence of purified laminin or fibronectin, either bound to the surface of the culture dish (insoluble form)
or added to the culture medium (soluble form). As had been previously

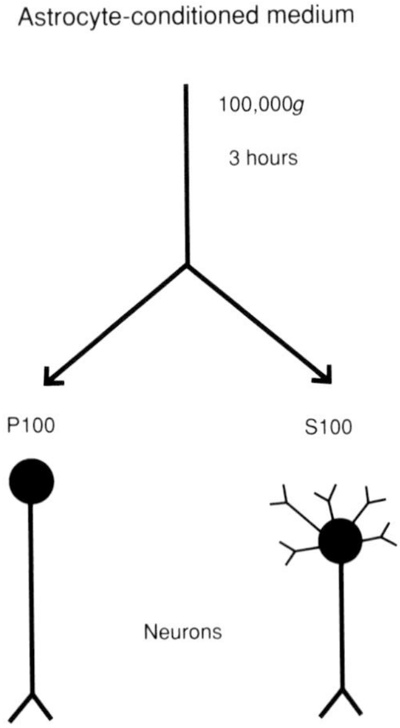

Fig. 2. Differential morphogenetic effects of the soluble (S100) and particulate (P100)
fractions derived from centrifugation of astrocyte-conditioned medium.

described, bound fibronectin and laminin increased the number of cells bearing neurites, whereas the soluble forms did not. However, a more extensive analysis of cell morphology revealed differential effects of laminin and fibronectin on neuronal polarity and shape. Neurons grown in the presence of soluble laminin or bound fibronectin were mostly unipolar with a long axon, suggesting that dendritic growth was inhibited under these conditions. In contrast, in the presence of bound laminin or soluble fibronectin, most cells were multipolar. In the case of bound laminin, a small (but significant) percentage of cells was unipolar, due to the leaching of laminin from the surface of the culture dish into the medium. The morphogenetic effects of soluble laminin are dynamic and reversible. If cells grown with soluble laminin for 24 hours (unipolar cells bearing a long axon) are treated with trypsin and then grown under standard culture conditions, they will become multipolar, bearing both dendrites and the axon. Conversely, if cells grown in normal culture medium or soluble fibronectin (multipolar cells) are subsequently exposed to soluble laminin, the growth of dendrites is inhibited and that of the axon is greatly stimulated (Fig. 3). These data indicate that exposure to soluble or insoluble isoforms of molecules of the extracellular matrix does not select specific populations of cells but, rather, regulates cell polarity. Interestingly, inhibition of dendritic growth is always accompanied by an enhanced elongation of the axon. Accordingly, in cells cultured with soluble laminin, the axon becomes twice as long as in cells grown in normal culture medium or in the presence of soluble fibronectin. This suggests that the spreading of the dendritic tree and the elongation of the axon are somehow in competition, at least when neurons are grown in culture.

Cells that bear dendrites (for example, those grown in the presence of soluble fibronectin or bound laminin) were found to be larger than unipolar cells (which are predominant in the presence of bound fibronectin or soluble laminin). This indicated that the growth of dendrites may require both a large degree of cell spreading on, and cell adhesion to, a substrate; whereas the growth of axons does not. Neurons plated under conditions that result in unipolar morphology were found to detach after shaking 3 hours later, whereas neurons plated under conditions that are permissive for dendritic growth did not. This finding was consistent with strong adhesion to a substrate being a necessary requirement for dendritic but not axonal growth (Fig. 4).

In summary, the axon can grow under low-adhesion conditions and its elongation is accelerated if dendritic growth is concomitantly inhibited. The extrapolation of this model to in vivo situations implies that a shift in the expression of different isoforms of cell adhesion molecules (CAMs),

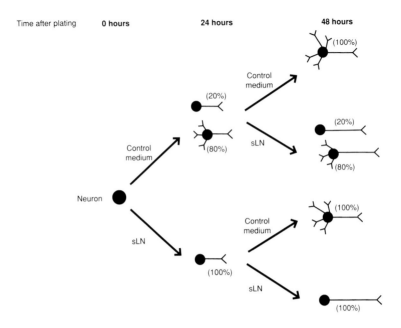

Fig. 3. The reversible and dynamic effects of control medium and soluble laminin (sLN) on dendritic and axonal growth. (**Lower part**) Cells grown in the presence of soluble laminin will all be unipolar both 24 and 48 hours after plating. However, if they are treated with trypsin 24 hours after being exposed to sLN, and then plated in control medium, they will express both axons and dendrites. (**Upper part**) If cells are cultured in control medium for 24 hours, 20% of them will be unipolar and 80% will bear both an axon and dendrites. After 48 hours, all cells will be multipolar. However, if sLN is added to the cultures 24 hours after plating, a significant number of cells will be unipolar with a long axon. [Adapted with permission of The Company of Biologists, Ltd., U.K., from Chamak and Prochiantz (1989).]

substrate adhesion molecules (SAMs), or extracellular matrix receptors may set the cellular program that initiates dendritic growth after the axon has reached its final target.

To explain how adhesion differentially affects the growth of axons and dendrites, one has to refer to a physical model based on the retracting force exerted by surface tension and the cortical actin network that prevents the elongation of any neurite unless it is counterbalanced by an opposing force. This can be achieved either by increased adhesion or increased viscosity. According to this model, if axons have higher viscosity than dendrites, then they can grow even under low-adhesion conditions. The number of molecules that contribute to the formation of the stable cytoskeleton is an important factor in determining the viscosity of a neu-

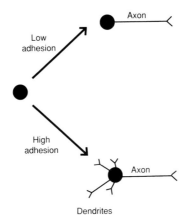

Fig. 4. Differential effects of low- and high-adhesion conditions on dendritic and axonal growth. [Adapted with permission from Prochiantz (1990). ©Gordon and Breach Science Publishers S.A.]

rite. For instance, although polymerized tubulin is present in dendrites, it is present in much greater amounts in axons, as shown by both electron-microscopic analysis and immunofluorescent staining.

A peculiar aspect of axonal growth, at least in culture, is that axons elongate by jumping from one specific attachment point to another, as opposed to dendrites, which spread on the substratum. At the attachment points, which correspond to the turning points of the elongating axon, the axon establishes strong contacts by forming adhesion plaques; whereas in the intersegmental regions, the concentration of tubulin is sufficiently high to counteract the retraction force of the surface tension.

Another important aspect of neuronal development concerns the intracellular mechanisms, in terms of specific gene expression and protein synthesis, that target the building materials used for neuronal growth to specific sites on the cell membrane, and thus determine neuronal polarity. In yeast, mutations in specific genes, termed *YPT1* and *SEC4,* decrease the ability of cells to form and transport secretory vesicles. These genes belong to the *ras* superfamily and code for small guanosine triphosphate (GTP)–binding proteins (20 to 25 kD). Genes equivalent to *YPT1* and *SEC4* have been cloned in mammals and have been termed *rab* genes. Different subtypes of *rab* proteins (*rab*p) are distributed within the cell at various sites involved in vesicle formation and transport. For example, *rab1*p and *rab2*p are found between the endoplasmic reticulum and the cis-Golgi apparatus; *rab6*p is located in trans-Golgi and post-Golgi vesicles; *rab4*p participates in endocytosis; and *rab3*p is found in synaptic vesicles. The expression of *rab1* in the central nervous system is developmentally regulated. A large molecular size form of *rab1* mRNA, which is neuron specific, is present in large amounts from E13 to P7 (postnatal day 7) and in very low amounts from P7 to P21, after which expression increases again. In contrast, the expression of the large molecular size form of *rab2* mRNA, which is also neuron specific, is maintained throughout embryonic and adult life.

Various *rab* proteins have been introduced into nerve cells in order to see if they contribute to the determination of polarity of neuronal growth. The *rab* proteins are able to penetrate cells easily when added just after cell trituration, as has been shown by incorporation of fluorescein-labeled *rab* proteins. If neurons injected with *rab1*p or *rab2*p are plated under low-adhesion conditions—a situation that normally results in the formation of cell clumps and aggregates—cell aggregation is greatly modified. The most obvious effects on neuronal morphology were seen after injection of large amounts of *rab2*p. It appears that *rab2*p increases dendritic growth and cell adhesion—only 3 hours after the introduction of *rab2*p into the soma, both cell adhesion and the surface area of the cell body were increased.

Interestingly, *rab2*p is able to reverse the inhibitory effects of soluble laminin on dendritic growth and cell adhesion. One can speculate that *rab2*p acts to accelerate the rate of insertion of adhesion molecules at specific locations on the cell membrane. In contrast to *rab2*p, *rab1*p appears to reduce adhesion and promote axonal growth (although its effect is less striking than that of *rab2*p on dendritic growth). The *rab1A* protein, which is a particular form of *rab1*p, increases the ratio of unipolar to multipolar neurons and reduces the number of dendrites. The *rab1B* protein—which differs from *rab1A*p by only 5% of its primary structure—is not as effective as *rab1A*p when introduced into neurons. However, a mutant form of *rab1B*p, which was modified in the region that encodes the GTP-binding domain in such a way that a superactivated protein was produced, was as effective as *rab1A*p. Hence, it appears that the morphogenetic action of *rab1*p depends on the ability of the protein to bind and hydrolyze GTP.

If *rab* proteins (or other proteins) act as targeting factors in the cellular programs that determine neuronal polarity, then which specific genes are regulated by an increase or decrease in adhesion in order to activate these programs (Fig. 5)? These switch genes probably code for DNA-binding proteins and may include homeotic genes. Homeotic genes are potential candidates for this function because they are expressed in the developing nervous system during neurite growth. Homeotic genes may contribute to the determination of cell shape and polarity by regulating specific cellular

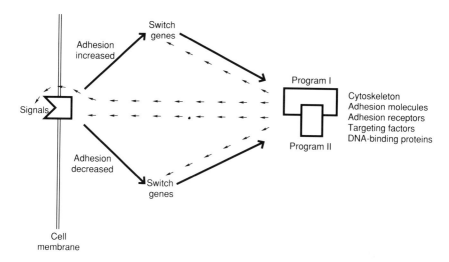

Fig. 5. Interaction between morphogenetic signals, cell adhesion, switch genes, and targeting factors in the development of three-dimensional shape.

programs that affect the pattern of interaction between cells and the substratum. These genes may achieve this effect by regulating the type, number, and distribution of specific adhesion molecules on the cell surface.

Homeobox proteins bind to canonical DNA sequences that have been characterized in detail. The DNA-binding domain of these proteins, the 60–amino acid homeobox domain, can interact with the canonical DNA sequences even without its flanking protein regions. Thus, if large amounts of a peptide corresponding to a particular homeobox domain were introduced into nerve cells, it can be assumed that the peptide would occupy and saturate the canonical DNA sequences and thereby prevent the action of endogenous homeotic proteins. To this end, the homeobox domain of Antennapedia, which shows great similarity to several other homeoboxes, has been synthesized and added to neurons grown in culture. Experiments performed with fluorescein-labeled Antennapedia peptide indicated that the peptide was able to penetrate cultured neurons and that it accumulated in the nucleus. The Antennapedia peptide induced profound morphological changes in cultured neurons: at the single cell level, the peptide induced neuronal spreading on the substratum. In addition, all cell aggregates disassociated and the growth of neurites increased. As expected, the effects of Antennapedia were dependent on protein synthesis because they were prevented by cycloheximide treatment. These results support a role for endogenous homeobox proteins in setting the programs that lead to the definition of neuronal shape and polarity.

In conclusion, signals resulting from homotopic or heterotopic interactions between neurons and glial cells lead to increased or decreased adhesion. This, in turn, switches on specific programs at the gene level. Specific isoforms of extracellular matrix molecules may have an important role in this process. Once a program is set up, specific factors (*rab* proteins?) will target the building material (such as adhesion molecules and extracellular matrix receptors) to the specific sites of growth, thus influencing neuronal polarity. This model provides a link between morphogenetic signals, gene expression, and the development of three-dimensional shape (Fig. 5).

Additional Reading

1. S. Denis-Donini, J. Glowinski, A. Prochiantz, "Glial heterogeneity may define the three-dimensional shape of mouse mesencephalic dopaminergic neurons," *Nature* **307,** 641 (1984).

2. B. Chamak, A. Fellous, J. Glowinski, A. Prochiantz, "MAP2 expression and neurite outgrowth and branching are coregulated through region-specific neuro-astroglial interactions," *J. Neurosci.* **7,** 3163 (1987).

3. A. Autillo-Touati *et al.,* "Region-specific neuro-astroglial interactions: Ultrastructural study of the in vitro expression of neuronal polarity," *J. Neurosci. Res.* **19,** 326 (1988).

4. A. Rousselet, L. Fetler, B. Chamak, A. Prochiantz, "Rat mesencephalic neurons in culture exhibit different morphological traits in the presence of media conditioned on mesencephalic or striatal astroglia," *Dev. Biol.* **126,** 495 (1988).

5. B. Chamak and A. Prochiantz, "Influence of extracellular matrix proteins on the expression of neuronal polarity," *Development* **106,** 483 (1989).

6. J. Ayala, N. Touchot, A. Zahraoui, A. Tavitian, A. Prochiantz, "The product of *rab2,* a small GTP binding protein, increases neuronal adhesion and neurite growth in vitro," *Neuron* **4,** 797 (1990).

7. A. Prochiantz, "Morphogenesis of the nerve cell," *Comments Dev. Neurobiol.* **1,** 143 (1990).

8. A. Rousselet, A. Autillo-Touati, D. Araud, A. Prochiantz, "In vitro regulation of neuronal morphogenesis and polarity by astrocyte-derived factors," *Dev. Biol.* **137,** 33 (1990).

9. A. Joliot, C. Pernelle, H. Deagostini-Bazin, A. Prochiantz, "Antennapedia homeobox peptide regulates neural morphogenesis," *Proc. Natl. Acad. Sci. U.S.A.* **88,** 1864 (1991).

Specification of Cerebral Cortical Areas

Pasko Rakic

Pasko Rakic, M.D., Sc.D., a native of Yugoslavia, has shaped his career in the United States; he was with Harvard Medical School for 12 years, and since 1978 has been with Yale University, where he presently is professor of neuroscience and chairman of the Section of Neurobiology.

Rakic is best known for elucidating the role of genetic and environmental factors in the development of the primate brain, particularly the cerebral cortex. His initial studies of neuronal migration in the cerebellum of normal and mutant mice led to the radial unit hypothesis and to the concept of surface-mediated glial guidance as the mechanism by which some classes of neurons move and acquire a final position in the brain. His experiments on the development of binocular visual connections in monkey embryos challenged the belief that neuronal connections are precisely and immutably specified, instead showing that these connections are subject to competitive interactions. Rakic has conducted comprehensive analyses of neurogenesis and synaptogenesis in diverse areas of normal and experimentally altered primate brains. These studies provide insight into cerebral evolution, epigenetic regulation of cortical maps, and the pathogenesis of certain congenital malformations. His current research involves cellular and molecular mechanisms of cell migration, emergence of neurotransmitters and their receptors, formation of synapses, and neuronal plasticity.

Specification of Cerebral Cortical Areas

LECTURER:

Pasko Rakic

One of the main characteristics of the cerebral cortex is that it is divided into defined areas with distinct cell types, neurotransmitters, connections, and physiological characteristics. Certain areas are devoted to specific functions; for example, the visual area is devoted to vision, and the motor area controls functions concerning movement. When considering the evolution of the brain, it is important to remember that the brain of the human did not develop from that of the monkey, which did not develop from that of the rat. Rather, the brains of all of these species have common ancestors. Although there are only small differences in the cortical thickness of brains from these species, there are large differences in surface area: the surface area of the human brain is approximately 1000 times larger than that of the rat and a little more than 10 times larger than that of the monkey. In addition, brain areas are not expanded equally in different species, and new areas have been introduced during the course of evolution. There are also variations in brain structure between individuals. In fact, humans are more different from one to another with respect to the structure of the cortex than for any other part of the body; for example, the neocortical area that specializes in speech, which is larger on the left side of the brain of right-handed individuals, can be three times larger in one individual than in another; and the visual area can differ by 50% between individuals (which is also the case in monkeys).

Are these variations in the size of brain areas due to different genetic information or to different sensory stimulations and "training" that the brain receives? Although many studies have investigated changes within a given area of the cortex, little effort has been made to compare one area to another. The major problems are large individual variations and lack of clear interareal borderlines. Recently, many new experimental techniques have been introduced that allow this type of investigation. Many researchers believe that cortical areas are very similar in their cellular organization, that they have a common circuitry, and that differences in information processing between different cortical areas are attributable simply to

This chapter was edited by Keith W. Brocklehurst, and was originally reported by Mariella Bertolino.

different inputs. Although, indeed, there are some basic principles that regulate the function of all areas, there are also large structural and molecular differences from one area to another, and one focus of attention has been how this diversity is generated.

This discussion will be concerned primarily with cortical area 17 (V1 or the primary visual cortex) and area 18 (V2 or the secondary visual cortex) in primates. Area 17 constitutes approximately 3% of the brain in humans and 15% in monkeys; area 18 in humans is twice as large as area 17, whereas in monkeys, area 18 is approximately equal in size to area 17. There are approximately 300 million cells in the primary visual cortex of both monkey and human.

The connectivity of the cortical visual areas in primates is well defined and is different from that in rat or cat. The primate area 17 receives inputs to particular layers and sublayers from the lateral geniculate nucleus (LGN), which receives inputs from the eyes. Area 18 does not receive input from the LGN; instead, it receives input from an adjacent thalamic nucleus known as the pulvinar. The LGN is divided into two regions: parvocellular and magnocellular. The parvocellular region comprises four layers and is concerned predominantly with color discrimination—that is, with wavelength sensitivity—whereas the magnocellular region comprises two layers and is concerned with motion and shape discrimination. Cortical inputs from each region project to different layers and sublayers in area 17. Fibers originating from the parvocellular layers of the geniculate terminate in layers IVA, IVCβ, and VIB of the cortex, whereas the magnocellular layers project to IVCα and VIA. Developmental biologists are interested in whether these cortical layers attract inputs from the magno- and parvocellular moieties of the geniculate, or are induced by them.

Advanced neurobiological techniques have revealed some basic information on the connectivity of neurons in different cortical areas and how this circuitry develops. The synaptic circuitry of each area is unique because each area processes a different type of information. Furthermore, distinct neurotransmitters contribute to the function of each cortical area, and the identity of these neurotransmitters is known in most areas. In order to trigger cellular events, neurotransmitters must act through receptors, and with the use of autoradiography and binding techniques, it is possible to study the distribution of these receptors in different cortical layers. For example, clonidine binding sites (α_2-adrenergic receptors) are particularly dense in the layers that process color in area 17. Furthermore, areas 17 and 18 show different distributions of receptors: of 15 different ligands that have been studied, none has an equal distribution of binding sites in the two areas; all of the ligands have binding sites in both areas, but each ligand has its own particular distribution of sites. Because of these distinct distributions, the borderline between areas 17 and 18 can be clearly seen by autoradiography. So, in addition to the cytoarchitecture of a cortical area, we can also describe its "chemoarchitecture."

Differences between and within layers can also be detected with other visible markers. If the surface of the cortex is cut parallel to the pia and stained histochemically for the enzyme cytochrome oxidase, "patches" or "blobs" of staining can be observed in area 17. With electrophysiological techniques, the cells in the blob and interblob regions have been shown to mediate different functions: the cells in the blobs predominantly mediate the perception of color, whereas the cells in the interblob regions mediate the perception of shape and motion. Cytochrome oxidase is a mitochondrial oxidative enzyme that is not directly involved in the process of color vision. However, the neurons in the circuit that analyzes color, for some reason, need more of this enzyme. In area 18, there are no patches or blobs, but there is evidence of thick and thin stripes of cytochrome oxidase staining that cross all the layers. These stripes have a specific connectivity with blobs and interblob regions—and represent an extension of the two-tiered system into secondary visual areas.

How is this circuitry of the cortex integrated with the mosaic of photoreceptors in the eye? In a neural circuit that processes color information, there must be sensory cells that are wavelength sensitive. The sensory cells in the eyes are termed cones and rods, and, although both respond to changes in wavelength, it is the cones that are sensitive to the wavelengths that are perceived as color. All these receptor cells project to the ganglion cell layer, which then projects to the magnocellular and parvocellular layers of the LGN (Fig. 1). The parvocellular layers of the LGN project to specific sublayers of area 17, which are cytochrome oxidase–positive, enriched in α_2-adrenergic receptors, and make separate connections to the blobs. Magnocellular layers project to layer IVCα, which in turn projects to the interblob regions. Areas 17 and 18 also communicate: fibers that originate in blobs project to the thin stripes, whereas fibers that originate from interblob regions project to the interstripe regions.

How does the synaptic circuitry of the visual system develop? To answer this question, we first need to know when cells of the cortex are generated. The method of [^{3}H]thymidine autoradiography has provided information about the timing of cellular generation. (Thymidine is a specific DNA precursor.) In this method, [^{3}H]thymidine is injected intravenously into pregnant monkeys. The [^{3}H]thymidine travels through the bloodstream and the placental barrier until it reaches the fetus, where it labels cells that are dividing and cells that have reached their last division;

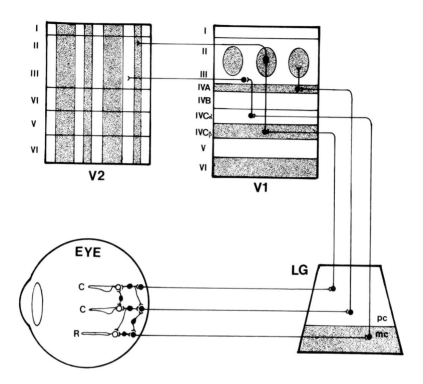

Fig. 1. Highly simplified schematic diagram showing the synaptic circuitry of the visual system. Inputs from the retina (C, cone; R, rod) project to the lateral geniculate nucleus (LG) (pc, parvocellular layers; mc, magnocellular layers), which sends projections to the primary visual cortex (V1), which in turn projects to V2. Shaded areas represent cytochrome oxidase–rich zones. [Courtesy Pasko Rakic, Yale University.]

cells labeled in their last division remain heavily labeled throughout the life of the monkey. Pregnancy in the monkey lasts approximately 165 days, whereas in humans the gestation period is 260 days. The baby monkey is allowed to grow to adulthood, when it is killed and its brain analyzed in order to determine which cells are labeled. Usually different animals are injected with thymidine at different times during pregnancy in order to determine a distribution of neuron "birthdays" during the development of the embryo.

By this method, it has been possible to determine that neuronal generation occurs during the middle of gestation; before embryonic day 30 (E30) no neurons are generated. The retinal cells are generated between E32 and birth, with ganglion cells completing their biogenesis by E70, and the generation of cones continuing throughout the fetal period. Cells destined for the geniculate nucleus are generated between E36 and E43.

Genesis of cortical neurons begins around E40. Cells located deep in the cortex are generated first, and the last, more superficial cells are generated between E90 and E100. No additional cortical neurons are generated during the rest of the pregnancy. Comparative analysis indicates that in humans all neocortical neurons are generated in the first half of the pregnancy; the first neurons are generated around E40 and neuronal generation continues until E125.

The generation of neurons follows an "inside-out" pattern; that is, the earlier-generated cells are located deep in the cortex, whereas late-generated cells are more superficial. No cortical neurons are generated within the cortex itself; the neurons are produced in the proliferative zone, near the ventricular zone, and then they migrate toward the cortex. The earlier-generated neurons settle in deeper positions and neurons that are generated late have to pass them and settle in positions situated more superficially. In this way, the distance between the place of origin and the final destination of the neuron becomes longer and longer; this is particularly true in humans and monkeys because the development of cortical convolutions forces the cells to migrate along paths that are several hundred times longer than the size of the cells. The migrating neurons are guided by radial organizations produced by elongated glial cells, and the neurons follow these pathways by means of surface-mediated interactions. Why is it necessary to bring the cells from the place of origin to their final position in such a fashion? The answer to this question may lie in the fact that earlier-generated cells interact with later-generated cells as the latter pass, so that each cell generation may receive information from the previous generation.

The dividing cells in the proliferative zone do not move laterally, and during their migration the cells maintain a columnar organization. In other words, a site within the proliferative zone produces several generations of cells, all of which migrate along the same radial glial fascicles and form an ontogenetic or embryonic column within the cortical plate. Each column therefore consists of a long chain of cells that originated from the same proliferative unit and, as a consequence, share common ancestors. Initially, before E40, cells divide symmetrically; that is, each cell produces two daughter cells with half the maximal amount of radioactivity derived from [^{3}H]thymidine injections. After E40, cells begin to divide asymmetrically, producing one cell that will migrate and become a neuron and another cell that will remain in the proliferative unit. Proliferative units do not correspond to single clones of cells; they are, in fact, polyclones containing from four to 12 clones. This heterogeneity is evident from [^{3}H]thymidine labeling studies, which show the existence, within the same column of labeled cells (which originate from the same progenitor) and unlabeled cells (which originate from a different progenitor).

This mechanism of cortical neuron generation has important consequences for the evolution of cortical size. An additional cycle of symmetrical division during the stage of proliferative unit formation (before E40) doubles the number of proliferative cells and therefore doubles the number of ontogenetic columns in the cortex; an extra cycle of asymmetrical division (after E40) only adds another neuron within each column. Therefore, the difference in cortical size between humans and monkeys could have been caused by a mutation in the common primate ancestor of humans and monkeys that produced, for example, three more symmetrical divisions. These three additional divisions would produce a cortex about eight to 10 times larger, because there would be many more proliferative units. Data are not available on the length of the cell cycle in any primate. However, if one cycle of cell division requires approximately 12 hours, as in other mammals, three more divisions would correspond to an additional 1.5 days at the stage of symmetrical division. Thus, small changes in timing could make a large difference in functional terms for an animal. The number of proliferative units is therefore critical for the development and evolution of the cortex.

As discussed above, the cortex is organized into specific areas with specific circuitry. There are three possible explanations as to how these areas develop. One possibility is that all of the proliferative units produce the same type of cell and that each cell assumes its specificity when it receives afferents from other regions. The cortical plate, in this case, is devoid of any intrinsic information and this hypothesis is known as the tabula rasa hypothesis. Another possibility is that the specificity of each cell is genetically programmed, and the nature of the afferent input to the cell is irrelevant. This model is known as the fate map hypothesis. The third, and most likely, possibility is that both genetic information and afferent inputs are necessary for formation of the correct circuitry. In this regard, the concept of a protomap in the proliferative zone has been introduced: a vague map, similar to a primordial blueprint, in which the details are not precisely defined until the afferent input is supplied.

The embryological development of the cortex therefore can be summarized as follows: neurons situated within a single radial ontogenetic column have a common site of origin, but have different birthdays. Thus, the position of a neuron in a particular cortical area depends on the position of its proliferative unit of origin, whereas its laminar position within the cortex depends on when it underwent its last mitotic division. The territorial expansion of a cytoarchitectonic area is a function of the number of contributing proliferative units; therefore, the size of any cortical area in each species and individual is the sum of the contributions of participating radial ontogenetic columns.

The functional specificity of cortical areas has been investigated by manipulating the size of the thalamic input into these areas. However, lesions to the source of the thalamic input to the visual cortex are difficult to interpret because they also result in the destruction of the cortical axon terminals that project back to the thalamus (for every axon that projects to the cortex there are 50 axons that project back to the thalamus). An alternative approach has been to destroy the retina in one eye at an early embryonic stage—the reasoning being that this might result in a reduction in size of the LGN and therefore in a reduced cortical input. However, the LGN of adult monkeys from which one eye had been effectively removed at E60 was found to contain the normal number of neurons (1,500,000), and no neuronal degeneration in the thalamus was apparent. The LGN of such manipulated monkeys was divided into parvocellular and magnocellular regions, but these regions were not further subdivided into layers as in normal monkeys. The number of neurons in the LGN did not decrease because of the presence of the remaining eye, which was found to project to the entire LGN. Therefore, the removal of input from a single eye does not affect the number of neurons in the thalamus or in the cortex. However, ocular dominance columns, which are normally observed in the cortex, were absent in the manipulated animals because the entire cortex receives input from one eye.

The LGN of adult monkeys in which both retinas had been resected at E60 was found to be smaller than the LGN of control animals and contained only approximately 400,000 neurons. The remaining geniculate neurons projected topographically to the cortex, but the occipital lobe contained additional sulci and gyri. The diminished thalamic input could theoretically have affected area 17 in various ways (Fig. 2). One possibility is that the reduced input would have no effect on cortical structure—the size and number of ontogenetic columns would be identical to those in the control; there would just be fewer afferents because there are fewer cells in the LGN (Fig. 2B). A second possibility is that transneuronal degeneration of the thalamic cells would result in a secondary neuronal degeneration of cortical cells—the number of columns would be unchanged but the thickness of the columns would be reduced (Fig. 2C). A third possibility is that there would be a reduction in the number of ontogenetic columns, with each maintaining the same number of cells—that is, the thickness of the cortex would be normal (Fig. 2D). Results indicate that the third possibility reflects the real situation: there are fewer columns in area 17, but

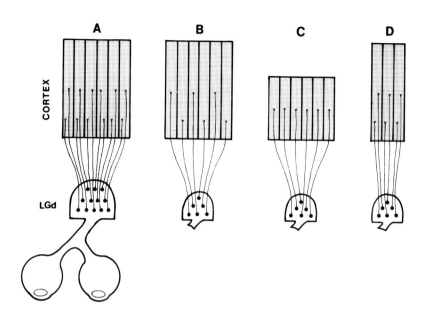

Fig. 2. Possible mechanisms by which ontogenetic columns could be altered by removal of their input. The loss of visual information from the periphery, achieved by removal of both eyes, decreases the number of cells (dots) in the dorsal lateral geniculate nucleus (LGd), and, as a consequence, the input to the cortex is diminished. (**A**) Control situation. (**B, C,** and **D**) Three mechanisms by which ontogenetic columns can be altered. See text for further details. [Reproduced with permission from Rakic (1988), ©AAAS.]

each single column appears normal. Thus, area 17 appears well differentiated from the adjacent area 18, even if it does not receive any information from the retina. The distribution of various neurotransmitter receptors in the different layers of areas 17 and 18 is normal in the lesioned animals. Moreover, cytochrome oxidase staining reveals the presence of the usual blobs—the distance between the blobs and their number are unchanged by manipulating input to the cortex.

These experiments show that the biochemical, cytological, and synaptic properties of area 17 can develop in the absence of afferent input from the retina. However, the number of ontogenetic columns is modified by the absence of afferents. There are several possible explanations why area 17 is smaller after afferent input is removed (Fig. 3): (i) Most of the columns in area 17 degenerate because the cells die, whereas area 18 maintains its normal size (Fig. 3B). (ii) Input from the pulvinar invades area 17, which then becomes transformed into part of area 18 (Fig. 3C). This is a version of the tabula rasa hypothesis—any cortical region can acquire any functional specificity if it receives the correct input. (iii) Abnormal

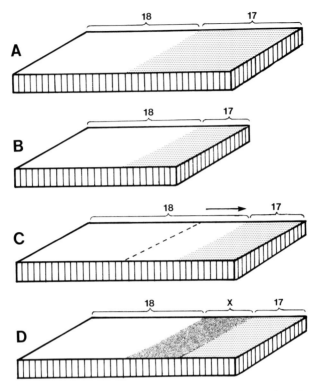

Fig. 3. Schematic representation of the different ways in which the size of area 17 could decrease after reduction of its input from the LGN. (**A**) Control animal. (**B, C,** and **D**) Various hypotheses. See text for further details. [Reproduced with permission from Rakic (1988), ©AAAS.]

input to the vacant region results in the formation of a new hybrid area that is neither area 17 nor 18 but which has some features of each (Fig. 3D). This is a version of the protomap theory.

Serial sections of areas 17 and 18 indeed show the existence of a new hybrid area that differs cytoarchitectonically from both areas 17 and 18. The portion of the developing cortical plate that was deprived of normal thalamic afferents may therefore develop as a new area (Fig. 3D, labeled X), consisting of cells that would normally be genetically destined for area 17 but which are modified by new inputs. The layer structure, cell density, and receptor distribution of the hybrid area also differ from those of areas 17 and 18. Thus, the final neuronal and synaptic organization of the neo-cortex depends on both intracellular genetic programs and extracellular signals.

How can these data be interpreted in terms of evolution, in order to understand how new cytoarchitectonic areas can be introduced into the neocortex? It was found that after the thalamic input decreases, a part of area 17 becomes empty and other inputs may compete to innervate this empty region. This could result in the creation of new cellular relations and may affect functional capacity. In evolution, an imbalance between inputs and targets in the cortex could occur by retaining the same thalamic input, but enlarging the size of cortical areas. For example, a mutation that caused additional cell cycles in the ventricular zone during the phase of proliferative unit formation could result in a larger number of ontogenetic columns. Such a mutation could enlarge one cortical area, and, subsequently, various inputs could compete and form new hybrid cortical areas that are different from those that already exist. If such new neuronal relations are beneficial for the animal, then natural selection will act to maintain the mutation. In this way, new species with larger cortices and new areas could be generated. During embryogenesis, genetic alterations as well as mechanical or chemical lesions that result in decreased input to the cortex may also affect the development of cortical areas and generate new cellular relations. The functional significance of such new cortical areas is not known.

Additional Reading

1. P. Rakic, "Mode of cell migration to the superficial layers of fetal monkey neocortex," *J. Comp. Neurol.* **145,** 61 (1972).
2. P. Rakic, "Neurons in the monkey neocortex: Systematic relation between time of origin and eventual disposition," *Science* **183,** 425 (1974).
3. P. Rakic, "Prenatal genesis of connections subserving ocular dominance in the rhesus monkey," *Nature* **261,** 467 (1976).
4. P. Rakic, "Neuronal-glial interaction during brain development," *Trends Neurosci.* **4,** 184 (1981).
5. P. Rakic and K. P. Riley, "Overproduction and elimination of retinal axons in the fetal rhesus monkey," *Science* **219,** 1441 (1983).
6. P. Rakic, "Limits of neurogenesis in primates," *Science* **227,** 154 (1985).
7. P. Rakic, J.-P. Bourgeois, M. F. Eckenhoff, N. Zecevic, P. S. Goldman-Rakic, "Concurrent overproduction of synapses in diverse regions of the primate cerebral cortex," *Science* **232,** 232 (1986).
8. P. Rakic, "Specification of cerebral cortical areas," *Science* **241,** 170 (1988).
9. J.-P. Bourgeois, P. J. Jastreboff, P. J. Rakic, "Synaptogenesis in visual cortex of normal and preterm monkeys: Evidence for intrinsic regulation of synaptic overproduction," *Proc. Natl. Acad. Sci. U.S.A.* **86,** 4297 (1989).
10. I. Kostovic and P. Rakic, "Developmental history of transient subplate zone in the visual and somatosensory cortex of the macaque monkey and human brain," *J. Comp. Neurol.* **297,** 441 (1990).
11. R. O. Kuljis and P. Rakic, "Hypercolumns in the primate cerebral cortex develop in the absence of cues from photoreceptors," *Proc. Natl. Acad. Sci. U.S.A.* **87,** 5303 (1990).

The Role of Hormones as Mediators of a Changing Brain

Bruce S. McEwen

Bruce S. McEwen's research has contributed significantly to the understanding of how stress and gonadal hormones influence the brain during development and in adult life. Using the rat brain as a model, McEwen and colleagues have studied the mechanisms by which stress hormones secreted by the adrenals and sex hormones secreted by the gonads shape the brain's structure and function during early development and regulate nerve cell activity in adult life. Their research has shown that the brain contains highly specific receptors for stress and sex hormones, and these receptors are found only in some brain regions. These findings have implications for sex differences in human brain function and behavior, and for abnormalities such as Alzheimer's disease, depressive illness, and Parkinson's disease, as well as the aging process.

McEwen, currently a professor at the Rockefeller University and dean of its graduate programs, received his Ph.D. in cell biology there in 1964. His doctoral thesis provided valuable new information about how the cell nucleus stores energy. As a postdoctoral fellow at the Institute of Neurobiology in Göteborg, Sweden, from 1964 to 1965, McEwen studied the biochemical processes underlying the function of nerve cells, particularly the role of brain proteins. He returned to Rockefeller in 1966.

The Role of Hormones as Mediators of a Changing Brain

LECTURER:

Bruce S. McEwen

The brain both regulates and responds to the endocrine system, and so the changing environment and the experiences of an animal can alter and shape the properties of hormone-sensitive nerve cells. For example, depending on the physiological state of the organism, steroid hormones can be either trophic or damaging to the nervous system. Thus, the endocrine system helps to determine the individual traits of an animal in terms of brain function and behavior.

There are many similarities but also many differences between the members of a pair of identical (monozygotic) twins. For example, the probability of two twins manifesting concordance (that is, the chance that, if one twin has the disease, the other twin will also express it during his or her lifetime) for familial Alzheimer's disease or several other genetic diseases is only on the order of 50%. This finding shows that there are characteristics of disease susceptibility that are influenced by environmental factors. In fact, environmental factors influence all aspects of biological development. Which of these factors influence the development of, and hence the adult function of, the brain? Environmental factors can influence the physiology of steroid hormones, which act on the nervous system itself and modulate its two-way relation with the endocrine system (Fig. 1).

The brain controls the endocrine system through the hypothalamus and pituitary gland. These neuroendocrine organs coordinate the rhythmicity of reproductive cycles and also respond to unpredictable, situational information from the external environment (such as stress). Ongoing neural activity regulates the output of hormones from the hypothalamus that control pituitary hormone secretion. Pituitary peptide hormones (such as luteinizing hormone, follicle-stimulating hormone, adrenocorticotropic hormone, and thyroid-stimulating hormone) stimulate steroid secretion from the gonads, adrenals, and thyroid gland; these steroids, in turn, influence neural activity and behavior and regulate further hormone output, thus forming a complex feedback loop. Classically, the

This chapter was edited by Keith W. Brocklehurst, and was originally reported by Maria Luisa Barbaccia.

96

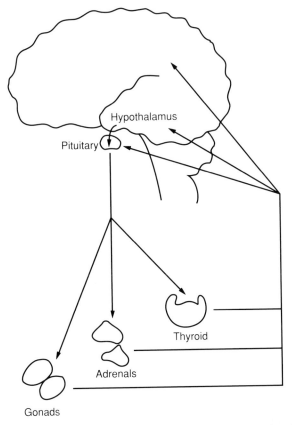

Fig. 1. Hormonal feedback from the peripheral endocrine organs to the pituitary gland, hypothalamus, and other parts of the brain. [Courtesy Bruce McEwen, Rockefeller University.]

action of hormones on the brain has been divided into two categories: "organizational" and "activational." The organizational effects occur during development and are permanent, involving changes in neural circuitry, whereas the activational effects are reversible and manifest themselves as changes in the biochemical properties of neural tissue in response to changing concentrations of steroids, such as occur as a result of reproductive cyclicity.

Whereas these two categories have remained largely correct after many years, new information has revealed diverse hormone effects on the brain that do not fit into the classical organizational or activational groupings. For example, steroids can exert damaging and destructive effects on the brain, particularly in conjunction with stress and aging. These effects are permanent and therefore not activational; and organizational is a mis-

nomer for effects that are disorganizational and lead to a disruption of
neural structure. In addition, activational effects are now known not to be
restricted to regulation of the biochemical properties of neurons, because
neuronal structures, such as synapses and dendrites, of the adult brain
have been shown to be cyclically altered by steroid hormones. Furthermore, activational effects of steroids are not necessarily all mediated by
the intracellular nuclear steroid receptors: There are also membrane effects of steroids that occur along with their genomic effects. Finally, the
organizational and activational effects of steroid hormones are interdepen-
dent; the developmental influences of steroids actually program and sometimes restrict the occurrence of the reversible activational effects.

Steroid hormones and thyroid hormone share a common mechanism
of action (Fig. 2). They first bind to an intracellular receptor, which comprises both a specific hormone binding domain and a DNA binding domain. Binding of the hormone to the receptor results in exposure of the
DNA binding domain, which binds to specific nucleotide sequences that
are present in the promoter region of target genes. By these means, the
receptor regulates the expression of genes that contain receptor binding
domains (Fig. 3).

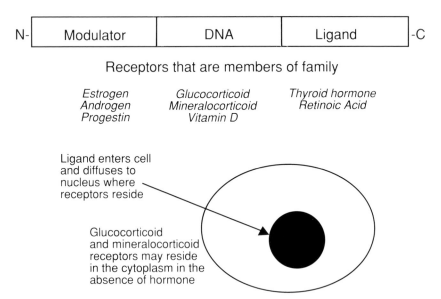

Fig. 2. Domain organization and cellular localization of the members of the steroid
hormone receptor family. N, amino terminus; C, carboxyl terminus; DNA, DNA binding domain; Ligand, ligand binding domain. [Courtesy Bruce McEwen, Rockefeller University.]

In brain, steroid hormone receptors, which resemble those found in the rest of the body, are present mainly in neurons but also in glia. In the past, attention centered on the most obvious tissues where steroids act, such as the uterus, liver, and kidney. Research on the brain lagged behind because the brain was complicated and yielded little information after the expenditure of great effort. Nevertheless, in the fields of psychology and animal behavior there was a distinguished tradition of research on hormone effects on behavior, and this provided the impetus for studies on steroid receptors in the brain. Fortunately, the high affinity and specificity of steroid receptors, and their intracellular localization in the cell nucleus, aided in their identification by autoradiography and other biochemical techniques. Thus, it was shown that the brain is a target organ for every steroid hormone class, with each class of hormone receptors showing a characteristic distribution pattern in the brain. For example, pyramidal neurons in the hippocampus of rhesus monkey were shown to accumulate [³H]glucocorticoids in their cytoplasm and nucleus; and the ventromedial hypothalamus of the rat was shown to contain progesterone receptors, which can be induced by estrogen priming—this is thus an example of a receptor system that is regulated by another hormone and is an important component of the synergistic interaction between estrogen and progesterone that occurs during the female reproductive cycle.

The task in recent years has been to relate the presence of steroid hormone receptors to function, both at the cellular level and in terms of neu-

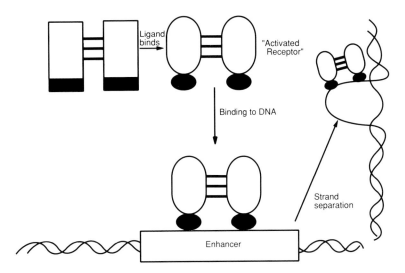

Fig. 3. Classic mechanism of action of steroid hormone receptors. [Courtesy Bruce McEwen, Rockefeller University.]

roendocrine events and behavior. However, ordinary biochemical proce-
dures proved inadequate for this task because of the small amounts of
these receptors present in the brain and the discrete localizations of recep-
tor-containing cells. Examination of restricted brain areas containing steroid receptors by sensitive methods, such as microdissection or quantitative histology, revealed that the brain responds in a similar manner to
other hormone-sensitive tissues and shows induction of enzymes and
other proteins, and even of cellular structures. One example is the induction of the enzyme choline acetyltransferase by estradiol in the basal forebrain of the female rat. This induction is blocked by inhibition of protein
synthesis and results in increased amounts of enzyme protein—not just
increased enzyme activity. As another example, treatment with estradiol
for 72 hours induces a four- to fivefold increase in oxytocin receptors in
the ventromedial nuclei of the hypothalamus.

Steroids can induce reversible changes in the structure of nerve cells.
Steroid hormones can cause rapid modifications in cell nuclei and perinu-
clear cytoplasm—which are indicative of genomic activation and an increased capacity for protein synthesis—as well as somewhat slower
changes related to synaptic transmission, which appear to affect neural
circuitry. For example, a 2-hour pulse of estradiol induces increases in
cell body, nuclear, and nucleolar size in neurons of the ventromedial hypothalamus. There are also increases in the amounts of stacked rough endoplasmic reticulum and of hybridizable 28S ribosomal RNA in these neurons, findings which indicate that there is a massive increase in the
capacity of the cell to make new proteins within hours of estradiol treatment. Why do these neurons show such a massive increase in protein synthesis? Examination of the dendrites of these neurons with the technique
of Golgi silver impregnation revealed that estradiol treatment increases the
number of dendritic spines; similar effects of estradiol have been seen in
the hippocampus. Spines are specialized dendritic structures at which synaptic contacts are made, and the induction of new spines indicates either
that new synapses are formed or that existing ones are changed. There is
further evidence to suggest that new synapses may indeed be forming, at
least in the hypothalamus. Perhaps the most significant finding is that
spines on dendrites appear and disappear during the course of the ovarian
estrous cycle of the female rat, which suggests that synaptogenesis is a
cyclic event that is important in reproductive cycling. Future studies will
need to focus on the structural proteins that underlie formation of new
spines and on the intracellular sites at which these proteins are synthesized and assembled, such as the polyribosomal clusters within neuronal
dendrites.

For many years it has been known that infusion of steroids such as estradiol or cortisol, or their local application to neural tissue, causes rapid perturbations in neuronal electrical activity. Yet only recently has there been a concerted effort to study these effects and to understand their mechanisms. The most successful investigations to date concern the type A γ-aminobutyric acid ($GABA_A$) receptor, which controls the opening of a Cl^- channel. The $GABA_A$ receptor contains a steroid-sensitive domain that recognizes a variety of A-ring–reduced steroids, notably 5α-pregnan-3α,20α-diol, 5α-pregnan-3α-ol-20-one, and 5β-pregnan-3α-ol-20-one. These steroids facilitate the opening of the Cl^- channel and synergize with GABA and with ligands for the coupled benzodiazepine receptor. The site to which the steroid metabolites bind to facilitate GABA-induced Cl^- fluxes was originally thought to be identical to that responsible for barbiturate binding; experimental results now suggest that the two sites are distinct, however. Moreover, the GABA-facilitating steroids may be produced locally in the brain by the metabolism of progesterone and desoxycorticosterone in mitochondria of glial cells. Because alterations of the function of the $GABA_A$ receptor may play a role in various disease states—such as anxiety, affective disorders, and epilepsy—the modulation of $GABA_A$ receptors by steroids is of clinical interest.

In addition, progesterone and related metabolites potentiate the release of dopamine from the rat corpus striatum and of luteinizing hormone–releasing hormone (LHRH) from the median eminence. To study the membrane activity of steroids, investigators have conjugated them to bovine serum albumin in order to reduce the likelihood of their acting intracellularly. Conjugated progestins produce the same effects as unconjugated steroids on dopamine and LHRH release. Radioactive conjugated steroids have also been used to label membrane receptor sites.

Some of the membrane effects of steroids depend on prior genomic actions by related steroids; this has been inferred from the observation that gonadectomy decreases the degree and frequency of the rapid, direct electrical effects of iontophoretically applied estradiol on preoptic area neurons. Another illustration of this phenomenon relates to the observation that whereas estradiol induces receptors for oxytocin in the ventromedial hypothalamus of the female rat, progesterone does not. However, the induced oxytocin receptors are present in an area of the neuronal membrane that is removed from the region of the neuron closest to the oxytocin-containing nerve fibers. It has recently been observed that progesterone rapidly (within 30 to 60 min) promotes spreading of oxytocin receptors into the membrane area adjacent to the oxytocin-containing fibers. This effect appears to be important in the facilitation of female sexual behavior, and the rapidity with which it occurs suggested that it might result from a direct membrane action of progesterone. The further observation that progesterone caused a rapid spread of oxytocin receptors in brain sections that had been cut fresh and then frozen and mounted on glass slides for autoradiography strongly indicated that the effect was unlikely to be genomic or intracellular. Rather, progesterone may activate the conversion of estrogen-induced oxytocin receptors to a high-affinity state or may facilitate a rapid movement of these receptors along the surface of the dendrites of ventromedial hypothalamic neurons.

Thus, progesterone has actions that can be distinguished on the basis of their time course as genomic or nongenomic (Fig. 4). The nongenomic effects include (i) the progesterone-induced spreading of oxytocin receptors and (ii) the potentiation of GABA action through $GABA_A$ receptors by certain metabolites of progesterone.

Gonadal steroids and thyroid hormone exert important developmental influences on the brain, which result in permanent changes in neuronal circuitry. Gonadal steroids and glucocorticoids can cause permanent neural damage and cell loss in the adult brain. For example, persistent low levels of estrogens lead to the hypothalamic disconnection syndrome,

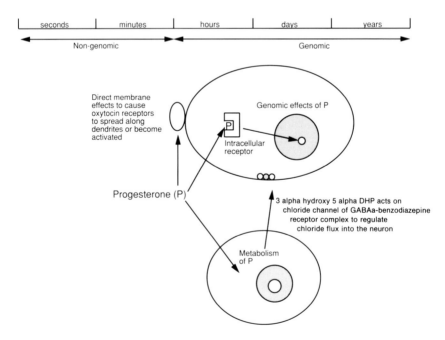

Fig. 4. Genomic and nongenomic actions of progesterone. [Courtesy Bruce McEwen, Rockefeller University.]

which is accompanied by a marked change in the morphology of the arcuate nucleus and reproductive acyclicity. Moreover, an excess or deficiency of glucocorticoids can result in the degeneration of specific populations of hippocampal neurons.

The hippocampus contains three principal types of interconnecting neurons: (i) the granule cells of the dentate gyrus, which receive afferents from the entorhinal cortex, one of the main input pathways to the hippocampus from the rest of the brain; (ii) the CA3 neurons of Ammon's horn, which receive the input of the axons (mossy fibers) of the granule cells; and (iii) CA1 pyramidal neurons, which receive input from the CA3 cells and are responsible for the main output of the hippocampus (Fig. 5). Neurons of the dentate gyrus atrophy and die after bilateral adrenalectomy, and this response can be prevented by low replacement doses of adrenal steroids after surgery—thus suggesting that glucocorticoids are themselves trophic substances or that they induce a trophic substance. One possible indirect mediator is nerve growth factor, the concentration of which is decreased in the hippocampus after adrenalectomy. In contrast to the

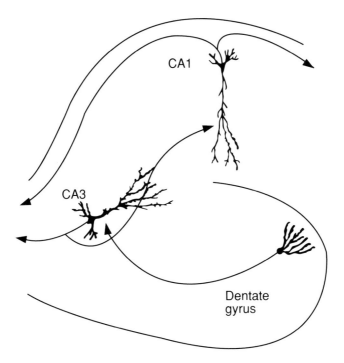

Fig. 5. Neuronal connectivity of hippocampal CA1 and CA3 cells and granule cells of the dentate gyrus. [Courtesy Bruce McEwen, Rockefeller University.]

effects of steroids on the dentate gyrus, repeated injections of corticosterone to young adult rats results in atrophy and eventual death of neurons in
the CA3 region. One possible cause for this effect may be excessive stimulation of CA3 neurons by the input from the dentate gyrus—the release of
excitatory amino acids from neurons of the dentate gyrus' is a primary
component in the cascade of events that leads to neuronal death after transient ischemia and head trauma. Glucocorticoids exacerbate neuronal loss
promoted by excitatory amino acids and may do so by inhibiting the uptake of glucose into neurons. According to this scenario, neurons that are
unable to generate enough energy to resequester the Ca^{2+} mobilized by
the excitatory amino acids enter a cascade of self-destruction—which involves osmotic damage, free-radical formation, lipid peroxidation, and
membrane damage (Fig. 6).

Neuronal loss in the hippocampus also occurs during aging, and glucocorticoids contribute to this process. As neurons are lost, the capacity of
the hippocampus to participate in turning off pituitary-adrenal function is
impaired, with the result that increases in the plasma concentration of glu-

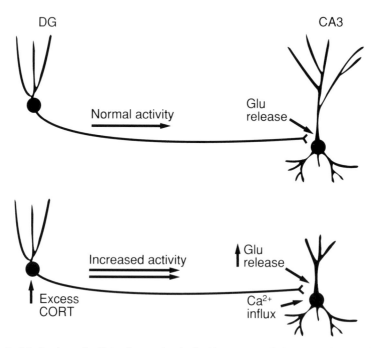

Fig. 6. Mechanism of cellular destruction in the hippocampus induced by glucocorticoids.
CORT, corticosterone; Glu, glutamate; DG, dentate gyrus. [Courtesy Bruce McEwen,
Rockefeller University.]

cocorticoids, particularly after stress, are prolonged; this may further exacerbate the damage and lead to accelerated neuronal destruction. It has also been shown that there is a selective destruction of neurons in CA3 and CA4 hippocampal regions in the brains of monkeys that lead subordinate, and therefore stressful, lives. Because this effect was observed only in male monkeys, it seems to be a sex-dependent phenomenon, probably related to the lack of a priming or protective effect of estrogens (or estrogen metabolites) in males.

Neurons of the hippocampus are also targets for thyroid hormone. If T_3 (triiodothyronine) is administered to an adult male rat for a period of 7 to 8 days, the rat will develop symptoms of hyperthyroidism. As a result of such treatment, there is a selective decrease of about 30 to 35% in the spine density in hippocampal CA1 neurons. A different response is seen if T_3 is administered to male rats on days 1, 2, and 4 after birth (when the sexual differentiation of the male rat, which is induced by testosterone secretion, is in progress). If the rats are allowed to mature and are examined 70 to 80 days after this treatment schedule, the hippocampal CA3 neurons are found to be larger and more branched than in control rats; this may also reflect or allow for an increased number of mossy fiber inputs, an increased survival of dentate gyrus granule neurons, and an increased CA3 neuronal output that is apparent from the greater number of spines present on CA1 neurons, which receive projections from CA3 (Fig. 7). Although the CA3 neurons appear larger and more branched, the hippocampus does not seem to function better. Behavioral experiments with these hyperthyroid rats showed that they were in fact less efficient at learning a spatial-cognitive task than normal rats.

Whereas the destructive actions of steroids alter the way the brain responds to the environment, the developmental actions of steroids determine the potential of the brain and set limits on its response. Permanent developmental effects of hormones place limitations on both the quantitative and qualitative nature of some of the activational responses to hormones after the developmental period is over. Whereas it has been clear that this concept applies to behavioral and neuroendocrine responses, particularly in the realm of reproductive function, it is now becoming evident that the concept also applies at the cellular level. For example, recent evidence has suggested that there are developmentally programmed sex differences in some, but not all, of the responses of the ventromedial hypothalamus to estradiol. The ventromedial hypothalamus plays an important role in hormonal stimulation of female mating behavior in the rat. Male rats, or females exposed at birth to testosterone, fail to show female mating responses to priming with ovarian steroids. Both male and female rats

NORMAL

CA1 pyramidal cell

CA3 pyramidal cell   granule cell

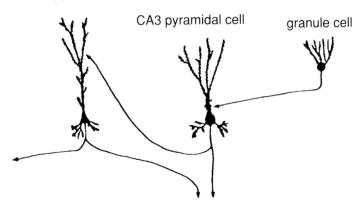

THYROID HORMONE TREATED

increased   increased
dendritic spines   cell size   increased
                                            numbers of cells

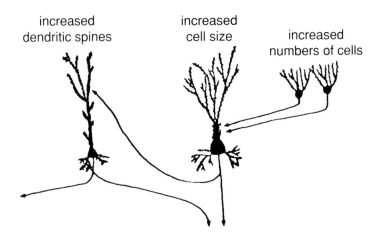

Fig. 7. Effect of thyroid hormone on CA1 and CA3 pyramidal cells of the hippocampus and granule cells of the dentate gyrus. [Courtesy Bruce McEwen, Rockefeller University.]

have estrogen receptors in the ventromedial nuclei of the hypothalamus (VMN), and, indeed, estradiol increases the number of oxytocin receptors equally in the male and female VMN. Yet estradiol does not induce significant numbers of dendritic spines in the male VMN, in contrast to its large effects on spine density in the female VMN. Furthermore, the extent of progestin receptor induction in the female VMN as a result of estrogen priming exceeds that in the male by a factor of two. These latter results suggest that the male VMN have a lower sensitivity to estradiol than the female VMN; however, the extensive induction of oxytocin receptors in both sexes, together with the very presence of estrogen receptors in the male VMN, indicates that the VMN of males are not totally insensitive to estradiol. One possibility is that the sexually dimorphic and nondimorphic responses occur in distinct cell populations; that is, sexual differentiation may affect certain populations of cells differently. Alternatively, these two different types of response may occur in the same cells; this may be possible because of a differentiation at the genomic level with regard to the regulation of transcriptional processes for individual genes. The existence of multiple transcription factors that control gene expression in differentiated cells is consistent with this second model.

In conclusion, studies of the actions of steroid hormones on neuronal structure and biochemistry have shown that the adult brain is quite plastic and responsive to the environment. Because the brain both controls the endocrine system and responds to it, the changing environment, as well as the experiences of an animal, can change and shape properties of hormone-sensitive nerve cells. This shaping is clearly central to the cyclic regulation of reproductive function, and it may also be important in other endocrine cycles, such as that responsible for diurnal rhythm. However, the endocrine system can also have destructive effects on the nervous system. The deleterious effects of constant low concentrations of estrogens on the rodent hypothalamus and the destructive effects of glucocorticoids on the rodent hippocampus emphasize the point that neural dysfunction may also result from the impact of the environment on the brain. A key question for future research will be to distinguish between the beneficial and destructive effects of hormones on the brain and to determine whether the pattern of hormone secretion, the dose, or the operation of other factors concurrently with hormones is important in initiating the damage.

The quality and quantity of steroid action in the adult brain are restricted by events during development. In addition to brain sexual differentiation, early experiences that affect thyroid and pituitary-adrenal function, such as the handling of newborn rats for the first 14 days after birth or random prenatal stress, determine characteristics of the adult stress response. In addition, the rate at which glucocorticoid-induced damage of the hippocampus accumulates with age is reduced in rats handled during the neonatal period; in such rats, pituitary-adrenal function in response to stress is less pronounced. Thus, the endocrine system is at least partially responsible for determining the characteristics of an individual animal with regard to brain function and behavior.

Additional Reading

1. B. S. McEwen, "The brain as target for steroid hormone action," *Annu. Rev. Neurosci.* **2**, 65 (1979).
2. V. Luine and B. McEwen, "Sex differences in cholinergic enzymes of diagonal band nuclei in the rat preoptic area," *Neuroendocrinology* **36**, 475 (1983).
3. B. Parsons, T. Rainbows, B. S. McEwen, "Organizational effects of testosterone via aromatization on feminine reproductive behavior and neural progestin receptors in rat brain," *Endocrinology* **115**, 1412 (1984).
4. R. Sapolsky, L. Krey, B. S. McEwen, "The neuroendocrinology of stress and aging: The glucocorticoid cascade hypothesis," *Endocr. Rev.* **7**, 284 (1986).
5. B. S. McEwen, K. Jones, D. Pfaff, "Hormonal control of sexual behavior in the female rat: Molecular, cellular and neurochemical studies," *Biol. Reprod.* **36**, 37 (1987).
6. H. Coirini, A. Johnson, B. S. McEwen, "Estradiol modulation of oxytocin binding in the ventromedial hypothalamic nucleus of male and female rats," *Neuroendocrinology* **50**, 193 (1989).
7. E. Gould, C. Woolley, M. Frankfurt, B. S. McEwen, "Gonadal steroids regulate dendritic spine density in hippocampal pyramidal cells in adulthood," *J. Neurosci.* **10**, 1286 (1989).
8. M. Schumacher, H. Coirini, M. Frankfurt, B. S. McEwen, "Localized actions of progesterone in hypothalamus involve oxytocin," *Proc. Natl. Acad. Sci. U.S.A.* **86**, 6798 (1989).
9. M. Frankfurt, E. Gould, C. Woolley, B. McEwen, "Gonadal steroids modify dendritic spine density in ventromedial hypothalamic neurons: A Golgi study in the adult rat," *Neuroendocrinology* **51**, 530 (1990).

Construction of the Visual Image by the Cerebral Cortex

Semir Zeki

Semir Zeki has served as professor of neurobiology at University College, London, U.K., since 1981. In 1967 he received his Ph.D. there in medicine with a focus on anatomy. He also has held posts as a research associate at St. Elizabeth's Hospital in Washington, D.C., and as assistant professor of anatomy at the University of Wisconsin.

Zeki has used anatomical and physiological techniques to study his main research interest, the primate visual cortex. His most recent studies have applied his findings to a study of the human brain using noninvasive imaging techniques.

Construction of the Visual Image by the Cerebral Cortex

LECTURER:

Semir Zeki

The study of color vision has provided a fascinating insight into the workings of the brain. Historically, during the first half of this century, three concepts greatly influenced researchers working on the visual cortex. The first of these concepts originated from observations of the anatomical connections between the retina and the cortex. These connections are organized in a point-to-point manner—adjacent points in the retina connect with adjacent points in the primary visual cortex (area V1). This defined cortical area was termed the "cortical retina" by Henschen because of the detailed topographical representation of the retina that it contains. The term "cortical retina" encapsulates much of the thinking in the field during this period. The first concept can thus be summarized as follows: An impression of the visual world—which includes color, form, movement, and depth information—is formed on the retina and is then transmitted to be "received" by the primary visual cortex.

The second concept concerns the duality of the cortical processes involved in vision. Two processes were suggested to be involved in vision: the reception of the visual impressions formed on the retina, leading to perception—a function performed by the primary visual cortex—and the association of these received visual impressions with previous impressions of a similar kind, leading to recognition. This latter function was supposedly performed by a cortical area surrounding the primary visual cortex, known as the visual association cortex. The doctrine of duality of the visual process received powerful support from the studies of Flechsig, who was interested in the mechanism by which cortical neurons are myelinated. He found that certain cortical areas ("primordial" areas), which include the primary visual cortex, are myelinated at birth, whereas other cortical regions ("associational" areas) are myelinated at various stages after birth. He noted that the primordial cortical areas are connected with sensory organs but not with each other, whereas the associational areas are not connected with sensory organs but receive inputs from the primordial areas. These observations suggested that the brain contains anatomically

This chapter was edited by Keith W. Brocklehurst, and was originally reported by Maurizio Memo.

defined cortical areas dedicated to the reception of impulses from the external world and areas that are important for the association of these impulses with previously received impulses. Flechsig thus referred to the association cortex as the organ of psyche.

One problem with the concept of duality, however, was the observation that brain lesions lying outside of the primary visual cortex are responsible for a syndrome—known as cerebral achromatopsia—in which the affected individual specifically loses the ability to see colors. Two features of cerebral achromatopsia are worth noting. First, the deficit is specific to color vision—the entire world being commonly described by affected individuals in terms of shades of gray. Perception of forms is often unimpaired, as is perception of depth and motion. The second feature of cerebral achromatopsia is that it is not necessarily accompanied by any defect in retinal mechanisms responsible for color vision. Indeed, all retinal mechanisms are intact, although affected individuals are unable to perceive colors. It is as if the sensory input to the cortex is intact, but because the relevant cortical area is damaged, the cortex is unable to make use of the information that it receives. These observations thus implied either that color is not a mere received visual impression or that the receiving visual cortex (Henschen's cortical retina) was much larger than was previously thought.

The third concept is that of cortical architecture. It has been generally supposed that functional differences between cortical areas should be reflected anatomically and, conversely, that a cortical area of uniform structure should also be one of uniform function. However, the histological methods used in the past have not always been equal to the task of revealing all the anatomical differences in the cerebral cortex. The preferred method was the cytoarchitectonic method, which showed how cells in the cortex are organized into separate layers. This approach readily revealed that the visual cortex can be subdivided into striate (primary visual) and prestriate (visual association) cortex; however, it did not reveal further differentiation within either zone. The prestriate cortex was, therefore, commonly thought of as a uniform cortical area. Thus, although clinical evidence suggested that a specific region of the prestriate cortex might be specifically involved in color vision, this evidence was dismissed partly because the region concerned could not be differentiated cytoarchitectonically from the surrounding regions.

These three concepts were considered as dogma until the 1970s. A fourth concept, which is still prevalent, is that of hierarchies. Simply stated, the hierarchical doctrine maintains that the nervous system uses a building-block strategy to construct the visual image, analyzing and bringing together different components of the image in a cascade. This functional hierarchical organization is reflected anatomically in a general sense—visual images are formed in the retina, received in the primary visual cortex, interpreted in the visual association cortex, and committed to memory in the cortex of the temporal lobe.

Recent anatomical and electrophysiological studies on monkeys, however, have shown that any given point in the primary visual cortex—which receives information about the visual field from a corresponding retinal point—sends independent and parallel outputs to different parts of the visual association cortex. Several conclusions can be drawn from this single observation: (i) This pattern of projections is not consistent with a simple hierarchical cascade model. (ii) It is difficult to believe that the primary visual cortex would send the same signals in these different projections; it is more logical to suppose that the primary visual cortex segregates information and parcels out different signals to different regions of the visual association cortex. This latter interpretation is supported by the finding that the diameters of the projecting fibers are themselves different. (iii) If different areas of the visual association cortex receive different kinds of signals, it follows that they must be specialized for handling different attributes of the visual image.

Indeed, with new anatomical techniques, it is now possible to divide the visual association cortex into a number of areas: V2, V3, V3A, V4, V5, and V5A. Thus, the notion that a specific modality of vision, such as form or color, might be represented in a specific area outside the primary visual cortex and the notion that such areas can be specifically damaged by vascular lesions are not so fantastic.

Electrophysiological recordings from these different areas of the visual association cortex have made it possible to assign specific functions to each of them. Thus, 100% of the cells in V5 are motion sensitive, and 95% are directionally selective; V5 cells are not selective for color and most are not selective for the form of the stimulus. Similar cells, but with larger receptive fields, are found in V5A. The V4 region, which is almost certainly made up of more than one area, contains cells that are selective for the color of the stimulus, some of which are also sensitive to its orientation. The cells in V3 and V3A are orientation selective but are not selective for color.

Thus, the demonstration of the existence of these three separate regions in the visual association cortex for processing form (V3 and V3A), color (V4), and motion (V5) led to the concept of functional specialization; that is, different attributes of vision are processed separately. Within the last decade it became possible to demonstrate functional specialization in the human visual cortex by positron emission tomography (PET), which measures increases in regional cerebral blood flow when a subject undertakes particular tasks. These studies have demonstrated that specific areas of the human visual cortex are responsible for processing information relating to motion (human V5) and to color (human V4). Both of these areas have also been shown to receive parallel inputs from the human primary visual cortex. Finally, brain lesions that give rise to cerebral achromatopsia fall within the area of the human V4 region as detected by PET scanning.

The theory of functional specialization predicts that signals related to different attributes of the visual world must be processed separately before they reach the specialized areas of the visual association cortex. This functional diversity of the primary visual cortex should therefore be reflected anatomically. Although cytoarchitectonic studies of the primary visual cortex revealed different layers parallel to the cortical surface, there were no obvious differences within the layers. However, staining of the primary visual cortex for the metabolic enzyme, cytochrome oxidase, revealed a set of columns of high metabolic activity that extend from the cortical surface to the white matter. These columns are especially prominent in layers 2 and 3, where they are commonly referred to as blobs— which is how they appear when viewed from above. Electrophysiological recordings from cells inside and outside the blobs have confirmed the general notion of separation of visual functions. Generally, cells inside the blobs are wavelength selective and not orientation selective, and cells outside the blobs are orientation selective and are not concerned with the color of the stimulus. These results show that the pathways for color and form are segregated within V1. Similarly, by retrograde labeling with horseradish peroxidase, area V5—which is specialized for visual motion—has been shown to receive its input only from directionally selective cells in layer 4B and upper layer 6 of V1. Cells in layer 4B of V1 that project to V5 are separated from each other by orientation-selective cells that project to V3. Thus, there is a segregation within layer 4B of V1 of cells that project to V5 and cells that project to V3. These findings support the notion that V1 acts as a segregator of function.

The concept of functional specialization and segregation can be extended to the V2 area. This area surrounds V1, receives a strong input from it, and, like V1, contains a heterogeneous population of cells, as shown by cytochrome oxidase histochemistry. Staining of V2 for metabolic activity thus reveals a set of alternate thick and thin stripes, which are separated from each other by more lightly staining interstripes. Physiological studies show that most cells in the thin stripes are wavelength selective but are not concerned with the orientation of the stimulus. The thin stripes receive input from the blobs of V1 and project to V4. Directionally selective cells are found in the thick stripes only; but not all the cells in the thick stripes are directionally selective. The thick stripes receive inputs from layer 4B of V1 and project both to V3 and V5. The interstripes receive inputs from the interblob areas of V1 and project to V4 and to other cortical regions. Thus, V2, like V1, acts as a segregator of function.

In order to summarize the concept of separate functionally specialized pathways, recent results of studies on the structural organization of the visual cortex can be combined with anatomical studies of the retino-geniculo-cortical pathway. The input from the eyes travels to the cortex through the lateral geniculate nucleus, which is composed of two main subdivisions: the magnocellular (M) layers and the parvocellular (P) layers. The M· and P layers have different cortical destinations, and the two pathways are involved in processing different attributes of the visual scene. Thus, the color pathway is P layers $\rightarrow$ blobs of V1 $\rightarrow$ thin stripes of V2 $\rightarrow$ V4. The motion pathway is M layers $\rightarrow$ layer 4B of V1 $\rightarrow$ thick stripes of V2 $\rightarrow$ V5. There are two pathways for form: one associated with color, which is P layers $\rightarrow$ interblobs of V1 $\rightarrow$ interstripes of V2 $\rightarrow$ V4; and the other, which is not associated with color, is M layers $\rightarrow$ layer 4B of V1 $\rightarrow$ thick stripes of V2 $\rightarrow$ V3.

With this knowledge, it is possible to account for certain neurological syndromes. In the case of cerebral achromatopsia, it is possible to account for the fact that color vision is impaired, whereas form vision is intact, by supposing that human area V4 is destroyed but the form system based on V3 is still active. Circumstantial evidence indeed suggests that such patients use the V3 form system. The syndrome of cerebral akinetopsia, in which the ability to detect motion visually is specifically affected, can be explained by lesions in area V5.

In summary then, the visual image is not analyzed in V1 and interpreted in other areas. Rather, the visual image is constructed in the brain, with different visual attributes being constructed in different areas. The functional specialization of the visual cortex raises the question of how different cerebral cortical areas interact to produce a visual image—a problem that is not unique to the process of vision. There is no single area to which the different visual areas all connect. Instead, there are many connections at different levels: (i) The specialized areas of the visual association cortex connect back with V1 and V2 through diffuse, return projections. (ii) Direct connections between the specialized areas allow them to communicate with each other. (iii) Convergent projections to higher brain areas allow signals from different areas to be combined. This complex network of connections forms the basis for one theory of multistage integration.

Additional Reading

1. S. Zeki, "Functional specialization in the visual cortex of the rhesus monkey," *Nature* **274,** 423 (1978).
2. S. Zeki, "Uniformity and diversity of structure and function in rhesus monkey prestriate visual cortex," *J. Physiol. (Lond.)* **277,** 273 (1978).
3. S. Zeki, "The construction of colours by the cerebral cortex," *Proc. R. Inst. Gt. Britain* **56,** 231 (1984).
4. S. Zeki and S. Shipp, "The functional logic of cortical connections," *Nature* **335,** 311 (1988).
5. S. Zeki, "A century of cerebral achromatopsia," *Brain* **113,** 1721 (1990).
6. S. Zeki, "Colour vision and functional specialization in the visual cortex," *Discuss. Neurosci.* **6,** 1 (1990).

Mechanisms of Growth and Synapse Formation During Regeneration

John G. Nicholls

John G. Nicholls, F.R.S., is a professor of pharmacology at the Biocenter, Basel University, and until recently was a professor of neurobiology at Stanford University School of Medicine. He has taught in England at University College, London, and Oxford University, and in the United States at Yale, Harvard, and Stanford University Medical Schools. In addition, he has given advanced courses worldwide including those at the Marine Biological Laboratory at Woods Hole, Massachusetts, and at the Cold Spring Harbor Laboratory, New York.

Nicholls was born in London, England, where he graduated in medicine from Charing Cross Hospital, London University. He received a doctorate in physiology from the Department of Biophysics at University College while working with Sir Bernard Katz. Nicholls' research has contributed to sensory and muscle physiology and to the physiology of neuroglial cells—an area in which he collaborated with Stephen Kuffler. Nicholls has used the relatively simple nervous system of the leech to study synaptic transmission and the regeneration of synaptic connections. Recently he has begun to study similar problems in the central nervous system of a small South American opossum in which much of development occurs after birth.

Mechanisms of Growth and Synapse Formation During Regeneration

LECTURER:

John G. Nicholls

This discussion will focus on the properties and connections of individual identified nerve cells of known function that have been dissected out of the central nervous system (CNS) of a simple invertebrate—the leech—and maintained in tissue culture for periods of days or weeks. In the first part of the discussion, emphasis will be placed on the manner in which these nerve cells form synapses. Whether a particular pair of cells forms a chemical, electrical, or mixed chemical-electrical synapse, or no synapse at all, depends on the identity of the cells. Furthermore, particular regions of a cell are favored in the formation of chemical or electrical synapses. A simple preparation consisting of a pair of cells is useful for studying the detailed mechanisms of synaptic transmission. The properties of transmitter release and synaptic transmission at these simplified synapses formed in culture are similar to those of synapses in intact animals. The second part of this discussion will be concerned with the mechanisms responsible for induction of neurite growth. The molecular composition of the substrate on which a cell is placed is of critical importance in determining whether the cell grows or not. Furthermore, each cell grows with a specific fingerprint, the characteristics of which depend on the identity of the cell and of the substrate. In addition to influencing the degree and pattern of growth, the substrate also influences the distribution of Ca^{2+} channels in the growing processes.

Regeneration and repair of the nervous system are of great importance to an organism. In mammals, the chances of recovery after lesions to a peripheral nerve are very good—axons will grow back and reestablish connections. However, until recently, it was thought that neurons in the mammalian CNS could not regenerate and repair connections after injury. In the last few years, experiments have shown that (i) neurons within the mammalian CNS do have powers of regeneration if they are supplied with a permissive pathway, and (ii) there are inhibitory molecules produced by glial cells in the CNS that prevent axonal growth. This discussion will be directed more to the problems of regeneration and repair in the leech ner-

This chapter was edited by Keith W. Brocklehurst, and was originally reported by Mariella Bertolino.

118

vous system. The nervous system of the leech repairs itself with high fidelity, and this process can be studied at the level of single, identified
cells. Even in the leech, however, the process of regeneration is complex,
which is one reason why synapse formation between pairs of cells has
been studied in culture.

The experiments reported here were performed by John Nicholls in
collaboration with S. Acklin, W. Adams, H. Aréchiga, S. Grumbacher-
Reinert, Y. Liu, L. Masuda-Nakagawa, K. J. Muller, W. N. Ross, and R.
Stewart, and were supported by the Swiss National Fund.

The leech nervous system is composed of a chain of similar ganglia
(Fig. 1), each consisting of approximately 400 cells. Each ganglion contains sensory T, P, and N cells, which are sensitive to touch, pressure, and
noxious mechanical stimulation, respectively; large Retzius cells, which
contain and secrete serotonin (5-HT); and anterior pagoda (AP) cells.
Each of these cells can be independently removed and kept in culture for
up to 4 weeks, during which time the cells retain their membrane properties and do not revert to a primordial undifferentiated state. Single cells are

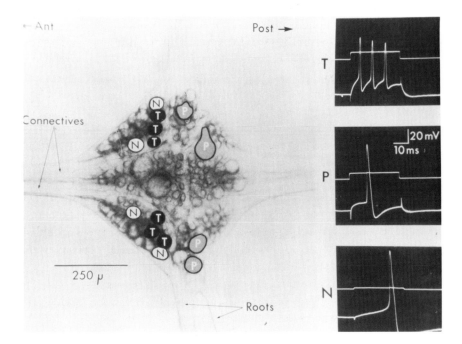

Fig. 1. (**Left**) The structure of a ganglion of the leech nervous system. T (touch), P (pressure), and N (noxious stimulation) sensory neurons are shown. Ant, anterior; post, posterior. (**Right**) Electrical activity of T, P, and N neurons after stimulation.

isolated by positioning a glass pipette with a large-diameter tip close to the ganglion and sucking up the desired cell (Fig. 2).

When a Retzius cell is placed in culture with a sensory P cell, the two cells form a chemical synapse, and the synapse always forms in the same direction, from the Retzius cell to the P cell. It has been determined that this association represents a true synapse—electron microscopic observations have revealed the presence of typical synaptic structures such as vesicles, active zones, a widened extracellular space, and postsynaptic specializations. Although the type of synapse formed between a particular pair of cells (electrical, chemical, or mixed electrical-chemical) is always the same, many times when two cells are simply placed together in culture, no synapse is formed. This is because there appear to be specialized regions of the cells that are favorable for synapse formation. For example,

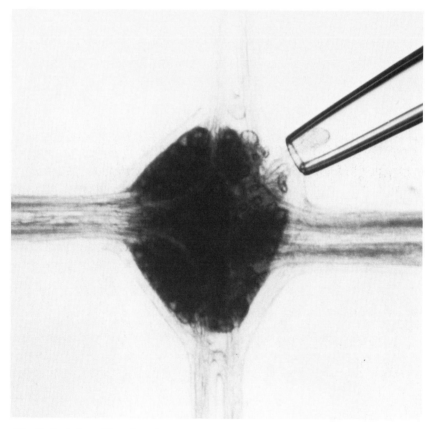

Fig. 2. Isolation with a glass pipette of single leech cells from a ganglion. [Reprinted with permission of the Physiological Society, U.K., from Dietzel *et al.* (1986).]

when two Retzius cells are placed so that their tips are touching (Fig. 3), a bidirectional chemical synapse develops within 6 hours, and by 2 days an electrical component also appears. This occurs in 100% of pairings. When the tip of one cell is placed so that it touches the body of another (Fig. 4), a unidirectional synapse is formed, with the tip as the release site. Finally, when the cell bodies of the two neurons are juxtaposed (Fig. 5), synapses have difficulty in forming, and many times do not form at all.

Electrical recordings made from Retzius cells paired at their tips show that, after 7 hours, an impulse applied to one cell gives rise to a synaptic potential in the other cell; and after 2 days, the synaptic potential becomes much larger. It has been shown that Retzius cells synthesize, store, and release 5-HT, and that application of 5-HT to the postsynaptic site of a Retzius cell mimics the action of the transmitter released from the presynaptic Retzius cell. Furthermore, the release of 5-HT seems to occur in multimolecular packets or quanta.

The Retzius cell–P cell synapse in culture also exhibits a feature that is common to synapses in the intact nervous system—facilitation. Facilitation refers to the phenomenon by which each successive impulse induces a

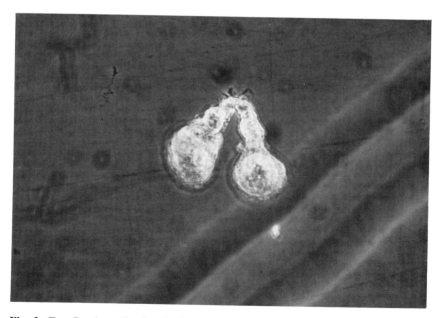

Fig. 3. Two Retzius cells placed with their tips juxtaposed. [Reprinted with permission from Liu and Nicholls (1989).]

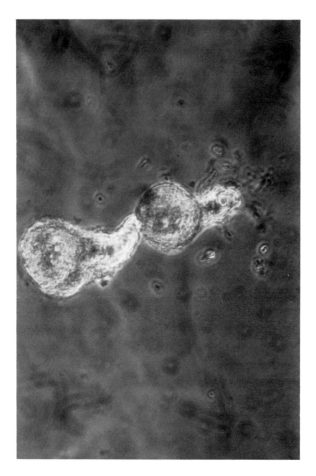

Fig. 4. The tip of one Retzius cell juxtaposed to the body of another. [Reprinted with permission from Liu and Nicholls (1989).]

larger synaptic potential than the previous impulse. Theoretically, the mechanism underlying facilitation could be an increase in the sensitivity of the postsynaptic cell to transmitter or an increase in the amount of transmitter released from the presynaptic cell with each successive stimulus. By measuring the number of quanta of transmitter released before and after facilitation, it can be demonstrated that facilitation is a presynaptic event and is due to an increase in the number of quanta of neurotransmitter released with each impulse. Because Ca^{2+} is required for the release of neurotransmitter, changes in Ca^{2+} regulation may be responsible for this phenomenon. One possibility is that each impulse could stimulate the entry of more Ca^{2+} into the cell than the previous impulse; this is referred to

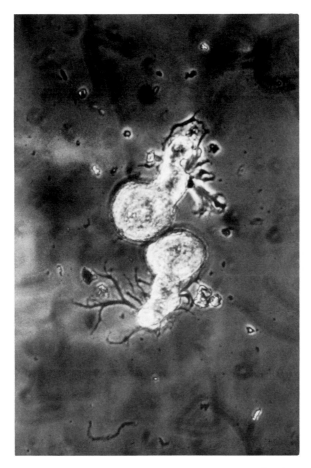

Fig. 5. Two Retzius cells with their cell bodies juxtaposed. [Reprinted with permission from Liu and Nicholls (1989).]

as the facilitated Ca^{2+} entry hypothesis. Another possibility is that each impulse allows the same amount of Ca^{2+} into the cell, but residual Ca^{2+} remains in the presynaptic cell between successive impulses; this is referred to as the residual Ca^{2+} hypothesis. These rival hypotheses have been investigated by measuring the Ca^{2+} that enters the Retzius cell during each impulse with the use of the voltage clamp technique. In this procedure, the presynaptic cell is electrically clamped with two microelectrodes, one for passing current and the other for measuring voltage. The cell is depolarized, and the inward and outward currents are measured. In this way, if the Na^+ and K^+ currents are blocked, Ca^{2+} entry can be measured. The presynaptic cell is stimulated with a series of electrical pulses, and the Ca^{2+} entry during each pulse is measured. The results from this kind of experiment show that the amount of Ca^{2+} that enters the cell during each pulse is the same (Fig. 6). It thus appears that the residual Ca^{2+} hypothesis is probably correct.

Optical recording techniques can also be used to measure Ca^{2+} current. A cell can be injected with the dye arsenazo III, which measures changes in the intracellular Ca^{2+} concentration (arsenazo III does not measure absolute Ca^{2+} concentrations, unlike the Ca^{2+} indicator, fura), and Ca^{2+} that enters a cell during an impulse can be visualized. Fig. 7 shows that the two Ca^{2+} transients produced from two successive impulses are of the same amplitude. These Ca^{2+} transients are blocked by Cd^{2+}, thus showing that the Ca^{2+} is not released from intracellular stores but enters the cell through membrane channels.

The loose-patch technique can also be applied to cultured leech neurons. In this technique, a patch electrode with a large-diameter tip is used to clamp a small patch of membrane, and current is measured. The advantage of this method is that populations of channels can be investigated in different regions of a single cell. Thus, regional current changes can be measured when cells form synapses. For example, by this technique, Na^+ currents have been shown to be larger at the growing tips of cells.

For synaptic contacts to be made during regeneration, the innervating neurons must be able to reach their targets. Neuronal growth depends crit-

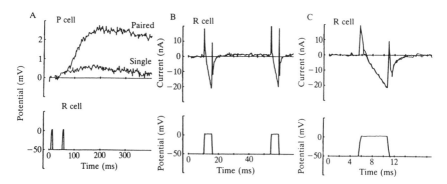

Fig. 6. Facilitation of P cell responses is not mediated by facilitated Ca^{2+} entry. (A) P cell synaptic potentials in response to single and paired voltage clamp stimuli to a Retzius (R) cell. (B) Ca^{2+} currents for each of the two stimuli. (C) Superimposition of the two Ca^{2+} current traces, showing them to be virtually identical. [Reprinted with permission of the Company of Biologists, Ltd., from Stewart, Adams, Nicholls (1989).]

ically on the molecular composition of the substrate. On a substrate of polylysine, for example, isolated neurons grow slowly or not at all, even though they adhere well to this substrate. In contrast, on a substrate of the plant lectin concanavalin A (Con A), neurons grow quickly and each cell grows with a characteristic fingerprint or branching pattern. A laminin molecule has been purified from the extracellular matrix (ECM) of the leech nervous system that promotes even faster growth than Con A. The branching pattern of a particular neuron on leech laminin is different from that of the same neuron on Con A. Leech laminin appears to have a similar structure to vertebrate laminin, although the amino acid sequence of leech laminin is not yet known. However, there must be some differences, because leech neurons do not grow on vertebrate laminin and vice versa.

Are the different branching patterns of a particular neuron that are evident on different substrates due to local interactions between the growing processes and the substrate or to commands sent from the cell body? This question has been addressed by growing an AP cell on the border of Con A and ECM substrates (at the border, the substrates meet but do not overlap) (Fig. 8). The half of the cell growing on Con A gives rise to thick

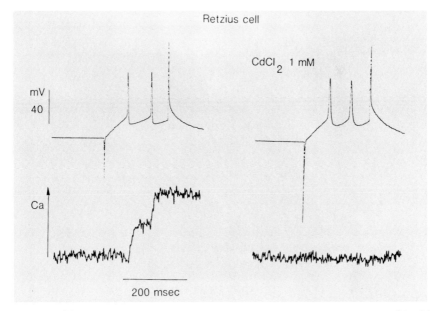

Fig. 7. Ca^{2+} transient from the soma of a Retzius cell in the absence or presence of 1 mM $CdCl_2$. The scale for the amount of Ca^{2+} is arbitrary but is the same for each panel. (**Upper traces**) Action potential recordings. (**Lower traces**) Ca^{2+} signals. [Adapted with permission from Ross *et al.* (1987).]

and curly neurites, whereas the half of the cell on ECM produces straight and thin neurites. Thus, local interactions largely determine the form of the neurites.

Because the nature of the substrate influences both the degree of growth and its pattern, it might be expected that the distribution of Ca^{2+} channels in the neuronal membrane might also be influenced. The sites of Ca^{2+} entry into neurons have been examined in cells injected with arsenazo III. In the case of Retzius cells grown on a Con A substrate (Fig. 9), Ca^{2+} entry is clearly evident in the cell body and in the initial segment adjacent to the cell body, but no Ca^{2+} entry can be detected at the growth cones. The possibility that action potentials cannot spread into the fine processes and reach the growth cones has been ruled out with the use of a voltage-sensitive dye that can optically detect changes in membrane potential (Fig. 10). These results indicate that when Retzius cells are grown on a Con A substrate, there are many fewer Ca^{2+} channels on the growing processes than on the cell body. In contrast, optical recordings from Retzius cells grown on a laminin substrate (although measurements are more

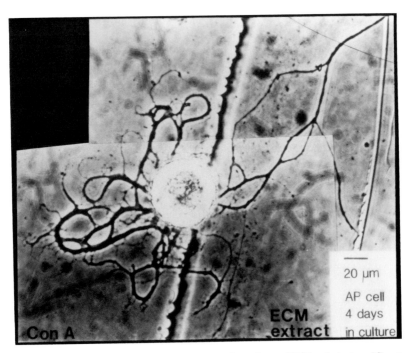

Fig. 8. An AP cell grown partly on Con A and partly on ECM substrates. [Courtesy Simone Grumbacher-Reinert, University of Basel.]

difficult to make on the fine processes that are typical of growth on this substrate) show the presence of Ca^{2+} transients in the distant processes (Fig. 11). Therefore, the nature of the substrate not only influences the growing pattern of the neurites but also the distribution of Ca^{2+} channels.

Because leech laminin influences the growth of neurons in tissue culture, it is important to determine the distribution of this laminin in the nervous system of the intact animal and to investigate its effect on the growth of neurons in situ. When the nervous system of an adult leech was stained with specific monoclonal antibodies to laminin, it was found that laminin is not present around the neurons; it is present in the ECM that surrounds the nerve cord but it is not in contact with the neurons. However, after a crush injury, there is an accumulation of laminin at the site of the crush, as well as an accumulation of wandering macrophage-like microglia. Nerve fibers grow through the zone of the crush and branch extensively.

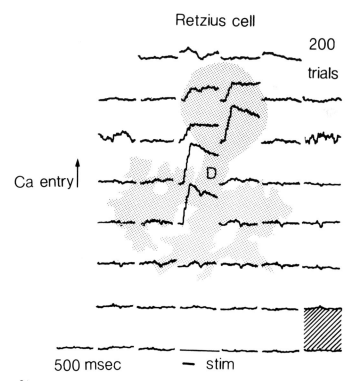

Fig. 9. Ca^{2+} transients in different regions of a Retzius cell grown on a Con A substrate. Stim, stimulation. D, initial segment. [Adapted with permission from Ross *et al.* (1987).]

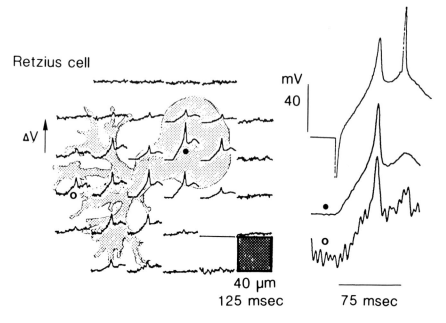

Fig. 10. Voltage transients in different regions of a Retzius cell grown on a Con A substrate. The upper trace at the right is an electrical recording; the two lower traces are optical signals from a voltage-sensitive dye. [Reprinted with permission from Ross *et al.* (1987).]

It therefore seems that in the adult, laminin is not normally present in contact with neurons. Laminin is present in the embryonic nervous system, however, and it appears at the site of a crush injury together with microglia. The source of the laminin that accumulates in the area of the crush is not known. The axons cannot be responsible because they are regenerated after laminin accumulation. Similarly, it has been shown experimentally that glial cells are not responsible for laminin accumulation.

In summary, neuronal regeneration mechanisms can be studied with individual leech cells in tissue culture. The factors that determine the specificity of synapse formation can be investigated in great detail. Finally, with regard to substrate molecules, it might be speculated that on reaching an ECM molecule such as laminin, a growing axon could receive instructions to branch and to insert Ca^{2+} channels into its terminals in order to form synapses. A second axon from a different neuron could receive a different message from its interaction with the same ECM molecule and, for example, turn and grow in another direction. Therefore, particular ECM molecules may influence different neurons in different ways.

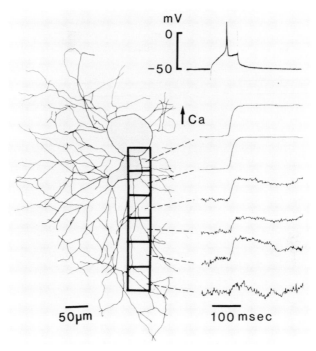

Fig. 11. Ca^{2+} transients in the cell body and terminals of a Retzius cell grown on a laminin substrate. [Reprinted with permission from Ross *et al.* (1988).]

Additional Reading

1. B. Katz and R. Miledi, "The effect of calcium on acetylcholine release from motor nerve terminals," *Proc. R. Soc. Lond. (Biol.)* **161,** 496 (1965).
2. K. J. Muller and J. G. Nicholls, "Different properties of synapses between a sensory neurone and two different motor cells in the leech C.N.S.," *J. Physiol. (Lond.)* **238,** 357 (1974).
3. P. A. Fuchs, J. G. Nicholls, D. F. Ready, "Membrane properties and selective connections of identified leech neurons in culture," *J. Physiol. (Lond.)* **316,** 203 (1981).
4. P. A. Fuchs, L. P. Henderson, J. G. Nicholls, "Chemical transmission between individual Retzius and sensory neurones of the leech in culture," *J. Physiol. (Lond.)* **323,** 195 (1982).
5. L. P. Henderson, D. P. Kuffler, J. G. Nicholls, R. Zhang, "Structural and functional analysis of synaptic transmission between identified leech neurons in culture," *J. Physiol. (Lond.)* **340,** 347 (1983).
6. I. D. Dietzel, P. Drapeau, J. G. Nicholls, "Voltage dependence of 5-hydroxytryptamine release at a synapse between identified leech neurons in culture," *J. Physiol. (Lond.)* **372,** 191 (1986).
7. J. G. Nicholls, W. N. Ross, H. Arechiga, "Membrane potential and calcium transients recorded optically from neuronal cell bodies and processes of identified leech neurons in culture," *Soc. Neurosci. Abstr.* **12,** 370 (1986).

8. W. N. Ross, H. Arechiga, J. G. Nicholls, "Optical recording of calcium and voltage transients following impulses in cell bodies and processes of identified leech neurons in culture," *J. Neurosci.* **7,** 3877 (1987).

9. W. N. Ross, H. Arechiga, J. G. Nicholls, "Influence of substrate on the distribution of calcium channels in identified leech neurons in culture," *Proc. Natl. Acad. Sci. U.S.A.* **85,** 4075 (1988).

10. S. Grumbacher-Reinert, "Local influence of substrate molecules in determining distinctive growth patterns of identified neurons in culture," *Proc. Natl. Acad. Sci. U.S.A.* **86,** 7270 (1989).

11. Y. Liu and J. G. Nicholls, "Steps in the development of chemical and electrical synapses by pairs of identified leech neurones in culture," *Proc. R. Soc. Lond. (Biol.)* **236,** 253 (1989).

12. R. R. Stewart, W. B. Adams, J. G. Nicholls, "Presynaptic calcium currents and facilitation of serotonin release at synapses between cultured leech neurones," *J. Exp. Biol.* **144,** 1 (1989).

13. R. R. Stewart, J. G. Nicholls, W. B. Adams, "Na^+, K^+ and Ca^{2+} currents in identified leech neurones in culture," *J. Exp. Biol.* **141,** 1 (1989).

14. S. E. Acklin and J. G. Nicholls, "Intrinsic and extrinsic factors influencing properties and growth patterns of identified leech neurons in culture," *J. Neurosci.* **10,** 1082 (1990).

15. L. M. Masuda-Nakagawa, K. J. Muller, J. G. Nicholls, "Accumulation of laminin and microglial cells at sites of injury and regeneration in the central nervous system of the leech," *Proc. R. Soc. Lond. (Biol.)* **241,** 201 (1990).

Activity and Chemoaffinity in the Development of Sensory Maps

Martha Constantine-Paton

In 1976 Martha Constantine-Paton obtained a Ph.D. from Cornell University for research in visual development, auditory physiology, and behavior. Her postdoctoral studies at Cornell focused on neuroanatomy and electron microscopy. Her current research aims to uncover the mechanism for the activity-dependent process that fine-tunes maps and sets up response properties within the central nervous system. Her work involves a variety of in vitro, in vivo, and biochemical studies.

Constantine-Paton was on the faculty of Princeton University from 1976 to 1985. After a sabbatical year in the Laboratory of Neurobiology at Rockefeller University, she joined the faculty at Yale University as a professor of biology. She currently serves on the Council of the Society for Neuroscience and is codirector of the Interdepartmental Neuroscience Program at Yale, and of the Neural Systems and Behavior course at the Marine Biological Laboratory in Woods Hole, Massachusetts.

Activity and Chemoaffinity in the Development of Sensory Maps

LECTURER:

Martha Constantine-Paton

Sensory receptor surfaces are reproduced in the central nervous system (CNS) with extremely high fidelity by a process that has two basic properties: the first allows for stereotypic alignment of projections and the second for a precise and predictable point-to-point fidelity. At least two mechanisms are thought to be operative in this developmental organization process: one that sets the alignment and makes use of cell surface molecular cues for pathway finding; and a second, which is a potentially completely independent mechanism, that sets the fidelity and organizes the local circuits in the brain.

All nervous systems are derived from a simple sheet of cells in the early embryo, and regions can be identified within this neural plate that will stereotypically project to other regions. Furthermore, if regions of the neural plate are rearranged, then the mature CNS will also be rearranged in a similar way. Thus, very early in development there are fixed alignment cues. The developmental pattern of CNS formation can be easily identified in all vertebrate species from early developmental stages.

There are at least three different phases in the development of sensory maps. In the first phase, the axons from the sensory receptor organ—which in the case of the visual system comprises the retinal ganglion cells—grow into the CNS via the appropriate pathways. Very early in development, the retinal ganglion cell axons leave the retina through the primitive optic stalk and enter the brain at the optic chiasma. At this stage, the retinal axons are faced, in mammals, with the decision of whether to cross to the opposite side, to project to the ipsilateral side, to continue growing forward into the forebrain, or to grow out of the other optic nerve. This process appears to be regulated by several molecules—including cell surface proteins and lipids—that are involved in pathway formation in what amounts to a combinatorial type of guidance system. Monoclonal antibodies have been used in order to identify antigens that are distributed along these pathways and which are specific to particular areas.

This chapter was edited by Keith W. Brocklehurst, and was originally reported by Roberto Dal Toso.

Anterograde labeling studies have shown that, as the retinal axons grow into the optic nerve, they maintain the relative dorsal-ventral order of the retina. Once the axons cross the optic chiasma, however, they reorganize, so that axons from the dorsal retina are located laterally in the brain and ventral axons run medially. For some time, the development of the visual system was explained by the fiber-pipe theory, which postulated that neighboring ganglion cell axons in the retina maintain strict spatial relations as they grow through the optic nerve and that the axons are organized in the target according to those relations. However, this theory is not consistent with experimental observations; there are reorganizations in the pathway that cannot be accounted for by the maintenance of initial relations.

A molecule that is approximately 44 times more abundant in the dorsal retina than the ventral retina of the chick was identified by the monoclonal antibody approach. This topographically distributed molecule (TOP molecule) appears to be a glycoprotein and has a complementary distribution in the optic tectum (or superior colliculus) of the chick; that is, it is more abundant in the lateral tectum than in the medial tectum, which is exactly how the retinal axons distribute. However, the TOP molecule is probably not the only pathway-determining molecule in this system. For example, a second molecule has been shown to display conformational differences in a similar dorsal-ventral retinal distribution in the mouse.

A third type of molecule that has a differential distribution within the visual system is a 9-*O*-acetylated ganglioside, which appears in the retina when the neurons become postmitotic. As the retina matures, the daughter cells leave the mitotic cycle and migrate from the proliferative layer. The ganglioside is located where neuronal migration begins and appears to be associated with migration of cell bodies as well as with axonal growth. This molecule is also present along the pathway of the optic tract and is highly enriched on the surface of the endfeet of the radial glia in the diencephalon. Immunocytochemical staining for the neural cell adhesion molecule, N-CAM, shows it to have a very similar distribution to the ganglioside in the same region. The ganglioside is also present in the target of the retinal axons, the superior colliculus. One important feature of adhesion molecules is that their expression is subject to a strict temporal regulation: They will appear abruptly at a particular stage of development, and then rapidly disappear. This is also the case for the ganglioside, which is closely associated with the growth of retinal axons; when this growth phase is over, the molecule disappears.

The second phase in the development of cortical maps occurs when the axons reach the target area and make contact with specific subsets of

cells. Although the cells within the superior colliculus appear to be anatomically homogeneous, particular projecting axons will produce synapses in particular regions of the target very selectively. The differential
growth of retinal ganglion cell axons on membranes prepared from different regions of the optic tectum has been investigated by creating, in culture dishes, alternating strips of anterior and posterior tectal membranes,
which are used as substrates for axonal growth. In this situation, in which
retinal axons have the opportunity to preferentially select the type of substrate on which to grow, it has been shown that temporal retinal ganglion
cells always avoid posterior tectal membrane strips and grow on the anterior tectal membranes. On the other hand, nasal retinal axons have no
preference for either anterior or posterior tectal membranes. However, if
only the posterior tectal membranes are available as a substrate, then the
temporal retinal axons will grow; it is just that when given a choice, the
growth cones will discriminate. When the posterior tectal membranes
were heated at 63°C for approximately 8 min and then used as a substrate,
it was found that temporal retinal axons could no longer discriminate between anterior and posterior tectal membranes. This finding implied the
existence of a molecule in the posterior tectal membranes that does not
inhibit, but rather is not attractive for, the growth of temporal retinal axons. Although this molecule has not been characterized, it appears to be a
protein that has a lipid linkage to the plasma membrane.

The third phase in the development of sensory systems is synaptogenesis. In pioneering experiments on the goldfish and amphibian visual systems, Sperry studied the distribution of retinal axon terminals in the optic
tectum. He showed that after ablation of a portion of the retina and
transection of the optic nerve, the regenerating axons did not grow to
cover the entire surface of the tectum; instead, they tended to remain restricted to the appropriate termination zone, as if the whole retina was
present. From experiments like this, Sperry formulated the chemoaffinity
theory, which states that there are molecules on particular subsets of axons
within the source population of neurons that are complementary to molecules on subsets of neurons in the target population. Hence, the process of
synapse formation is the result of combining two complementary molecules.

Experimental evidence has shown, however, that the process is not
that simple. As mentioned above, many molecules are actually involved.
Furthermore, Sperry's experiment only revealed the initial stages of a
more complex process. With time, the terminal innervation fields of axons
from the remaining portion of the retina will expand to cover the entire
target area. This process does not occur randomly; instead, it appears to
represent an ordered enlargement of the available retinal input. The con-

verse experiment, in which a portion of the optic tectum is removed, also shows that, with time, the entire retinal surface becomes compressed into the remaining vestige of the target in a very organized pattern. This type of experiment has now been performed in several animal species, including mammals, and with many different tectal regions. A graded type of plasticity, therefore, appears to allow the system to readjust and rules out a rigid lock-and-key hypothesis.

In the developing vertebrate, the first synapses that form generally never remain in the adult. This indicates that young synapses are extremely labile entities, which can be formed, broken, made at inappropriate sites, withdrawn, and the density and anatomy of which differ from adult synapses. The process of synaptogenesis can be visualized directly in *Xenopus* by following the growth of labeled retinal axons through the transparent head of the larva. With this preparation, it can be shown, for example, that nasal retinal axons may initially form branches in the anterior tectum but then branch more profusely in the posterior tectum, which is the appropriate region of termination; the early branches then retract. Hence, very labile and plastic processes underlie the initial synaptogenic events, and the refining of projections depends critically on the presence of synapses that allow presynaptic cells to sample potential postsynaptic sites. The synapses that survive in the adult are the result of a rigorous trial-and-error sorting process in which potential postsynaptic sites are tested, and synapses only remain in regions where the postsynaptic neuron can effectively be driven. Therefore, selective pattern discrimination is based on action potentials and functional synaptic activity.

This type of mechanism was first proposed by Hebb as a basis for associative learning. He postulated that an input that succeeds in triggering the firing of a postsynaptic partner is selectively reinforced. Hebb was not necessarily referring to structure, but rather to synaptic efficacy. The importance of experience in neuronal connectivity and function was further underlined by Hubel and Wiesel. They showed that kittens raised with one eye muscle cut, so that their retinas could not converge on the same point in visual space during the early postnatal period, lost a significant number of binocularly driven cells in the visual cortex. This result suggested that temporal convergence of activity from the retinas is a requisite for the maintenance of binocular neurons. Thus, young kittens at the time of eyelid opening possess binocularly driven neurons, the synapses of which are labile and will be functionally lost if the kitten cannot use its eyes to constantly drive inputs to these neurons simultaneously.

Stent resurrected Hebb's postulate in stating that for a population of neurons that converge on a central target or on a given postsynaptic cell, in such a way that temporal summation of the excitatory postsynaptic events they trigger can occur, there is a positive feedback system that stabilizes those inputs that are effective in producing depolarization, and, similarly, there is probably a negative feedback system for inputs that are silent. Later, Changeux proposed that young synapses have distinct states. Synapses may be functional but unstable until a subsequent series of events, which is still not understood, is triggered that causes a true structural stabilization of the synapse. The transition from the destabilized to the stabilized state depends on the ability of the presynaptic cell to drive the target cell.

Thus, during development, the visual cortex receives an array of inputs from roughly the appropriate region of the retina but without precise point-to-point ordering. Growth cones then converge on single target cells, and the subset of those neurons that show synchronous activity will produce temporal summation and a positive reinforcement of their synapses, whereas silent synapses will be lost. The types of temporal correlations in activity that are needed for this sorting process may be derived from the local circuitry of the presynaptic neuronal population. Indeed, recordings from neighboring retinal ganglion cells of the same response type have shown that if one cell fires, there is a high probability that its neighbor will also fire. Cells that are further separated have lower probabilities of firing in close temporal synchrony. Thus, spatial proximity or point-to-point ordering in the presynaptic cell population is coded in a very dynamic fashion in a temporal pattern of action potential activity. Most of the studies that have shown this have been performed with mature retina, but there is now evidence that even in embryonic retina, before photoreceptors are differentiated, neighboring ganglion cells have highly correlated patterns of spontaneous activity that can drive postsynaptic cells. This allows for a period of synaptic sorting during which synapses formed from nearest neighbors are reinforced, and gradually, during a period of continuous turnover of synaptic contacts, this process generates a highly ordered set of nearest neighbor synapses in the target area.

What are the mechanisms for this process? In early experiments, tetrodotoxin—an inhibitor of voltage-dependent Na^+ channels, and therefore of action potential activity—was injected into eyes during the period in which synapses were presumed to be labile. The conclusion from these experiments was that the point-to-point ordering of the retinal projections to the optic tectum was absent in injected animals—although there was still a reasonable alignment of maps. If synaptic sorting is activity dependent, then it may also depend on some particular type of neurotransmitter.

It is now clear that the retinotectal projections use the excitatory amino acid glutamate as the dominant transmitter.

Glutamate interacts with various different types of receptor, several of which operate cation channels (ionotropic receptors) and one of which stimulates inositol phospholipid turnover through an intermediary G protein (metabotropic receptor). Of critical importance to these studies is the ionotropic receptor gated by N-methyl-D-aspartate (NMDA)—which is antagonized by 2-amino-5-phosphonovaleric acid (APV) and blocked by physiological concentrations of Mg^{2+} at resting membrane potentials—and the ionotropic receptor gated by quisqualate and α-amino-3-hydroxy-5-methyl-4-isoxazole propionic acid (AMPA) and specifically antagonized by 6-cyano-7-nitroquinoxaline-2,3-dione (CNQX).

NMDA and AMPA receptors tend to be colocalized on CNS neurons, but they have quite different properties. Whereas the AMPA receptor is associated with a low-conductance Na^+ channel, the NMDA receptor channel is relatively large and allows the passage of both Na^+ and Ca^{2+}. Furthermore, the NMDA receptor can function as a gate: in addition to requiring the binding of agonist for activation, it requires a concomitant postsynaptic depolarization to remove the Mg^{2+} block. This property can account for detection of temporal summation and of associated synaptic events that have been shown to occur in learning. In hippocampal CA1 pyramidal cells, associative stimulation produces a great increase in synaptic efficacy, and this effect is specifically blocked—both in hippocampal slices and in vivo—by low concentrations of APV, thus indicating the involvement of NMDA receptors. Thus, if two excitatory presynaptic cells (A and B) form synapses on neighboring patches of a postsynaptic cell, and only A fires, then the glutamate that is released will interact with both AMPA and NMDA receptors but will produce a significant current only through the AMPA receptors—the NMDA receptors being blocked by Mg^{2+}. However, if both A and B release synchronously for a sufficiently long period of time, the current flowing through the AMPA receptors will depolarize the postsynaptic membrane to a point at which the Mg^{2+} block of the NMDA receptors is removed, and Na^+ and Ca^{2+} will flow into the postsynaptic neuron. This has important consequences, because an increased concentration of intracellular Ca^{2+} can affect a variety of intracellular processes and second messenger pathways.

It is therefore possible that the refinement of sensory maps during development depends on the activation of NMDA receptors on postsynaptic cells. NMDA receptors are present in the optic tectum and physiological evidence indicates the presence of both NMDA and AMPA receptors in the retinotectal pathway. This hypothesis has been tested by infusing—

from a slow-release plastic—low concentrations of APV onto the surface of the optic tectum in amphibian larvae. By injection of small amounts of horseradish peroxidase (HRP) at small defined sites in the optic tectum, it was possible to identify the regions of the retina that became stained with retrogradely transported HRP. In control animals, the region of labeled retinal ganglion cells was reproducibly small and defined, covering approximately 4% of the retinal surface. However, in animals treated with APV for 4 to 6 weeks, a much larger proportion of the retinal surface—14 to 15%—was labeled by HRP. This effect is not associated with an increase in the size of individual retinal terminal fields, but rather is due to more disordered terminations. This phenomenon can be demonstrated in amphibians because the process by which nearest neighbor synapses form is active and dynamic and involves constant synaptic turnover. If the mechanism is blocked, the system evolves toward disorder.

Encompassing this synaptic-ordering process is the development of a functional segregation pattern within a topographical projection. In the visual system, there is segregation along a variety of different modalities, such as orientation, color, and ocular dominance. The activity-dependent, synaptic-sorting mechanism actually predicts functional segregation, because what is selected and stabilized is similarity in the pattern of action potentials. Thus, in the case of two retinas projecting to the same target—layer IV in the cortex—there are two sets of neighborhood relations among the synapses that are competing for synaptic space. Because retinal ganglion cells located in different retinas do not have highly correlated patterns of activity and are not proximal neighbors, the final terminal field organization will segregate, during the point-to-point ordering, to maximize nearest neighbor proximity.

Experimentally, the generation of this type of segregation can be shown by implanting a third eye primordium in the forebrain region of amphibian larvae—which have completely crossed visual projections, so that each eye innervates the opposite tectal lobe. The manipulated animal grows up with two eyes innervating one tectal lobe. Injection of HRP into one of the two normal eyes reveals that, instead of the usual continuous termination zone, a pattern of alternating labeled and nonlabeled stripes is evident. Each retina is represented in an embryonically appropriate alignment—that is, nasal retina is still represented in the posterior tectum and temporal retina in the anterior tectum—but the retinal inputs have segregated within these zones. If the electrical activity of the eyes is blocked by administration of tetrodotoxin, the segregation is lost and the axons overlap, indicating that segregation is activity dependent. However, the segregation also has a chemoaffinity component. Stripes can also be produced in the remaining tectal lobe of a normal two-eyed animal after removal of the second tectal lobe, in which case both optic nerves innervate the remaining lobe to form the stripes. However, in the case of an incomplete ablation of the posterior segment of one tectal lobe, in the region of the intact tectum corresponding to the missing part of the other tectum the axons that would normally terminate in the ablated tectal segment are able to exclude the normal projections and segregate. If these axons were just sorting to minimize local synaptic density, they should spread out and stripe in the entire remaining tectum. But this does not occur; there is segregation and high-density innervation only in the topographically appropriate part of the remaining tectum. Chemoaffinity is therefore necessary to achieve the proper neuronal alignment that is required before activity-dependent, point-to-point ordering can occur.

In model terms, if chemoaffinity was the only driving force behind segregation and both eyes were forced to converge onto a target, then there should be a complete overlap of the two terminal projection fields (Fig. 1A). If activity-dependent nearest neighbor sorting was the only driving force, the result would be some form of binary partitioning of the target (Fig. 1B). Only if both processes are operative will an ordered segregation of terminal projections occur (Fig. 1C). Segregation into stripes is a way of maximally covering a surface but minimizing the boundary area where nonneighbors have to interact.

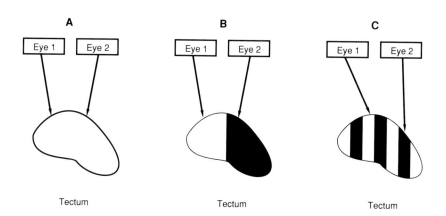

Fig. 1. (**A**) Chemoaffinity alignment as the only driving force for target innervation would produce a complete overlap of the two projection fields. (**B**) Activity-dependent nearest neighbor sorting as the only driving force would produce a binary partitioning of the target area. (**C**) If both processes were simultaneously active, then the target area would be segregated in an ordered pattern of alternating projection fields.

If NMDA receptors are critical for point-to-point ordering of a topographical map, then the application of APV to the tecta of animals with two retinas innervating one tectal lobe should produce a desegregation. Indeed, a 4-week application of APV disrupted the segregation pattern and resulted in a complete coverage of the tectal surface by the supranumerary eye, with complete overlap of the two projections. This disruption of the segregation pattern is reversible; after removal of the APV implant and allowing the animal to survive, the segregation reappears.

In conclusion, it appears that there are at least two phases to the process of forming an organized projection: in the first phase, the appropriate subset of presynaptic axons sort within a particular region in the target; and then in the second phase, an activity-dependent sorting occurs that increases the point-to-point fidelity of the system and which, at least in the case of amphibians, involves the NMDA receptor.

Additional Reading

1.   M. Constantine-Paton and J. J. Norden, "Synapse regulation in the developing visual system," in *Development of Order in the Visual System*, S. R. Hilfer and J. B. Sheffield, Eds. (Springer-Verlag, New York, 1986), pp. 1–14.

2.   M. Constantine-Paton, A. S. Blum, R. Mendez-Otero, C. J. Barnstable, "A cell surface molecule distributed as a dorsoventral gradient in the perinatal rat retina," *Nature* **324**, 459 (1986).

3.   M. Constantine-Paton and P. Ferrari-Eastman, "Pre- and post-synaptic correlates of interocular competition and segregation in the frog," *J. Comp. Neurol.* **255**, 178 (1987).

4.   R. Mendez-Otero, B. Schlosshauer, C. J. Barnstable, M. Constantine-Paton, "A developmentally regulated antigen associated with neural cell and process migration," *J. Neurosci.* **8**, 564 (1988).

5.   B. Schlosshauer, A. S. Blum, R. Mendez-Otero, C. J. Barnstable, M. Constantine-Paton, "Developmental regulation of ganglioside antigens recognized by the JONES antibody," *J. Neurosci.* **8**, 580 (1988).

6.   H. T. Cline and M. Constantine-Paton, "NMDA receptor antagonists disrupt the retinotectal topographic map," *Neuron* **3**, 413 (1989).

7.   M. Constantine-Paton, H. T. Cline, E. Debski, "Neural activity, synaptic convergence and synapse stabilization in the CNS," in *Assembly of the Nervous System*, L. Landmesser, Ed. (Liss, New York, 1989), pp. 279–300.

8.   H. T. Cline and M. Constantine-Paton, "NMDA receptor agonists and antagonists alter RGC terminal morphology in the frog retinotectal projection," *J. Neurosci.* **10**, 1197 (1990).

9.   M. Constantine-Paton, H. T. Cline, E. Debski, "Patterned activity, synaptic convergence, and the NMDA receptor in developing visual pathways," *Annu. Rev. Neurosci.* **13**, 129 (1990).

Making Maps in the Brain

Hendrik Van der Loos

Hendrik Van der Loos was born in The Netherlands, where he studied medicine in Leiden and Amsterdam. After receiving an M.D. in 1956 and a Ph.D. in 1959 from the University of Amsterdam, Van der Loos departed Europe to conduct postdoctoral research with David Bodian, and, later, to go through the ranks from assistant to full professor of anatomy at the Johns Hopkins University School of Medicine over a period that spanned from 1961 to 1971. Van der Loos also was a Joseph P. Kennedy, Jr., Memorial Foundation senior research scholar in mental retardation from 1961 to 1973. He subsequently returned to Europe and became director of the University of Lausanne Institute of Anatomy in Switzerland, where he has since remained. Research at the institute has centered mostly on problems of brain development and plasticity.

Van der Loos' current research interests encompass juvenile and adult plasticity of the brain, the manufacture of maps in the brain, neurogenetics, the design of devices that facilitate characterization of neuronal form, and the history of neuroscience.

Making Maps in the Brain
LECTURER:

Hendrik Van der Loos

Mice have whiskers (vibrissae) on their muzzles, which are sensory organs that signal to particular regions in the brain. Virtually all mammals
have a system of this kind—notable exceptions are the orders to which
whales, elephants, and humans belong. In the mouse, the whiskers are
implanted in follicles, which contain large numbers of four different types
of receptor. Innervating each follicle are about 100 myelinated axons, the
cell bodies of which lie in the Gasserian ganglion. From this ganglion, the
central axons penetrate the rhombencephalon to synapse in the trigeminal
sensory complex. Axons from neurons in the main sensory nucleus of V,
and in the three subnuclei of its descending tract, make the conventional
decussation and project to the contralateral ventrobasal nucleus of the thalamus. From there, the axons of the third order neurons travel, via the
internal capsule, to the "barrelfield" of the primary somatosensory cortex.
For each whisker on the muzzle of the mouse, there is a corresponding
"barrel" in layer IV of the somatosensory cortex, each barrel consisting of
approximately 2000 neurons. The barrels in turn project to a variety of
structures. There are back-connections to VB and the trigeminal nuclei,
but, in addition, the barrels also project beyond the somatosensory system
to, among other places, the motor cortex. From the motor cortex, fibers
descend into the brainstem to innervate, via an unknown set of interneurons, the large motoneurons of the facial nucleus. These cells in turn innervate, via the facial nerve, the muscle-slings that surround each of the
vibrissal follicles. These specializations of the facial musculature are so
designed that, when activated, whiskers whisk—a prerequisite for the animals to use their vibrissae as sensors.

What makes this system so unique is that it shows a high degree of
topological order, which, moreover, in all but one central station, can be
readily visualized. Traditionally, neuroscientists have used two basic
techniques to define maps in the brain: Penfield, for one, defined human
brain maps by stimulating the cortex at various sites and then asking the
patient what he or she felt; Mountcastle, on the other hand, was one of the
pioneers of the reverse strategy, in which natural stimuli are applied to

*This chapter was edited by Keith W. Brocklehurst, and was originally reported by David
Armstrong.*

superficial and deep body structures of the experimental animal, and the corresponding electrical activity from various sites in the brain recorded. The distinct advantage of the mouse whisker-to-barrel system is not only that the peripheral sensory fields are punctiform and easily definable, but also that their corresponding representations in the cortex and in all subcortical relays can actually be seen with the aid of conventional histological techniques.

On the muzzle of the mouse, the whiskers are arranged in precise order and are referred to by letters and numbers. In the cortex, the barrels—33 per hemisphere—are distributed according to an equally precise pattern, which is isomorphic to that of the whiskers. This map is gigantic: its scale is about 1:4, which speaks to the fact that, for the animal, the system is important indeed.

In coronal, Nissl-stained sections of the somatosensory cortex, distinct vertical bands of high cell density can be observed within layer IV. These bands are the "sides" of the barrels. The anatomy of barrels and, particularly, of their ensemble, the barrelfield, can be appreciated by looking down onto the surface of the brain: in sections cut tangential to the pial surface over the barrelfield, the roughly cylindrical and tub-shaped barrels are readily apparent. The sides of the barrels are densely packed with neurons and surround "hollows" that contain few cells. Between barrels are thin, cell-sparse domains, or septa. The barrels have two types of stellate cells—spiny and nonspiny—and it is these neurons that receive most of the thalamic input. The spiny neurons are believed to be excitatory; they send their axons downward (in the direction of the white matter). In contrast, the nonspiny stellate neurons are thought to be inhibitory; they send their axons upward (in the direction of the pia). The dendrites of the barrel neurons remain confined to their hollow, although a few cells have "promiscuous" dendrites that branch either in the septa or into neighboring barrels. Although the ventrobasal thalamus is the major source of afferent innervation to the barrels, the barrelfield receives additional inputs, including inputs from the ipsi- and contralateral cortex. These projections are primarily to the septa. From the above, it is clear that the anatomy of this system is highly ordered, and that this order adds to its attractiveness for studies of development and brain plasticity.

It is of interest that not all whisker-bearing mammals display such a system in which order is visible; for example, cats, and even certain rodents, do not seem to possess this system, whereas some marsupials do. Therefore, the question arises as to the utility of the system. What is its function? It would appear that the whisker-to-barrel system is geared to delivering, in a highly precise manner, space-specific data to the cerebral cortex. This can be demonstrated with conventional techniques: deflecting whiskers and recording the electrical activity from the corresponding barrels; or analyzing the metabolic activity of barrels with deoxyglucose autoradiography.

It has been considered important to ascertain the basic principles that govern both the development and maintenance of such a system. The basic thesis that will be developed is that the central organization of the system is a reflection of that in the periphery and is not of the brain's own making.

In considering whether this thesis is valid, one must first take into account certain salient events in the development of a mouse. The mouse fetus requires 19 days to be ready for delivery, and during this period several events occur that are critical to the whiskerpad-to-barrelfield system. First, on gestational day 9, the Gasserian ganglion is laid down. During the next few days (gestational days 10 to 12), the generation of the whisker follicles and the pattern that they form is completed. In the brain, the barrel neurons are born on gestational day 14, but it is not until postnatal day 3 that the radial migration of these cortical neurons is complete. It is only on postnatal day 4 that the barrel pattern can be discerned. The fact that the development of the peripheral pattern temporally precedes that occurring in the brain would seem to support the thesis that the development of order in this system is controlled in the periphery. However, this evidence cannot be viewed as conclusive, because it is possible that the pattern develops independently in the brain, only later. This would require much from the genome. In this case, proper further development of the system would mean proper hook-up between the whisker follicles, the subcortical stations, and, finally, the barrels. If, however, the pattern so characteristic for this system is indeed conceived in the periphery, then it should be possible to predict the outcome of experiments designed to study the effects, if any, on the brain of damaging the follicles.

In Fig. 1, the whisker-to-barrel system is schematized and reduced to nine whiskers and nine barrels in order to illustrate the central point of these lesion experiments. On one side of the face, the whiskers marked with a Y were injured in the neonate. In the adult hemisphere corresponding to the intact side, the (simplified) barrelfield was found to possess nine barrels, whereas in the hemisphere to which the injured side reports, the region corresponding to barrels whose whiskers were damaged was reduced to a thin band. Furthermore, the remaining barrels were enlarged. This marked alteration in cortical cytoarchitecture is the result of a relatively small insult made at a critical period of development in the periphery, which is placed three synapses and a long distance away. Although

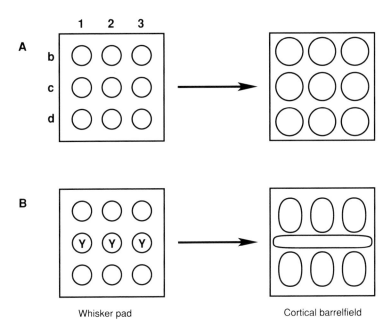

Fig. 1. (A) Simplified representation of the adult mouse whiskerpad-to-barrelfield system, consisting of only nine whiskers—arranged in three rows (b, c, d), each row having three whiskers (1, 2, 3)—and their cortical barrels. In real life, there are five rows of between four and eight elements. (B) The whiskers of row C, marked with a Y, were injured at birth, which resulted in the adult barrel pattern shown. Note enlargement of barrels of rows b and d.

these data again support the thesis that the periphery leads the way in the making of the cortical map, it is nevertheless possible that embedded within the telencephalic matrix that leads to the neocortex is a tiny "protomap," and that all this map needs for the expression of a barrel pattern is for some factor from the periphery to percolate up to the developing pallium. What is interesting about the above experiment is that the effects on cortical structure are only apparent if the lesions are performed before postnatal day 5.

However, certain experimental manipulations of whiskers in the adult animal also have an effect on the barrelfield. One such experiment is represented in Fig. 2. The whiskers marked with an X of a normal adult mouse were stimulated for 45 min, and the somatosensory cortex was then examined by deoxyglucose autoradiography. The barrels corresponding to the stimulated whiskers showed increased metabolic activity. If, however, the experiment was repeated with animals in which those whiskers marked with a Y were denervated previously, then all nine barrels showed in-

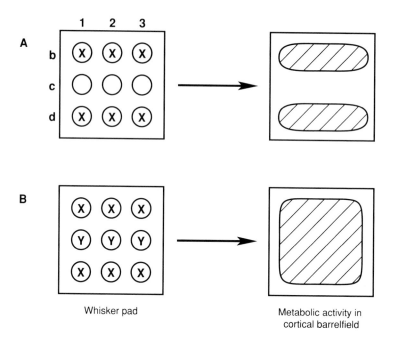

Fig. 2. (**A**) Schematic representation of a simplified adult mouse whisker pattern and the associated metabolic activity of the cortical barrelfield (defined by deoxyglucose autoradiography) after stimulation for 45 min of the whiskers of rows b and d (marked with an X). (**B**) As in (**A**) except that the row c whiskers (marked with a Y) had been denervated 160 days before stimulation.

creased metabolic activity. Importantly, this increased area of metabolic activity was not accompanied by anatomical change. These results clearly reflect cortical plasticity, and this notion is supported by the finding that shortly after removal of a set of whiskers, there is a dramatic decrease in the expression of glutamic acid decarboxylase (GAD)—the rate-limiting enzyme in the biosynthesis of γ-aminobutyric acid (GABA)—in the corresponding part of layer IV of the somatosensory cortex. This observation is important because GABA is the major inhibitory neurotransmitter in the central nervous system. A decrease in GAD, and thus presumably in GABA, implies decreased inhibitory input to the neurons within, above, and below the barrels. This lack of inhibition may, in fact, serve to unmask weak excitatory inputs and thus, in part, explain the "colonization" of regions of the cortex deprived of their "own" peripheral innervation by inputs from the intact neighboring follicles. Metabolic changes such as those evoked in the cortex also are observed in the nuclei of termination in the brainstem.

After this introduction of the two forms of experimentally evoked brain plasticity, "developmental" and "adult," we turn to a third and last form: genetically evoked plasticity. This will bring us back to the question, Where are brain maps made?

There are mice that have supernumerary whiskers. Each one of the two sides of the upper lip of the mouse is formed from three distinct anlagen, which, in normal development, merge to make one smooth, whole surface. In an extreme situation, these hillocks do not merge and what in clinical terms is known as a harelip results. The three hillocks, from medial to lateral, are termed the medial nasal fold, the lateral nasal fold, and the maxillary bud, and they are separated by what have been called the medial and lateral lines of mergence. In mice with a normal distribution of whiskers, the whiskers are present on the lateral nasal fold and on the maxillary bud. When supernumerary whiskers are present, however, they are, in the great majority of cases, found in the zones corresponding to the medial and lateral lines of mergence. Importantly, when extra whiskers are found in given sites on the muzzle of a mouse, there is a corresponding increase in the number of barrels, which are found at corresponding locations in the somatosensory cortex. Likewise, additional barrels in the cortex imply the presence of corresponding whiskers. Nowhere other than the muzzle in the pathway from periphery to cortex is there an initial discontinuity in what will become a continuous sheet of tissue. It can therefore be concluded that the extra sensory "pipelines" connecting periphery with cortex in animals with extra whiskers are created, in fact, in the periphery. And because the pipelines of the standard set of whiskers resemble in all ways those of the supernumerary ones, what has been proposed for the latter holds for the standard pipelines as well. Hence, the map of the entire system seems to be created in the periphery.

The fact that, by and large, the whisker pattern is so stereotyped implies that it must be genetically determined. It has been suggested that when full mergence of the three anlagen of the mouse muzzle occurs, a normal pattern of whiskers results; however, when such mergence fails to occur, or is incomplete, more space is created on the muzzle surface and, consequently, there is an opportunity for development of additional follicles. And, as mentioned above, when mergence fails to occur in the periphery and extra whiskers are formed, it has been shown that the brain is induced to form extra barrels.

Is mergence of the muzzle, with its important central implications, due to an "accident of development," or is it genetically determined? It is the latter: it has been shown that it is possible to breed mice specifically to select for the development of additional whiskers, and usually there is correspondence between the number and location of whiskers on the muzzle and the number and location of barrels in the somatosensory cortex. Twenty-two different mouse strains have been created, each with its own characteristic whisker and barrel patterns, some bilaterally symmetrical, others exhibiting left-right asymmetries. Early in the breeding program, mice with extra whiskers had extra barrels that were rather small and narrow, but with ongoing selective inbreeding larger barrels developed. Interestingly, it was found that for a whisker to "create" a barrel, a minimum of approximately 40 nerve fibers innervating the follicle was necessary. In some of the newly formed, "enriched" strains of mice, the entire barrel-field is enlarged so as to accommodate the extra barrels. It is not yet known, however, if this expansion occurs to the detriment of surrounding cortical areas or whether the entire pallium is pushed out.

Mice have now been bred that have as many as 33 extra whiskers—a sizeable increase in number on a total standard set of 66 (one champion had 36 extra whiskers). In such mice, there are also changes in the peripheral innervation. Each of the extra whiskers receives its own innervation, so as to increase the total number of nerve fibers innervating the whisker-pad. Furthermore, the standard set of whiskers in these mice receives 20% more fibers as well, when compared with mice with the standard whisker pattern. This finding would seem to imply that as the number of sense organs increases in the periphery, the Gasserian ganglion responds by creating more primary sensory neurons or by submitting to less developmental cell death.

In conclusion, the results of experiments that have examined three different types of brain plasticity—that which is surgically evoked in development, that which is surgically evoked in adulthood, and that which is genetically evoked—have provided support for the notion that the cortical pattern representing a peripheral sensory sheet is induced by the distribution of sensory organs in that sensory sheet. From an evolutionary point of view, it is worth emphasizing that the genome may be asked to modify the brain—in this case to modify the size and compartmentalization of a sensory representation—and can do so via its impact on the periphery.

Additional Reading

1. K. H. Andres, "Ueber die feinstruktur der rezeptoren an sinus-haaren," *Z. Zellforsch.* **75,** 339 (1966).
2. T. A. Woolsey and H. Van der Loos, "The structural organization of layer IV in the somatosensory region (SI) of mouse cerebral cortex. The description of a cortical field composed of discrete cytoarchitectonic units," *Brain Res.* **17,** 205 (1970).

3. H. Van der Loos and T. A. Woolsey, "Somato-sensory cortex: Structural alterations following early injury to sense organs," *Science* **179**, 395 (1973).

4. E. L. White, "Identified neurons in mouse Sml cortex which are postsynaptic to thalamocortical axon terminals: A combined Golgi-electron microscopic and degeneration study," *J. Comp. Neurol.* **181**, 627 (1978).

5. D. Jeanmonod, F. L. Rice, H. Van der Loos, "Mouse somatosensory cortex: Alterations in the barrelfield following receptor injury at different early postnatal ages," *Neuroscience* **6**, 1503 (1981).

6. J. Dörfl, "The innervation of the mystacial region of the white mouse. A topographical study," *J. Anat.* **142**, 173 (1985).

7. P. Melzer *et al.*, "A magnetic device to stimulate selected whiskers of freely moving or restrained small rodents: Its application in a deoxyglucose study," *Brain Res.* **348**, 229 (1985).

8. H. Van der Loos, E. Welker, J. Dörfl, G. Rumo, "Selective breeding for variations in pattern of mystacial vibrissae of mice; bilaterally symmetrical strains derived from ICR-stock," *J. Hered.* **77**, 66 (1986).

9. E. Welker and H. Van der Loos, "Quantitative correlation between barrel-field size and the sensory innervation of the whiskerpad: A comparative study in six strains of mice bred for different patterns of mystacial vibrissae," *J. Neurosci.* **6**, 3355 (1986).

10. E. Welker, P. V. Hoogland, H. Van der Loos, "Organization of feedback and feedforward projections of the barrel cortex: A PHA-L study in the mouse," *Exp. Brain Res.* **73**, 411 (1988).

11. H. Van der Loos, E. Welker, J. Dörfl, P. V. Hoogland, "Brain maps: Development, plasticity and distribution of signals beyond," in *The Neocortex Ontogeny and Phylogeny,* B. L. Finlay, G. Innocenti, H. Scheich, Eds. (Plenum Press, New York, 1991), NATO ASI Series A: Life Sciences, vol. 200, pp. 229–236.

12. E. Welker, H. Van der Loos, J. Dörfl, E. Soriano, "The possible role of GABA-ergic innervation in plasticity of adult cerebral cortex," in *The Neocortex Ontogeny and Phylogeny,* B. L. Finlay, G. Innocenti, H. Scheich, Eds. (Plenum Press, New York, 1991), NATO ASI Series A: Life Sciences, vol. 200, pp. 237–243.

The Development of Cortical Connections

Giorgio M. Innocenti

Giorgio M. Innocenti was born in Italy, where he obtained a medical degree in 1967 from Turin University with a specialization in neurology and psychiatry. He has taught throughout Italy at the Institutes of Physiology of the Universities of Turin, Rome, Sassari, Catania, and Ferrara. His interest in the function and structure of the central nervous system led him to work in several other laboratories worldwide, including the Max-Planck Institutes (Germany), l'Instituto de Biofisica Federal de Rio de Janeiro (Brazil), and the University of Alicante Department of Morphology (Spain). Since 1974, he has served at the Institut d'Anatomie of Lausanne University in Switzerland.

Innocenti has applied electrophysiological, anatomical, and biochemical techniques to the study of cortical organization and its development, using the callosal connections between visual areas as his favorite model. His most recent findings highlight the existence of transient structures in cortical development, which may provide the basis for developmental plasticity and the evolution of the cerebral cortex.

The Development of Cortical Connections

LECTURER:

Giorgio M. Innocenti

The cerebral cortex is organized in a precise fashion; each cortical cell sends a specific set of efferent fibers to, and receives afferent projections from, restricted sets of neurons. The corpus callosum can be viewed as a model system in which to study the development of cortical-cortical connectivity. Most of the axons contributing to the corpus callosum originate from cortical neurons in one hemisphere and terminate on cortical neurons in the other hemisphere. If the corpus callosum is cut, no interaction between the two hemispheres is possible. The functional deficits that arise from such a lack of interaction between the hemispheres have been referred to as "disconnection syndromes."

Although the basic principles underlying the development of cortical-cortical interactions are applicable to many species, emphasis will be placed on studies of cats and kittens and on the callosal projections that arise from the visual cortex (areas 17 and 18). Retrograde tracing techniques have shown that callosal fibers arising from neurons in areas 17 and 18 of the adult cat are largely restricted to a single band, which is located near the border between areas 17 and 18—this border corresponds to the midline of the visual field. The location of these neurons is thus functionally important and is related to the organization of visual areas. The callosally projecting cells are also restricted to a supragranular band (most are present in layer III, but some are present in layers IV and VI). These supragranular neurons—which will be the focus of this discussion—project axons across the corpus callosum that terminate more or less symmetrically at the border of areas 17 and 18 in the contralateral hemisphere. This projection is therefore precise and anatomically well defined. The restricted origin of these callosal projections can thus be defined by its tangential and radial specificity.

In the kitten, during the first postnatal week, the pattern of callosal projections is very different from that in the adult cat. All of areas 17 and 18, and in fact all visual areas, contribute axons to the corpus callosum at this time. However, by 90 days after birth, many of the fibers that projected through the callosum are lost, resulting in the pattern that is ob-

This chapter was edited by Keith W. Brocklehurst, and was originally reported by David Armstrong.

152

served in the adult. The excess callosal fibers are referred to as exuberant projections. These projections are observed in nearly every species. Moreover, this concept of exuberant fibers is applicable not only to callosal fibers but also to cortical-subcortical projections, intrahemispheric projections, and intra-areal projections. These observations suggest that cortical development is not a unitary process but, rather, involves a series of steps, which may be linked to one another but which need not necessarily depend on one another. If these processes are independent, they may be caused by different factors.

What causes the transformation of the juvenile pattern of projections to the adult pattern, and how is this process regulated? One way of addressing these questions is to see what happens when the transient (exuberant) projections are eliminated. One such experiment involved injecting a retrograde tracer into one side of the brain of a kitten on postnatal day 3 (P3). Then, at P27, after the disappearance of most of the transient projections, a second tracer was injected into the same hemisphere. Three days after the second injection, the distribution of the two populations of labeled cells was examined. The first tracer revealed the neurons that were responsible for sending the exuberant projections, and all cells in area 17 were labeled. The second tracer revealed a more restricted distribution of cells near the border between areas 17 and 18. Thus, the neurons that generated the exuberant fibers did not die. Instead, they eliminated axons that crossed the callosum and formed connections within the ipsilateral hemisphere.

Examination of the cells projecting initially through the callosum reveals that they are of at least two major classes; one class projecting to the contralateral area 17-18 border and another projecting to the contralateral lateral suprasylvian cortex. After elimination of callosal axons, however, some of these neurons form short connections (for example, from area 17 to area 18). It appears to be a general principle, that certain cortical neurons replace long projections with short ones during development.

When the process of axonal elimination is examined by electron microscopy, the actual number of axons can be seen to peak around birth and then to drop dramatically in the ensuing postnatal period. In fact, approximately 70% of the axons projecting through the callosum are eliminated during maturation. The decrease in the number of axons observed by electron microscopy correlates temporally with the elimination of projections observed by retrograde transport studies, and thus it is likely that both methods reveal the same phenomenon. The elimination of axons observed by electron microscopy and changes in the cross-sectional area of the corpus callosum observed by light microscopy in sagittal sections of kitten brain are also temporally correlated. Morphometric measurements of the cross-sectional area of the corpus callosum reveal that the area of the callosum first increases, and then decreases slowly during axon elimination. Later, however, the corpus callosum enlarges, and this growth is associated with myelination of the callosal axons.

The massive elimination of callosal axons therefore appears to be reflected macroscopically by a decrease in the size, or a pause in the growth, of the corpus callosum. If the data on projection elimination, axon number, size of the corpus callosum, and synaptogenesis in the visual cortex are compared, it is apparent that the loss of axons and the decrease in callosal size precede myelination; and, furthermore, that axonal loss occurs at a time of increasing synaptic density. These data suggest that (i) most of the axons that are eliminated during development are probably not myelinated and (ii) the elimination of axons is probably not a consequence of a decrease in the number of synapses in the cortex. Although synaptic loss is a normal occurrence in development, it nevertheless takes place after the massive decrease in callosal axons. The increase in synaptogenesis and the elimination of axons may in fact be related events: it is possible that during synaptogenesis, callosal axons will be eliminated if they do not form synapses.

As stated above, the basic principles of cortical development are thought to be applicable to most species. Yet these common developmental processes give rise to different brains. In the cat and rat, for example, the temporal courses of the elimination of callosal axons, synaptogenesis, and myelination are comparable. On this basis, it might be predicted that in humans the elimination of axons will be mostly a postnatal event. Because retrograde studies are not possible in humans, this prediction has been addressed by examining the cross-sectional callosal area in the brains of human fetuses and infants. The callosal area increases during the fetal period, but then there is a growth pause and the area decreases slightly. This decrease lasts until the middle of the 2nd postnatal month, after which callosal size begins to increase again. This finding suggests that callosal axons are eliminated in man during a period that spans the end of gestation and the first weeks of postnatal life. As for cat and rat, the pause in the growth of the corpus callosum in humans occurs before myelination and during the initial rapid phase of synaptogenesis in the visual cortex. In the monkey, like the cat, the pause in the growth of the callosal cross-sectional area corresponds to a period of elimination of axons and occurs during a period of synaptogenesis. In the monkey, the number of callosal fibers increases early in development and then falls precipitously (approximately 70% of the axons are lost). If data on the elimination of axons are compared with data on the number of growth cones in the corpus callosum, axon elimination is seen to occur when new axons are probably being established. Thus, the temporal relations between these various morphogenetic events appear similar in cat and monkey. The two species appear to differ, however, in the relation between these morphogenetic events and birth: most of the morphogenetic events are at an advanced phase at birth in the monkey, whereas in the cat and man, these events occur later and extend to early postnatal periods.

What are the cellular events that underlie the elimination of axons? In the white matter underlying area 17, and in regions close to the corpus callosum that are crossed by transient axons, clusters of phagocytic cells can be detected by labeling with horseradish peroxidase. By electron microscopy, processes of these macrophage-like cells can be seen to envelop axons, which thus may be eliminated by phagocytosis. This process is of interest because of a syndrome in children that seems to be caused by overelimination of cortical axons. Children with this disorder are severely hypotonic at birth and die during the 1st year of life. At autopsy, the brain displays gross atrophy of the corpus callosum and the pyramidal tract. In the white matter, there are also signs of axonal degeneration.

Because the failure to maintain certain axonal projections appears to underlie this disorder, it is of particular interest to understand the process by which axons are maintained. To this end, recent work has focused on cytoskeletal elements. The neuronal cytoskeleton consists largely of microtubules and neurofilaments, each of which form interconnected networks in the mature axon. The neurofilaments comprise three subunits: NF-L, NF-M, and NF-H (of "low," "medium," and "heavy" molecular mass, respectively). NF-H has a molecular mass of approximately 200 kD and is present in the sidearms that connect filaments. Microtubules also consist of heterogeneous subunits, which, in addition to several forms of tubulin, include microtubule-associated proteins (MAPs) such as MAP-5 and tau—both of which appear to be located in the sidearms between microtubules. During the period of callosal axon maturation, the amounts and characteristics of these various proteins change. For example, on protein immunoblots, NF-H first appears at P25, although it can be detected slightly earlier in callosal axons by immunocytochemistry. NF-H can be heavily phosphorylated. The antibody to NF-H used in the above study recognized a phosphorylated epitope of the protein. When the study was repeated with an antibody that recognized a nonphosphorylated epitope, NF-H was first detected much later in development (P39). The appearance of the nonphosphorylated epitope suggests that NF-H may undergo developmental modifications that result in the unmasking of the nonphosphorylated epitope.

Two sets of tau proteins exist: a juvenile set and an adult set. The transition between the juvenile and adult sets occurs between P19 and P28 in the cat. MAP-5 appears in the cortex as two bands on protein immunoblots (MAP-5A and MAP-5B). In the cortex, these two bands are present together until P28; between P28 and P39, only the lower molecular mass form (MAP-5B) persists, after which the amount of this protein also decreases until it is no longer detectable. In the corpus callosum, the situation is different than in the cortex: only the higher molecular mass band is visible until P28, and between P28 and P39 this band shifts in molecular mass. The conversion from high to low molecular mass forms of MAP-5 probably results from the loss of phosphate, because treatment of both molecular species of MAP-5 with alkaline phosphatase results in the persistence of only the lower molecular mass form. Thus, both MAP-5 and NF-H may undergo important dephosphorylation reactions during axonal maturation. The loss of phosphate may change the binding properties of these proteins. This appears to be the case for MAP-5, because in cell extracts MAP-5B appears in the soluble fraction, whereas MAP-5A does not.

These changes in the components of the cytoskeleton occur after the period of elimination of callosal axons. Thus, it is the axons that survive elimination that undergo alterations in their cytoskeleton. It is unclear whether the transformation of cytoskeletal proteins causes axons to become stabilized or whether the axonal stabilization results in the transformation of these proteins. With the use of high-power electron microscopy, the relative positions of individual neurofilaments and microtubules in callosal axons can be studied, and certain features of axonal morphology, such as the distance between a neurofilament or microtubule and its nearest neighbor, can be ascertained. In the cat, the mean distance between individual microtubules decreases after birth until P30, and thereafter stabilizes. In contrast, neurofilaments undergo more complex organizational changes, which are characterized by an initial phase of increasing interfilament distance that reaches a peak around P20, followed by a period in which the nearest-neighbor measurement decreases and finally stabilizes around P40. This stabilization of the organization of microtubules and neurofilaments correlates with the molecular transformations of the corresponding proteins (tau, MAP-5, and NF-H).

What controls the maintenance of some axons and the elimination of others? Tracer experiments have shown that callosal axons from the contralateral hemisphere arrive at areas 17 and 18 and grow into the cortex only at selective locations—at the area 17-18 border and other locations where axons persist. Very few axons grow into the medial part of area 17, which loses the callosal projections. This selective pattern of innervation suggests that an interaction occurs between the callosal axons and the target. Indeed, during the phase of exuberance, the axons that originate at the area 17-18 border (which are destined to remain) seem to enter the contralateral area 17-18 border (and probably stay there); whereas the axons from the medial aspect of area 17 cross the midline and project either to the medial aspect of the contralateral area 17 or to the area 17-18 border, where they may compete with projections from the area 17-18 border. However, the axons originating from the medial aspect of area 17 do not appear to penetrate far into the gray matter. This finding suggests that stable connections may require a dual form of recognition: the neurons from the area 17-18 border may follow signals to send their axons to the appropriate region of the contralateral cortex, and the target may have a mechanism to identify the appropriate axons.

This idea was explored further by injecting the excitotoxin ibotenic acid into the cortex of kittens at P2 or P3—ibotenic acid acts at the N-methyl-D-aspartate (NMDA) subtype of glutamate receptor and kills neurons by causing excessive stimulation. Later, on gross examination, the lesioned cortex appears to be shrunken. Microscopically, the contralateral (nonlesioned) cortex retains its typical six-layer structure; in contrast, on the lesioned side, there is little, if any, evidence of the infragranular cortex or of layer IV. Rather, this severely atrophic cortex (microcortex) consists solely of the supragranular layer and resembles a human pathology known as microgyria, which is thought to result from an ischemic insult that occurs near the end of neuronal migration during prenatal development.

When activity in the normal visual cortex of the cat is examined by 2-deoxyglucose uptake after monocular stimulation, there is a heavy band of excitation in layer IV with some patchiness, which may represent ocular dominance columns. In contrast, in the cortex lesioned with ibotenic acid, the band of activity corresponding to layer IV is missing. Rather, small clusters of activity are seen, which appear to be remnants of ocular dominance columns. This result suggests that this functional feature may be preserved even in a severely damaged brain. Moreover, microelectrode penetrations into brains lesioned with ibotenic acid reveal that parts of the microcortex are still responsive to visual stimuli and that this responsiveness is comparable to that in the intact cat.

Can the anatomy of the circuits in the microcortex give any clues about the involvement of cell-cell recognition in the formation and maintenance of neuronal connections? In the intact cat, the projections from the lateral geniculate body to the visual cortex consist of a major projection to layer IV and smaller projections to layers I and VI; there is also a projection from layer VI back to the thalamus. In contrast, in the microcortex, the thalamic afferents are much less dense and are restricted to the base of the cortex—they appear to be restricted to their normal target area and do not invade the supragranular layers. These data suggest that some kind of recognition occurs between thalamic afferents and those layers of the cortex that normally receive their input.

The callosal afferents to the microcortex are similar to those in the intact brain; fibers from the intact cortex still cross the midline to invade the microcortex and remain restricted to the area 17-18 border. Thus, callosal connections that are normally eliminated are not maintained in the microcortex. Tracers injected into the microcortex also label intrahemispheric connections that are characteristic of the intact visual cortex. However, in addition to these normal connections, there is a cluster of labeled cells in the auditory cortex, which indicates that there is a projection from the auditory cortex to the visual cortex. This projection appears to represent a transient projection that has been stabilized by the experimental manipulation of the cortex. Indeed, injection of a retrograde tracer into the visual cortex of a normal kitten during the 1st postnatal week results in the labeling of cells in the auditory cortex. This projection may have become stabilized in the microcortex because of the absence of the infragranular layers—neurons in the infragranular layers may ordinarily compete with other afferents to the cortex, and this competition may lead to the elimination of certain afferents and the maintenance of others.

The role of astrocytes in neural development has also been examined by staining normal cortex for the presence of the glial marker, glial fibrillary acidic protein (GFAP). In normal developing brain, GFAP-positive cells are found throughout the white matter of the cortex. One day after injection of ibotenic acid, the astrocytes that contain GFAP have degenerated in the lesioned cortex. However, 1 to 2 weeks after the injection, the population of GFAP-positive cells increases dramatically and forms what appears to be a glial scar. (Glial scars are also characteristic of microgyria in humans.) This increase in the number of glia is accompanied by an increase in the number of macrophage-like cells.

In conclusion, when the transient callosal projections were first observed, it was theorized that they may provide greater flexibility or plasticity to the developing brain. It was further proposed that they may also be valuable in phylogenesis for the "hooking up" of new cortical areas to the rest of the cortex. The demonstration that transient projections can be maintained by experimental manipulation validates these basic ideas. The "choice" of which juvenile axons are maintained appears to involve a number of "controllers," including activity and interactions with neuronal and nonneuronal elements at the target. At present, we can only speculate as to the nature of these interactions.

Additional Reading

1. G. M. Innocenti, "General organization of callosal connections in the cerebral cortex," in *Cerebral Cortex,* E. G. Jones and A. Peters, Eds. (Plenum Press, New York, 1986), vol. 5, pp. 291–353.
2. A. Guadano-Ferraz, B. M. Riederer, G. M. Innocenti, "Developmental changes in the heavy subunit of neurofilaments in the corpus callosum of the cat," *Dev. Brain Res.* **56,** 244 (1990).
3. G. Lyon *et al.*, "A disorder of axonal development, necrotizing myopathy, cardiomyopathy, and cataracts: A new familial disease," *Ann. Neurol.* **27,** 193 (1990).
4. B. M. Riederer, A. Guadano-Ferraz, G. M. Innocenti, "Difference in distribution of microtubule-associated proteins 5a and 5b during the development of cerebral cortex and corpus callosum in cats: Dependence on phosphorylation," *Dev. Brain Res.* **56,** 235 (1990).
5. G. M. Innocenti, "Pathways between development and evolution," in *The Neocortex Ontogeny and Phylogeny,* B. L. Finlay, G. Innocenti, H. Scheich, Eds. (Plenum Press, New York, 1991), NATO ASI Series A: Life Sciences, vol. 200, pp. 43–52.
6. G. M. Innocenti, "The development of projections from cerebral cortex," *Prog. Sensory Physiol.*, in press.

Pioneer Neurons and Target Selection in Cerebral Cortical Development

Carla J. Shatz

Carla J. Shatz received a Ph.D. in neurobiology in 1976 from Harvard University and continued her postdoctoral studies at Harvard Medical School until 1978. She then joined the Stanford University School of Medicine, where she is now a professor of neurobiology.

Shatz's research focuses on understanding how the adult pattern of precise and orderly connections in the mammalian central nervous system is achieved during development. Her major subject of study is the development of the cat visual system, particularly the sets of connections between the retina, the lateral geniculate nucleus (LGN), and the primary visual cortex. Since many of these connections form during prenatal life, the principal goal of her research has been to learn more about the sequence of early fetal events associated with the formation of connections in the visual system. Shatz's work has extended knowledge of the development of connections between the retina and the LGN, from the system to the cellular level. Her current experiments involve making intracellular recordings from and deleting the pioneer neurons to learn how the cellular interactions during fetal life may direct the development of the cortex.

Pioneer Neurons and Target Selection in Cerebral Cortical Development

LECTURER:

Carla J. Shatz

The development of the central nervous system (CNS) entails at least three general processes: neurogenesis, neuronal pathfinding (target selection), and the ordering of connections within targets. These processes will be discussed with regard to the development of connections between the thalamus and cerebral cortex in the mammalian CNS.

In the invertebrate nervous system, it has been shown that axons begin to grow toward their targets in the brain very early during development. The advantages of this early growth are that the distances involved are short and the pathways and cues are presumably simple; thus, the problems associated with pathway selection and target selection are minimized. This principle is also followed in the development of the mammalian visual system; that is, the axons of the thalamic neurons begin to grow toward the cortex soon after the thalamic neurons themselves have been generated and have completed their migration. However, the axons of the thalamic neurons arrive in the cortex before their target neurons are in place—this is a consequence of the time required for the large number of cell divisions that generate the neurons of the mammalian cerebral cortex to occur. Thus, questions arise concerning the behavior of the axons of the thalamic neurons in the absence of their target cells. These questions will be addressed with regard to the development of connections between the thalamic nucleus that subserves vision—the lateral geniculate nucleus (LGN)—and the primary visual cortex, but the underlying principles of this process are generalizable to other thalamic-cortical connections. Furthermore, although the cat visual system will form the focus of this discussion, the development of the monkey and human visual systems appears to be similar.

The ganglion cells in the retina send their axons to the LGN through the optic tract. The LGN neurons, in turn, send their axons through the internal capsule—a large bundle of fibers that is essentially the gateway between the thalamus and the cortex—to layer IV of the visual cortex. A

This chapter was edited by Keith W. Brocklehurst, and was originally reported by Maurizio Memo.

162

number of targeting problems have to be solved in the pathway from thalamus to cortex: Axons of the LGN have to grow (i) up toward the cortex and not down into the spinal cord, (ii) toward the visual cortex and not to the auditory cortex, and (iii) to layer IV (a few connections are also made in layer VI) of the visual cortex and not to other cortical layers. This discussion will be concerned with the problem of how LGN neurons recognize the visual cortex—and not with their specific targeting to layer IV of the visual cortex.

As mentioned above, the LGN axons grow out very early in development, shortly after the neurons become postmigratory, and the axons reach the developing cortex at a time when the neurons of layer IV are not yet present. Evidence now suggests, however, that a transient neuronal scaffold, which is formed by a specialized population of early-generated neurons—subplate (SP) neurons—acts as a temporary target for the thalamocortical axons. After layer IV is generated, the scaffold is dismantled.

The development of the cat fetal nervous system can be studied with modern techniques of fetal neurosurgery. Techniques are also available, however, that allow the tracing of developing pathways in young embryos without necessitating the use of live animals. For example, lipophilic dyes can be introduced into the LGN of aldehyde-fixed fetal brains and these dyes then diffuse along the axons and reveal the chosen pathways. In this way, the time course of development of connections between the LGN and cortex can be established.

After neurons of the developing visual cortex have undergone their last round of cell division, they leave the ventricular zone (VZ) and migrate along radial glial cells to the forming cortical plate (CP). As a result of successive waves of neuronal migration, the CP becomes thickened until all the neurons that form the six layers of the mature cortex are present. Two other main zones are present in the embryonic cortex: the marginal zone (MZ), which turns into layer I in the adult; and the intermediate zone (IZ), which lies between the base of the CP and the top of the VZ and which can be further subdivided. One of the component subzones of the IZ is the SP, which lies below the CP and contains the axons of the LGN neurons. When the LGN axons first reach the developing CP, they do not grow into the CP itself but instead they accumulate in the SP and branch. LGN axons are present in the internal capsule at embryonic day 30 (E30) (birth occurs around E65), which is just a few days after the LGN has formed, and the axons reach the developing visual cortical area at E35. The LGN axons then remain in the SP, and it is not until E50 that the first tips of the axons can be seen in the CP. By E55 the axons are finally present in the CP. The axons of LGN neurons thus wait for a period of 2 weeks in the SP before entering the CP, and at least part of the reason for this is that their target neurons of cortical layer IV are not yet present in the CP.

The birthdates of cortical neurons can be determined by [³H]-thymidine labeling studies, and from these studies it has been shown that the cortical layers are generated in an ordered sequence, with the deep layers being generated first and the superficial layers later. For example, if [³H]thymidine is administered to a fetal cat at E33 and the brain of the animal is examined by autoradiography in adulthood, then the most heavily labeled cells are present in cortical layer VI. On the other hand, when [³H]thymidine is administered at E56, the neurons in cortical layers II and III are labeled. Thus, the cortex develops according to an inside-first, outside-last pattern. Labeled cells can be detected in layer IV when [³H]thymidine is administered between E38 and E44. The additional time taken for the neurons of layer IV to migrate to their position in the CP after their birth in the VZ has been measured by supplying a pulse of [³H]thymidine at E38 and determining the positions of the labeled cells on subsequent days. Thus, the cortical layer IV neurons achieve their final position above layers V and VI around E55, which coincides with the time of entry of the LGN axons into the CP.

The administration of [³H]thymidine between E24 and E30 results in the labeling of only a few cells in the adult brain, and these cells are present in two locations: in the white matter, which develops from the SP; and in layer I, which develops from the MZ. The life history of these cells—which represent the first postmitotic cells of the cortex—has been examined by supplying [³H]thymidine at E24 and examining the distribution of labeled cells on subsequent days. The cells thus leave the VZ on E24 and settle underneath the pial surface in a zone that has been termed the preplate. This preplate is then split into two halves—which develop into the MZ and SP, respectively—as neurons of the CP migrate through the zone and insert themselves between the two parts. With subsequent cell division and migration, the CP thickens, but the labeled cells in the MZ and SP are still present in large numbers. However, by 2 months after birth, a time at which the cortical layers have matured, there are very few of the MZ and SP labeled cells left in the cortex. Thus, the pattern of neurogenesis in the cortex is not strictly inside-first and outside-last, but rather resembles the making of a sandwich.

Many lines of evidence suggest that these first postmitotic cells of the cortex are neurons. By correlating [³H]thymidine labeling and immuno-histochemical staining it has been shown that these cells contain neu-ropeptides—neuropeptide Y, somatostatin, cholecystokinin—γ-amino-butyric acid (GABA) and glutamic acid decarboxylase (GAD), and the neuron-specific microtubule-associated protein–2. Evidence also suggests that the disappearance of these early-generated cells as the cortex matures during the first 2 months after birth occurs by a process of cell death; that is, almost 90% of these cells die and are not present in the adult brain. Although the cause of this massive cell death is not known, it is possible that the cells are dependent on a trophic factor that is only present during development—this notion is supported by the finding that shortly after they become postmitotic, the SP neurons are immunoreactive for the receptor for nerve growth factor (NGF); however, about 1 week before the period of cell death begins, this immunoreactivity is lost.

Anterograde and retrograde tracing studies have shown that whereas some SP neurons make local circuit connections, others make long-distance projections; for example, they project down to the thalamus and across the corpus callosum. These projection neurons have also been shown to transport retrogradely [^{3}H]aspartate, which suggests they may use an excitatory amino acid as a transmitter. The mature SP neurons also are located in a fairly extensive synaptic neuropil. The first synapses that can be detected in the forming cerebral wall are present in the SP and the MZ, and it is only later that synapses appear in the CP.

The close proximity between the waiting axons of LGN neurons and the SP neurons and the fact that the SP is filled with synapses suggest that waiting LGN axons may make synaptic contacts onto SP neurons. Although the presynaptic terminals that make contact with SP neurons have not yet been definitively identified, electrophysiological recordings from fetal cortical slices in vitro have shown that the synapses onto SP neurons are functional.

The facts that the SP neurons are born so early and that they make long-distance projections back down to the LGN suggest that the SP neurons may lay down some of the first cortical pathways. Indeed, the lipophilic dye tracing technique has shown that if dye I is placed in the thalamus at E30, the SP neurons are retrogradely labeled. Thus, at E30, the growth cones of the LGN neurons have reached the internal capsule and the growth cones of the SP neurons have reached and passed through the internal capsule. The two sets of axons may therefore fasciculate with each other and form this early thalamocortical connection reciprocally. Although the timing and spatial relations of the growth of these neurons are consistent with this possibility, there is no direct evidence that this is the case. The axons of CP neurons could follow this pathway later in development.

The question of whether the SP neurons are required for the development of thalamocortical connections needs to be addressed by selectively lesioning the SP neurons, but this has not yet been attempted successfully.

However, SP neurons have been selectively deleted at E43—when the LGN axons are waiting in the SP—by injecting the excitotoxin kainic acid into the SP. Examination of such lesioned brains at later embryonic and postnatal stages reveals that the LGN axons fail to enter the visual cortex; instead, they remain in a tight fascicle within the white matter and grow past the visual cortex. Thus, interactions between the SP neurons and the waiting LGN axons appear to be essential for the LGN axons to be able to enter the visual cortex. Furthermore, deletion of the SP neurons at E43 also appears to prevent the formation of connections from the cortex to the thalamus.

In conclusion, the major logistical problem in the construction of the cerebral cortex that arises from the mismatch in the timing of the arrival of the LGN axons and the timing of the generation of their target neurons in layer IV may be solved in part by the construction of a temporary scaffold made of SP neurons. The SP neurons are the first postmitotic cells of the cerebral cortex. The axons of these neurons pioneer pathways, after which the neurons mature, become functional, and then die. Lesion experiments suggest that SP neurons are critical for the formation of normal connections between the thalamus and cortex. Finally, a clinically relevant point is that any damage to the fetus that destroys the SP neurons will not leave an obvious trace in the adult or postnatal brain unless connections themselves are traced—the CP appears normal in animals with small SP lesions even though the pattern of axonal projections is abnormal.

Additional Reading

1. C. J. Shatz and D. W. Sretaven, "Interactions between retinal ganglion cells during the development of the mammalian visual system," *Annu. Rev. Neurosci.* **9,** 171 (1986).
2. C. J. Shatz, "Development of the mammalian visual system," in *Fundamental Mechanisms in Development,* L. J. Shapiro, I. Gross, H. R. Hill, Eds. (Perinatology Press, Ithaca, New York, 1987), pp.19–26.
3. J. C. Edmondson, R. K. H. Liem, J. E. Kuster, M. E. Hatten, "Astrotactin: A novel neuronal cell surface antigen that mediates neuron-astroglial interactions in cerebellar microcultures," *J. Cell Biol.* **106,** 505 (1988).
4. C. J. Shatz, J. J. M. Chun, M. B. Luskin, "The role of the subplate in the development of the telencephalon," in *The Cerebral Cortex, Vol. 7: The Development of the Cerebral Cortex,* A. Peters and E. G. Jones, Eds. (Plenum Press, New York, 1988), pp. 35–58.
5. J. J. M. Chun and C. J. Shatz, "The earliest-generated neurons of the cat neocortex: Characterization by MAP2 and neurotransmitter immunohistochemistry during fetal life," *J. Neurosci.* **9,** 1648 (1989).
6. S. K. McConnell, "The determination of neuronal fate in the cerebral cortex," *Trends Neurosci.* **12,** 342 (1989).

7. S. K. McConnell, A. Ghosh, C. J. Shatz, "Subplate neurons pioneer the pathway from cortex to thalamus," *Science* **245,** 978 (1989).

8. D. D. M. O'Leary, "Do cortical areas emerge from a protocortex?" *Trends Neurosci.* **12,** 400 (1989).

9. K. L. Allendoerfer, D. L. Shelton, E. M. Shooter, C. J. Shatz, "Nerve growth factor receptor immunoreactivity is transiently associated with the subplate neurons of the mammalian cerebral cortex," *Proc. Natl. Acad. Sci. U.S.A.* **87,** 187 (1990).

10. A. Ghosh, A. Antonini, S. K. McConnell, C. J. Shatz, "Requirement for subplate neurons in the formation of thalamocortical connections," *Nature* **347,** 179 (1990).

Ontogenetic Development of Cognitive Memory and Habit Formation in Rhesus Monkeys

Mortimer Mishkin

Mortimer Mishkin earned a Ph.D. in psychology from McGill University, Montreal, Canada, in 1951. He has made significant advances in neuropsychology since he joined the National Institute of Mental Health, Bethesda, Maryland, in 1955, where he currently serves as chief of the Laboratory of Neuropsychology.

Mishkin has spent nearly 40 years studying the memory systems of the brain and is internationally recognized for advancing understanding of the brain's structure and function. Much of his pioneering work comes from research on monkeys. Contrary to the previously held belief that the brain had only one type of memory, Mishkin's revolutionary discovery showed that the brain actually stores habits and facts separately. This idea was a major breakthrough in the study of learning and memory. Mishkin's findings in animal models have brought researchers closer to understanding and developing effective treatments for diseases such as Parkinson's and Alzheimer's.

Ontogenetic Development of Cognitive Memory and Habit Formation in Rhesus Monkeys

LECTURER:

Mortimer Mishkin

Investigations into the neural mechanisms of memory formation in adult monkeys have revealed that there are at least two different cerebral systems in the forebrain that underlie information storage. Also of interest, however, is the development of memory in the infant monkey. Adult humans have poor recollection of events that occurred in early childhood and infancy. The lower limit beyond which humans cannot recall memories of childhood events appears to be 3 or 4 years of age. In exceptional circumstances, a particular event that occurred at an even younger age may be recalled, but, in general, our memory for these events is either poor or nonexistent and the question is, Why?

Information obtained on the neurobiology of memory formation in adult monkeys may prove useful in helping to understand childhood memory formation. First, however, it might be useful to review how the monkey forebrain is organized to serve two different kinds of memory.

In the visual system, information from the retina travels via the lateral geniculate nucleus to the striate cortex (V1), out of which originate three streams of visual processing: an occipital-parietal stream, which is important for spatial orientation; a stream that travels deep into the superior temporal sulcus, which is important for motion analysis; and an occipital-temporal pathway, which is important for object vision. All these pathways are organized in a similar fashion, with multiple areas reciprocally connected to the striate cortex; in the case of the occipital-temporal pathway, the pathway is V1 to V2 to V3 and V4, with V4 being the main input to the inferior temporal cortex—which is important for various kinds of memory and vision. The various stations are organized so that the feedforward projections of one station reach from the supragranular layer (mainly layer III) to the granular layer of the station that follows. The pathways are therefore organized in such a way that, if the early stations are missing, the later stations cannot be activated by the relevant sensory

This chapter was edited by Keith W. Brocklehurst, and was originally reported by Roberto Dal Toso.

170

modality. The feedback projections arise generally from the lower or infragranular layers and project back mostly to the plexiform layer and the deep layers of the preceding station; stations are therefore in a position to modulate the information that they receive. The feedback projections also appear to be a means by which central processes, such as attention, can modulate the information that is entering the central nervous system (CNS). In addition, the feedback projections are probably important for retrieving information that is stored in earlier stations.

An understanding of how the visual system is involved in memory was facilitated by studying the interactions between cortical areas and subcortical structures, such as the limbic system. There are two general principles of organization exhibited by the occipital-temporal processing system. The first is that the receptive fields of the neurons in this sequential processing pathway become progressively larger. For example, neurons in V1 have small receptive fields, whereas in later stations, neurons progressively receive and integrate inputs from preceding neurons, so that in the inferior temporal cortex, some neurons have receptive fields that encompass the entire visual world—they receive information not only from their own striate cortex, but also information from the opposite striate cortex that is conveyed through the corpus callosum and the anterior commissure. Thus, these neurons with large bilateral receptive fields are potential (although, maybe poor) representatives of external stimuli. The second feature of the pathway organization is that the filters become progressively more complicated; so that, for example, neurons in V1 may respond to lines and edges oriented in different ways, whereas in the inferior temporal cortex, neurons respond selectively to stimuli as complex as faces.

When an image of an object falls on the retina, a stream of information is initiated that reaches the inferior temporal cortex in approximately 100 ms. This process involves the activation of millions of neurons that constitute the current representation of the stimulus on the retina and which can be termed the neuronal ensemble. One important question is, How does this neuronal ensemble leave a trace in the CNS to make object recognition possible? It has been shown that this process depends critically on the interaction between the occipital-temporal processing stream and the limbic system (amygdala, rhinal cortex, and hippocampus). Only the last station of the occipital-temporal processing stream activates limbic structures; either directly in the case of the amygdala and rhinal cortex, or indirectly in the case of the hippocampus through the entorhinal cortex.

The important relation between the cortex and the limbic system in memory formation was recognized from the performance of adult monkeys in a simple one-trial object recognition task (Fig. 1). In this task, a

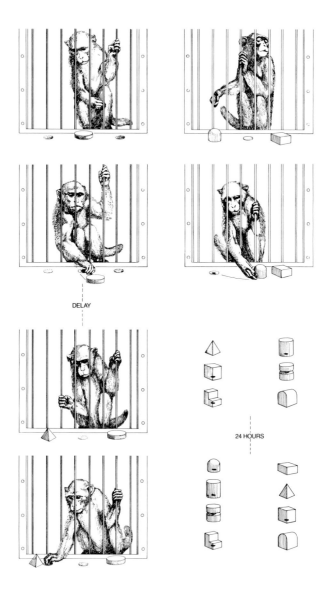

Fig. 1. Two tests allow the evaluation of different memory abilities. In the test known as delayed nonmatching the sample (**left**) the animal must choose the nonfamiliar object to receive a reward. The task can be made more difficult by increasing the delay between the sample and the choice. In a second task (**right**), 20 pairs of objects are successively presented to the animal and only one of them hides a reward each time. The same sequence is presented every 24 hours until the animal remembers the correct object of each pair. Lesions to cortical structures that impair memory in the first task do not impair performance in the second. [Reproduced with permission from Mishkin and Appenzeller (1987). ©1987 by Scientific American, Inc. All rights reserved.]

sample object is presented to the animal for a few seconds and if the animal displaces the object it receives a food reward. The same object is then presented together with a new object, and it is now the new object that must be displaced for the animal to receive a reward. New pairs of stimuli are presented in every subsequent trial so that trial-unique stimuli are used. The same arrangement, a sample followed by a choice test, is repeated in several trials, so that the principle—displacement of new stimuli is associated with a food reward—can be learned by the animal. Adult monkeys learn very quickly this principle of delayed nonmatching the sample, and once a monkey has learned the principle, it is possible to test its memory by progressively increasing the delay between the sample and the choice test. Another version of this test involves presenting to the animal a collection of objects (three to 10) one at a time. The principle is the same, and if the animal remembers the collection of samples, it performs perfectly on the choice test. Normal animals respond with more than 90% correct choices, both with prolonged delays and large lists of objects, indicating that monkeys have quite good visual object memory. This is true if the late stations of the occipital-temporal processing stream and the limbic structures to which they project are intact. If either one of these structures is removed bilaterally, the animals do not perform so well, although they can, with difficulty, reacquire the principle. This latter result indicates that the animals do not have problems with attention, motivation, discrimination, or problem solving. However, when the delay between the sample and the choice test is increased to more than 1 or 2 min, or the number of objects in the list is increased, the performance of these animals falls off dramatically. Thus, as a result of damage to either limbic structures or inferior temporal cortex, the animals are impaired in memory.

The projection from area TE of the inferior temporal lobe to the limbic system is essential for the participation of the limbic system in memory, because if this connection is interrupted, the animals also suffer memory impairment. This evidence therefore indicates that the visual processing stream must activate the limbic system before a trace can be left somewhere in the CNS for an animal to be able to remember a stimulus as familiar, and so avoid it in the task. The limbic structures are only the beginning, however, of an extensive pathway of projections from the temporal lobe to the medial thalamus and hypothalamus, and from these structures to the ventral medial prefrontal cortex. Damage to any one of these regions results in a similar memory impairment. Thus, all these structures appear to be essential stations for the translation of the neuronal ensemble into some form of trace. Furthermore, all these areas project to cholinergic

basal forebrain neurons, which project to the whole cortical mantle, including the limbic system. These cholinergic neurons may serve as a trigger for a cascade of intracellular events that leads to synaptic modification—either short term, by means of protein phosphorylation, for
example, or long term, by changes in gene expression.

All these results can be pieced together to construct a hypothetical
model of the interactions between perception and memory. Thus, visual
information enters the striate cortex, flows through the prestriate cortex,
and, in area TE, many different dimensions of the stimulus that may have
been processed independently—such as color, shape, size, and texture—
converge onto single neurons that are sensitive to modulation by all stimulus characteristics. It is on the basis of their large receptive fields and
complex trigger features or filters that it is thought that these latter neurons
can represent configurational stimuli. This process thus accounts for perception. Memory, however, requires the further activation of the extensive limbic structures and, through them, the activation of the basal forebrain cholinergic system, the nucleus basalis of Meynert, the medial
septal and diagonal band area, and feedback projections to the limbic system, area TE, and earlier stations in the processing stream. A small fraction of the neurons that were active at the time the stimulus was present on
the retina may have their synaptic properties changed as a result of this
feedback action and thereby form a cell assembly. A cell assembly thus
comprises a group of neurons that are linked together into a more-or-less
permanent trace—the degree of permanence depending on how far down
the cascade of intracellular events the process progresses to allow for either short-term or long-term synaptic changes. The next time the stimulus
that produced the trace falls on the retina, it can activate the cell assembly
again and, according to the model, it is the reactivation of the stored cell
assembly that leads to recognition.

How do infant monkeys perform on this type of object recognition
task? Adult monkeys learn the delayed nonmatching principle very rapidly, but 1-year-old or 6-month-old monkeys learn more slowly, and 3-
month-old monkeys cannot learn the principle at all; it is not until they are
5 months old that monkeys begin to perform correctly. However, even
after infant monkeys have learned the principle, their performance is not
very good when the delay between the sample and the choice test is increased; the performance of a 7-month-old monkey is comparable to that
of an adult with a partial lesion of the limbic system. Only when monkeys
reach 2 years of age do they become as proficient as adults. The obvious
question is, Why is such a long period of time needed for the development
of this ability?

The first hypothesis proposed was that the limbic system is immature in young monkeys. This hypothesis was supported by the finding that the occipital-temporal processing stream is sufficient for visual perception and, under certain circumstances, for certain types of learning even in the absence of the limbic system, as was illustrated by the following task. Animals are confronted with a pair of stimuli, one of which is positive and the other negative (Fig. 1). After this trial, they are exposed to a different pair of objects but with the same choice, one positive and one negative. This is repeated for a list of 20 pairs of objects. After 24 hours, the animals are presented with the same 20 pairs, in the same order, with the same stimuli positive and negative as the day before; the only change is the left-right position of the stimuli on the tray so that position habits cannot be used. The test is repeated 24 hours later, and so on for several days until the animals learn the entire set of discriminations.

Adult animals learn in about 10 sessions, and the inferior temporal cortex is essential for this performance, because after its removal the animals take three times as long to learn. Thus, although the animals do learn, they have great difficulty in acquiring the discrimination habit. Animals with limbic lesions (removal of the amygdala and hippocampus) do not differ from normal adults in acquisition time. The neurobiology of this type of learning seems to involve neostriatal targets (caudate nucleus and ventral caudal putamen) of the temporal cortex, because lesions to this pathway increased by two to three times the number of trials needed to learn the task. This form of learning is totally different from that which occurs in recognition memory—which is a form of cognitive memory stored in the cortex—because storage may take place in the neostriatum itself and the dopaminergic system may play an important role.

The inputs to the neostriatum from the temporal cortex are topographically organized and arrive at the neostriatum from early stations of the visual processing stream; unlike the limbic system inputs, which arise from the last station. Thus, whereas highly processed information appears to be needed for activation of the limbic structures, single stimulus elements may serve as inputs to the neostriatum, and the laying down of the trace probably occurs within the neostriatum itself because there are no feedback projections to the temporal cortex (unlike the situation for the limbic system). The neostriatal learning pathway courses from the occipital-temporal processing stream to the caudal portions of the neostriatum to the substantia nigra pars reticulata and globus pallidus to the ventral thalamus to the premotor and prefrontal cortex. This pathway thus provides a means for stimuli to activate responses fairly directly. Through this pathway, stimulus-response bonds are deposited in the CNS, in a form of response adaptation; by contrast, the limbic system is responsible for storage, not of responses, but of information and knowledge about what is or was present in the world.

How do infant monkeys perform on this second type of task? Infant monkeys perform as well as adults—not always as well on the first set of discriminations, but even faster than adults on the second set. On this task, therefore, infant monkeys are adultlike even when they are 3 months old. Whether or not young animals are slower on the first set depends on their sex: 3-month-old male monkeys take longer than adults, 3-month old females do not. At 6 months of age, there is no longer a difference between the sexes with regard to test performance. In 3-month-old animals, the sex difference in performance can be hormonally manipulated: orchiectomized males behave as females, and ovariectomized females receiving testosterone behave as males.

Thus, the data described so far suggest that the defect in the recognition or cognitive memory of the infant monkey is related to the limbic system; that is, the limbic structures are immature. However, the distribution of neurobiological markers—such as opiate receptors and cholinergic receptors, as revealed by autoradiography—in the amygdala and hippocampus was found to be virtually identical in adults and infants. On the other hand, in the cortex, there were differences. For example, in the cortex of a newborn monkey there is homogeneous labeling of opiate receptors, both across areas and across layers, whereas in the adult cortex there are rather large areal and laminar differences. This result therefore suggested that the recognition memory deficit in young monkeys might be related to cortical, rather than limbic, immaturity.

The 2-deoxyglucose (2DG) technique was used to detect areas of glucose utilization in the brains of infant and adult monkeys. The animals had one optic tract and the connections between the cerebral hemispheres cut, so that metabolic rates in a "blind" hemisphere and a "seeing" hemisphere could be compared with each other. On the day of the experiment, the awake animal was placed inside a rotating screen with high-contrast patterns to activate the visual system, while a bolus of radioactively labeled 2DG was injected intravenously to allow for later measurement of local cerebral glucose utilization by means of autoradiography. The results showed that in adult monkeys of 3 to 4 years of age, the percentage reduction in glucose utilization in the blind hemisphere versus the visually intact hemisphere was greatest in the striate and prestriate cortex and somewhat less in the inferior temporal cortex. In animals less than 3 months old, the levels of glucose utilization in the blind hemisphere were not greatly reduced compared to the visually intact hemisphere, because the levels of the latter were also extremely low. At 3 months of age, the levels of glucose utilization in the visually intact hemisphere were comparable to adult values in the striate and the prestriate cortex, even though at this age the temporal portions of the visual processing stream still showed an infant pattern of utilization. Only by 4 months of age did levels of glucose utilization in the intact hemisphere reach adult values throughout the entire pathway, and there was even an overshoot at 6 months of age before metabolic rates returned to adult levels. Thus, according to these measures, the cortical visual system is not mature in early infancy but appears to be so by the time the animals can learn visual discriminations and before they are able to perform adequately on the recognition memory task.

Lesions were introduced neonatally in the temporal lobe as another way to examine its functional maturity in infant monkeys. Either area TE or the limbic system was removed and the animals were tested in the delayed nonmatching-to-sample task; that is, the object recognition task. Surgery was performed in two stages, when the animals were 1 and 3 weeks of age—simultaneous bilateral, symmetrical surgery, as performed on the adult monkeys, may have been lethal to the young animals. The lesioned animals were then tested at 10 months of age, an age at which performance is still not up to adult standards. Young animals with limbic lesions performed poorly in this task compared to nonlesioned animals; as was also the case with adult monkeys with limbic system ablation. Young animals with ablation in area TE, however, were not greatly impaired in the object recognition task; unlike the situation with adult monkeys with the same type of lesion. What accounts for the ability of animals with early TE lesions to perform this task, given that in the adult, area TE is the only station that activates the limbic system?

To answer this question, the connectivity of the system, especially of area TEO—the posterior portion of the inferior temporal cortex—was examined, both in adults and in infants. It was found in the adult, that although cells in the lateral basal nucleus of the amygdala project back to area TEO, area TEO does not innervate the amygdala. However, in the infant, there is an extensive projection from area TEO to the amygdala; this is thus an example of an exuberant projection in the infant that regresses in the adult. Furthermore, it is not just to the amygdala that area TEO shows exuberant projections in the infant. Whereas in the adult, projections originating from area TEO remain confined to area TE and area TEO itself, in infant monkeys the projections reach the parahippocampal gyrus and area TF on the ventral surface of the temporal lobe, from where they can also reach the entorhinal cortex and the hippocampus. Thus, through both direct projections to the amygdala and indirect projections to the hippocampus, infant animals have visual input to the limbic system from stations in the posterior portions of the visual processing stream; and these projections have regressed in the adult. However, it has been recently shown that if there is early damage to area TE, then the exuberant projections are stabilized and are functional. Functionality was demonstrated by the finding that removal of area TEO from 2-year-old monkeys that had also received a TE lesion in early infancy caused the performance of the animals in the simple memory task to fall significantly. A partial explanation for the sparing of function that occurs after early damage to immature cortical areas thus appears to be that other cortical areas in the same processing stream can activate the limbic system and become responsible for the cortical-limbic interactions that are necessary for object recognition memory to occur.

The results presented have not revealed the neurobiological basis for the failure of adults to remember early events of childhood. These findings have explained why animals perform very poorly in early infancy and why it is possible to damage the late stations of the system early in infancy and still have the system preserved functionally to a large extent. However, it still remains to be explained why monkeys have poor memory not just for the first few months of life but up to the age of about 2 years. The explanation may depend, in part, not on the immaturity of the sensory processing pathway, but on the immaturity of the neuromodulatory and intracellular mechanisms that lead to synaptic modification from perceptual observations alone. To understand better what is occurring in "infantile amnesia" (which is not the same phenomenon as medial temporal amnesia), we must have a better understanding of the neuromodulatory events and the whole cascade of intracellular processes. It may be that short-term changes can take place in the infant to allow the type of memory that has been described and which lasts from seconds to minutes. But memories may not remain permanent until changes in gene expression have occurred. Presumably, this particular form of synaptic change is required for memories in childhood to be retrievable later in life.

Additional Reading

1. J. B. Bachevalier and M. Mishkin, "An early and a late developing system for learning and retention in infant monkeys," *Behav. Neurosci.* **98,** 770 (1984).
2. J. Bachevalier and M. Mishkin, "Visual recognition in infant rhesus monkeys: Effects of neocortical vs limbic lesions," *Neuroscience* **22,** S176 (1987).
3. M. Mishkin and T. Appenzeller, "The anatomy of memory," *Sci. Am.* **255,** 80 (1987).

4. J. Bachevalier, C. Hagger, B. B. Bercu, "Gender differences in visual habit formation in 3-month-old rhesus monkeys," *Dev. Psychobiol.* **22,** 585 (1989).
5. J. Bachevalier, M. Brickson, C. Hagger, M. Mishkin, "Age and sex differences in the effects of selective temporal lobe lesions on the formation of visual discrimination habits in rhesus monkeys," *Behav. Neurosci.* **104,** 885 (1990).
6. M. J. Webster, L. G. Ungerleider, J. Bachevalier, "Lesions of inferior temporal area TE in infant monkeys produce reorganization of cortico-amygdalar projections," *Soc. Neurosci. Abstr.* **20,** 285 (1990).
7. J. Bachevalier, "Ontogenetic development of habit and memory formation in primates," in *Development and Neural Bases of Higher Cognitive Functions,* A. Diamond, Ed. (New York Academy of Sciences, New York, 1991), pp. 457–484.
8. M. J. Webster, L. G. Ungerleider, J. Bachevalier, "Connections of inferior temporal areas TE and TEO with medial temporal-lobe structures in infant and adult monkeys," *J. Neurosci.* **11,** 1095 (1991).
9. J. Bachevalier, "Cortical versus limbic immaturity: Relationship to infantile amnesia," in *Developmental Neuroscience,* M. Gunnar and C. A. Nelson, Eds. (Erlbaum, New Jersey, in press).

Human Brain Growth and the Role of Communication

Colwyn Trevarthen

Colwyn Trevarthen was born in New Zealand, where he first specialized in marine botany at Auckland University and then studied animal ethology at Otago University. He began study in the United States in 1957 and received a Ph.D. in psychobiology from the California Institute of Technology in 1962. Since, Trevarthen has published numerous papers in neuropsychology and developmental psychology, including major reviews of the functions of the hemispheres and interhemispheric commissures, brain growth, and psychological development in infancy. In 1988 he helped establish the Edinburgh Centre for Research in Child Development, which he currently directs.

Trevarthen has conducted research at distinguished institutions including the CNRS Laboratory of Psychophysiology, Marseille, France; Cambridge University, England; Harvard University, Cambridge, Massachusetts; and the University of Edinburgh, Scotland. His early work explored how consciousness and learning are allocated in the divided brain by subcortical systems. His subsequent work on the visual awareness of human commissurotomy patients, the allocation of consciousness between the hemispheres, and the comparison of cognitive specializations is frequently cited. When infancy research became his main focus in the 1960s, Trevarthen studied communication in infancy, mother-child relationships, and social factors and cognitive development. He is currently attempting to relate his findings to the understanding of human brain growth and development.

Human Brain Growth and the Role of Communication

LECTURER:

Colwyn Trevarthen

Various theories have been advanced to explain the development of brain systems. These theories have different implications for the development and modification of psychological functions. The reflex assembly theory, which forms a conceptual basis for behavioristic psychology, assumes that only simple, elemental, and anatomically obvious features of the nervous system, the sensory-motor reflexes, and certain drives related to maintenance of the physiological equilibria of the body are determined by development inside the central nervous system and the body without intervention of stimulation from the environment. All higher functions develop as a result of "conditioning"; that is, some mechanism of learning that links up reflexes according to reinforcing feedback from the homeostatic regulators of physiological state. According to this theory, all higher psychological capacities develop as a result of patterns of stimulation and the temporal contingency of discrete stimuli with forms of action (responses and operants) that simultaneously affect physiological states. For example, Piaget's influential theory of cognitive development assumes that mental schemata are learned as a consequence of the way patterns of action regulate perception of environmental stimuli.

Sperry's chemoaffinity theory proposed that nerve circuits governing integrative and complex patterns of action and their guidance by uptake of whole patterns of stimulation (such as locomotor pathfinding through an infinitely varying layout of surroundings, or orientation to and capture of prey) are determined by some kind of cytochemical coding; that is, by a genetically determined mechanism. Elaborate perceptual functions (for example, the space-time frame for behavior, motion and movement perception, color vision), as well as complex innate sequences of behavior (for example, mating, care of offspring, capture of prey and feeding, hiding and escape), are supposedly determined by a code that labels neurons for different connective affinities. The nerve growth process is thought to

This chapter is an extended version of the abstract by Colwyn Trevarthen.

be a process of searching out the correct route through tissues to the correct target neuron, as had been proposed by Cajal on the basis of his anatomical studies on developing brains. This theory, although in direct conflict with radical learning theory, was highly attractive to ethologists, who had evidence that complex behaviors (species-typical behavior patterns) were equally important phenotypic reflections of evolutionary selection as any part of the anatomy of a species.

After gaining ground steadily over the 1940s and 1950s, Sperry's theory came under attack from proponents of the view that intricate, orderly patterns of nerve connections could arise, after an initial period of disorderly exuberance and intermingling of growing nerve branches and cell contacts, by selective removal of connections that had not been validated by coincident stimulation via two or more sensory inputs. Gaze and others sought to bring back the environment of temporally and spatially patterned stimuli as the principal formative agent in fixing orderly functional nerve systems. Hebb's theory, concerning the formation of neuronal assemblies by selective reinforcement of coincidently active endings on a neuron, and postsynaptic regulation, was a key element of this approach.

In the 1970s, a number of studies, including some that actually set out to disprove the chemoaffinity theory, provided evidence that key features of the anatomical design of the brain are determined before patterned stimuli have access. In certain experimental rearrangements, nerve connections grew in contradiction to the way stimuli were impinging—as shown in Sperry's classic studies. At the same time, dramatic examples of exuberance and selective reduction of connections with influence of stimulation were also obtained by Innocenti, Changeux, and others. A dual process theory (Willshaw and Von der Mahlsberg; Constantine-Paton) therefore became popular. Sperryesque determinism was admitted for many essential "boundary conditions," body-related mappings, and segregation of parallel processing systems adapted to different perceptual or motoric processes. On the other hand, growing neuronal systems were known to exhibit a high degree of plasticity, and reorganization can occur under the influence of stimuli that would be "gated" by forms of movement and by the embryogenically determined form of the receptor organs in their relation to the body. Spontaneous neuronal activity in immature systems was shown to be an essential source of energy, capable of driving "sorting factors" in the formation of ordered nerve connections.

In the 1980s, a major innovation came with demonstrations that the efficacy of environmental input, even in the optimal "sensitive period" of growth of a given system, is itself "conditional" on the concomitant activity of prewired motor and motivational or attentional systems in the core of the brain. Thus, for kitten binocular cells in the visual cortex, the precisely segregated convergent connections that mature after the eyes open developed correctly only if both oculomotor movements and inputs from the reticular system were normal (Singer; Imbert).

The inner muscular and interneuronal adjustments of attention in the brain "gate" the connections being retained in the visual cortex. These discoveries regarding the cell physiology of visual cortex circuit formation open the way to a new theory of the self-regulation of brain circuits, with motivating reticular and limbic systems acting as the vehicles of inherent rules governing the patterning of impressionable parts of the nerve net by experience.

These findings now require integration with new information on the cell-cell interactions, immunology, pharmacology, and biochemistry of developing neurons to determine how the regulatory systems are patterned. Finally, the way genes and peptides act as codes for these developments and their relation to different neural systems that develop in the embryo and fetus require elucidation.

Recent behavioral data from infants with their mothers demonstrate the importance of emotions transmitted in communication for the regulation of cognitive growth. In development of the brains of social species, various kinds of motivated interaction of growing brains with mature and experienced brains permit the transfer of adaptive behaviors without the need for the risky process of trial and error and exploration of unfamiliar environmental conditions by the young. Imitative behaviors and teaching have evolved to make such transfer of organization from older to younger brains more efficient; human cultural transmission being a new and powerful form of adaptive process that transforms the evolutionary process in all its aspects.

Such processes of social and cooperative adaptation cannot be understood from classical learning theory; instead, it is necessary to observe the regulations of perceptual uptake of information and learning that occur through transfer of emotions between teacher and learner, or model agent or actor and imitator. This intersubjective process is an evolutionary adaptation of the internal regulators of learning that developmental brain science is beginning to uncover. The regulatory states of motivation, appetite, attention, interest, and the like are made accessible to the young in affectionate, playful, or cooperative communication. These motivators give selective reinforcement for the child's experiences about events that occur in relation to, or contingent with, the reciprocal transfer of feelings between teacher and pupil. Cultural learning in humans requires the most efficient transfer of emotions, and this depends on the formation of affectionate attachments of the young to their parents or other mentors.

In the last 20 years, new descriptive methods, the development of which has been facilitated by the availability of inexpensive television equipment, have been applied to the study of the subtle and complex interplay of expressions of feeling, interest, and intention between infants and mothers. Frame-by-frame analysis of visible movements and microanalysis of vocalizations, especially those of the mother, have revealed hitherto unsuspected refinements of timing and expression. Precisely regulated interactions between mother and baby have been described. Important evidence has been obtained concerning the origins and functions of human emotion, and the means by which emotions are communicated.

This work poses far-reaching questions concerning the nature of human cognitive processes and their development. A young infant has the ability to enter into close-coupling with states of attention, intention, and feeling in another person, and mothers exhibit intuitive adaptations of feeling and expression that support the infant's experience and learning. Periods of intense brain-brain interaction are set up and the infant gains the capacity to direct another person into the role of a supporter of communicative expression, motivational states, and cognitive growth. The caretaker becomes a guide who can keep pace with the infant's psychological growth.

Imitation tests and perturbation experiments have shown that the infant is born with a specified neuropsychological "representation" or "schema" of a partner (another "subject") in communication, and that this "virtual other" becomes active in response to appropriate, intuitively patterned behaviors of an "actual other" in the first 2 months after birth—before the infant begins to build a concept of any physical object of manipulation. These events support a theory of intersubjective autopoesis for human consciousness—in other words, a human mind is, from the start, self-created in communication with other similarly motivated minds.

We are led by these findings to question any theory that proposes emotions to be merely a by-product of cognitive work of a subject taking in sensory information to control actions. Nor do emotions appear to be merely the expression of drives and appetites for the regulation of body state. Innate systems of the brain are elaborately and specifically adapted, not only for self-regulation within separate brains of individuals, but for regulating intermental or intersubjective engagements between communicating persons and their brains. This action requires communication by means of a specific, dedicated system of emotional expressions. Moreover, there is increasing evidence that the neural regulatory mechanisms of this communication are asymmetrical, at least from fetal stages of brain development. Infant communicative expressions have predictable asymmetries at birth.

Many experimental studies of infants in the past clearly started with hypotheses that are too restricting, being especially neglectful of the possibility that motivational and emotional organizations and processes are innate in the developing human brain and differentiated from the outset to distinguish between physical things and persons as they determine what action the baby will attempt to perform. All such questions become clearer when we observe closely what a baby expresses in actual interaction with the expressions of another person.

There is evidence from newborn rats and premature human newborns that emotional communication can affect brain growth by changing the balance of growth regulating hormones. Distortions of cognitive growth in infants are correlated with environmental stress affecting communication, such as maternal postnatal depression. Congenital defects in communicative expression or motivation, as in autism, are also linked to abnormal cognitive maturation. On the other hand, the severe distortion of development in the cerebral cortex that accompanies profound mental handicap can leave functional a basic level of human emotional communication that resembles the communication between an infant and its mother. We can conclude that the fundamental motivating machinery of the brain, which is established prenatally, is very robust; however, it is subject to congenital variation and deformity, and, if defective, it cripples intelligence and cultural learning.

Experimental and clinical neuropsychology provide data that confirm the existence of a motivating and emotion-generating system in the medioventral aspect of the brain. Limbic tissues of the forebrain and mediofrontal cortex are implicated in emotional expression and reception and in the regulation of social relations. Lesions in these structures produce failures in direct communication in adults, and in juvenile monkeys a condition resembling autism can be produced by removal of some parts of this system (Bachevalier and Mishkin). Abnormal development of the cerebellar vermis in autistic individuals (Courchesne) suggests that this part of the brain also plays an important role in the regulation of affective communication and development of higher brain functions. We are just beginning to discover the neuronal systems in the human brain that regulate its maturation, and this knowledge will change the way we see the environment as supplier of essential information for development.

Additional Reading

1. C. Trevarthen, "Neuroembryology and the development of perceptual mechanisms," in *Human Growth,* F. Falkner and J. M. Tanner, Eds. (Plenum Press, New York, ed. 2, 1985), pp. 301–383.

2. C. Trevarthen and H. Marwick, "Signs of motivation for speech in infants, and the nature of a mother's support for development of language," in *Precursors of Early Speech,* B. Lindblom and R. Zetterstrom, Eds. (Macmillan, Basingstoke, 1986), pp. 279–308.

3. C. Trevarthen, "Brain development," in *Oxford Companion to the Mind,* R. L. Gregory and O. L. Zangwill, Eds. (Oxford University Press, Oxford and New York, 1987), pp. 101–110.

4. C. Trevarthen, "Language mechanisms in the brain, development," in *Encyclopedia of Neuroscience,* G. Adelman, Ed. (Birkhauser; Boston, Basel, Stuttgart; 1987), vol. I, pp. 565–567.

5. C. Trevarthen, "Development of early social interactions and the affective regulation of brain growth," in *Neurobiology of Early Infant Behaviour,* C. von Euler, H. Forssberg, H. Lagercrantz, Eds. (Macmillan, Basingstoke and Stockton Press, New York, 1989), Wenner-Gren Center International Symposium Series, vol. 55, pp. 191–216.

6. C. Trevarthen, "Growth and education of the hemispheres," in *Brain Circuits and Functions of the Mind,* C. Trevarthen, Ed. (Cambridge University Press, New York, 1990), pp. 334–363.

Subject Index

A

Acetylcholine, 22–30
Acetylcholine receptor, 22–30
  binding sites, 24–25
  structure, 23
Adenosine 3',5'-monophosphate
  (cyclic AMP), 27, 55, 57
α-Amino-3-hydroxy-5-methyl-4-
  isoxazole propionic acid
  (AMPA), 137–138
2-Amino-5-phosphonovaleric acid
  (APV), 137–138
Astrocytes, 74–76, 158

B

Brain
  areas, 112–113
    17 and 18, 85–93
    in monkey, 170–178
    for vision, 110–115
  cerebral cortex, 84–93
  color vision, 110–115
  development of, 152–159,
    162–167, 171–174
  cortical plate, 163–166
  development, in monkeys, 88–91
  evolution of, 84
  growth, 182–187
  hormones as mediators in,
    96–108
  maps of, 132–140, 142–149
  pathways in, 112–114

C

Cadherins, 13, 38
Calcitonin gene–related peptide, 27
Calcium ion channels, 122–124,
  126–129
Catecholamines, 54–61
Cell adhesion molecules (CAMs),
  2–19, 38, 77–82, 133
  liver, 5
  neural, 5
  in neuronal development, 32–43
Cell-junction molecules (CJMs),
  4–5
Cell recognition, 32–43
Central nervous system (CNS)
  catecholaminergic neurons, 54
  cell functions, 118
  development of, 162, 170–178
  of *Drosophila*, 33–34
  of leeches, 65–66, 68–70
  maps of, 132–140, 142–149
  pathways, 132
Cerebral cortex, specification of,
  84–93
Chemoaffinity theory, 132–135,
  182–183
Chick embryo, 3–8, 10–12, 25–26,
  46–52
Chloramphenicol acetyltransferase
  (CAT), 27, 57
Communication
  between cells, 22–30
  role of, 182–187
Concanavalin A, 125–128

189

CONTENTS

PREFACE

York Notes are designed to give you a broader perspective on works of literature studied at GCSE and equivalent levels. We have carried out extensive research into the needs of the modern literature student prior to publishing this new edition. Our research showed that no existing series fully met students' requirements. Rather than present a single authoritative approach, we have provided alternative viewpoints, empowering students to reach their own interpretations of the text. York Notes provide a close examination of the work and include biographical and historical background, summaries, glossaries, analyses of characters, themes, structure and language, cultural connections and literary terms.

If you look at the Contents page you will see the structure for the series. However, there's no need to read from the beginning to the end as you would with a novel, play, poem or short story. Use the Notes in the way that suits you. Our aim is to help you with your understanding of the work, not to dictate how you should learn.

York Notes are written by English teachers and examiners, with an expert knowledge of the subject. They show you how to succeed in coursework and examination assignments, guiding you through the text and offering practical advice. Questions and comments will extend, test and reinforce your knowledge. Attractive colour design and illustrations improve clarity and understanding, making these Notes easy to use and handy for quick reference.

York Notes are ideal for:
- Essay writing
- Exam preparation
- Class discussion

The author of these Notes is Paul Beadle, who teachers English and Drama in a comprehensive school in the North-East of England. He is a senior examiner for one of the United Kingdom's largest GCSE examination bodies.

The text used in these Notes is the Harper Collins Lions edition, first published 1976.

Health Warning: **This study guide will enhance your understanding, but should not replace the reading of the original text and/or study in class.**

Part one

Introduction

How to study a novel

You have bought this book because you wanted to study a novel on your own. This may supplement classwork.

- You will need to read the novel several times. Start by reading it quickly for pleasure, then read it slowly and carefully. Further readings will generate new ideas and help you to memorise the details of the story.
- Make careful notes on themes, plot and characters of the novel. The plot will change some of the characters. Who changes?
- The novel may not present events chronologically. Does the novel you are reading begin at the beginning of the story or does it contain flashbacks and a muddled time sequence? Can you think why?
- How is the story told? Is it narrated by one of the characters or by an all-seeing ('omniscient') narrator?
- Does the same person tell the story all the way through? Or do we see the events through the minds and feelings of a number of different people.
- Which characters does the narrator like? Which characters do you like or dislike? Do your sympathies change during the course of the book? Why? When?
- Any piece of writing (including your notes and essays) is the result of thousands of choices. No book had to be written in just one way: the author could have chosen other words, other phrases, other characters, other events. How could the author of your novel have written the story differently? If events were recounted by a minor character how would this change the novel?

Studying on your own requires self-discipline and a carefully thought-out work plan in order to be effective. Good luck.

Robert C. O'Brien was the pseudonym of Robert Leslie Conly, who was born in New York City in 1922, one of a family of seven. He died in 1973, not long after *Z for Zachariah* had been published in the USA.

Youth

In his youth, Robert O'Brien had intended to become a professional pianist, but when he finished high school he took on a variety of jobs, including work in a mail room, a bookshop, and an advertising agency. His literary career probably had its beginnings when he was a student working in camps for boys during the summer vacations; here he would tell stories, sitting by night around the campfire or in the cabin. He realised this was excellent training for finding out what types of story young people like.

Writing

He worked on a newspaper as a reporter for a while, then as a re-write man for a news agency, a staff writer for various magazines, and a freelance writer of stories, poems and essays. He then took up a post on the staff of *National Geographic* magazine in Washington, DC. He became an editor for the magazine and spent the last twenty-two years of his life with this internationally famous publication which deals with scientific, geographic and ecological matters – subjects which are at the heart of *Z for Zachariah* (1974) and his other novels, *The Silver Crown* (1968), *Mrs Frisby and the Rats of NIMH* (1971) and *Report from Group 17* (1972).

Context & setting

Z for Zachariah is essentially a science-fiction novel, based on the fear, which was very real in the 1970s when the book was written, that nuclear war was certainly possible and, indeed, probable.

Political context

The end of the Second World War, when atomic bombs were dropped on the Japanese cities of

Hiroshima and Nagasaki, had proved how horrific the potential of nuclear power was when used in aggressive situations. After the war, from the 1940s onwards, there was a tension between some of the victors. The United States of America and the Union of Soviet Socialist Republics (USSR) had been allies in the fight against Japan and Hitler's Germany, but they were ideologically very far apart – the USA was a capitalist nation, while the USSR favoured communism. There developed between the two countries a situation known as the Cold War, in which fear of one another's ideologies and intentions led to mounting strain on their relationship.

Z for Zachariah is set in the United States after a nuclear war. The circumstances of the war are never alluded to – in fact, before Loomis arrives, Ann is even unsure of what kind of warfare had been employed – and it is not stated which other country was involved in this war with the USA. However, its consequences have been devastating.

The political situation which resulted in this terrible and sudden war are of little importance to the author. The fact that a war has occurred, and that the American (or even global) population has been destroyed, is the starting point of a novel which explores the essence of what it is to be human, the point of existence itself.

Science fiction   To categorise the novel as being part of the genre we generally call science fiction is perhaps a little misleading, although the best quality science fiction does address universal issues like those in *Z for Zachariah*. The novel is not, though, about aliens, robots, other planets or bizarre technology. It is written in diary form – the diary of a fifteen-year-old girl (she celebrates her sixteenth birthday half way through the novel) named Ann Burden. At the beginning of the story, Ann believes that she may be the only person left alive on the planet.

Geography   Ann has lived all her life on a farm in an area called Burden Valley, named after her long-established family who were the first settlers there. By some freak of nature, the valley has remained free from radiation pollution and is still capable of sustaining life. The valley seems to have been protected by the high surrounding hills. Claypole Ridge is fifteen miles to the north. Ten miles beyond this is the nearest settlement, Ogdentown, which she knows from having gone to school there. She also knows, from her family's explorations, that 'there is no one left alive in Ogdentown'. Near her homestead, Burden Farm, there is Burden Hill, six miles away, some woodland, and a cave; there are also two streams and a pond. In the valley itself there is a church, and a store which was owned by Mr and Mrs Klein. This store had served the Burdens, and an Amish (see Glossary on p. 15 of these Notes) community who had farms just to the south of the valley. There is a highway nearby which led to Dean Town, which Ann describes as 'a real city – twenty thousand people, much bigger than Ogdentown'. Ann had hoped to go to study at the Teachers' College in Dean Town, but she now knows there is no one left alive there, or in the Amish settlement.

This, then, is the apparently desperate situation in which we find Ann Burden at the beginning of the novel. She had lived with her family: father, mother, brother Joseph and cousin David. They, together with the Kleins, had gone to search for signs of life to the south, but they never returned. She was left alone, until Mr Loomis appears on the scene.

PART TWO

SUMMARIES

GENERAL SUMMARY

Chapters
1–5:
A stranger
arrives

A nuclear holocaust has taken place and fifteen-year-old Ann Burden believes herself to be the sole survivor – the valley in which she lives has somehow escaped the devastation. Ann's parents, brother, and cousin, and the only other people in the valley, the Kleins, who ran the store, had gone to search for signs of life, but never returned. Ann has been living by herself for over a year, when she sees, with a mixture of hope and fear, a column of smoke in the distance, gradually coming nearer.

Leaving behind no trace of her existence, Ann cautiously decides to move to a cave further up the hill, from where she watches a man approaching, who is dressed in an orange plastic suit and is pulling a wagon. Obviously amazed and relieved to find a green, living valley, the stranger checks for radiation and removes his mask.

The following day, he mistakenly bathes in the contaminated Burden Creek, rather than in the pure stream that Ann has been using as a water supply. Soon after this, Faro, cousin David's dog, who had run off some time ago, returns. Moving between the cave and house, Ann fears Faro may give her presence away.

The man goes looking around the valley, but becomes ill and drags himself to his tent. When he does not emerge, Ann goes to see what has happened. He has become very ill indeed, but comes around enough to tell her he has contracted radiation sickness. In his delirious sleep he keeps mentioning 'Edward'.

Chapters 6–10: Nursing the sick

Ann nurses the man and finds out that his name is John R. Loomis. Before the nuclear war, he was working on a type of plastic which would keep out radiation – the suit he was wearing, which is the only one of its kind, and the cover of the wagon are made out of this material. Loomis has scientific and mechanical knowledge which will surely be of help to Ann, but at the same time he displays a quirky and aggressive nature, especially when Ann enquires about Edward. He also continues to talk in his sleep in a worrying manner.

Despite this, Ann even begins to innocently consider the prospect of marriage to Loomis. Then he becomes seriously ill again. She continues to nurse him, but on her return home after doing some chores she sees Loomis stagger from the house, take his gun, and shoot at the top of the building. She calms him and puts him back to bed, but his nightmares return and Ann finds out that Loomis shot Edward because he tried to take the suit from the laboratory where they worked.

Chapters 11–15: Living with a murderer

Loomis is so ill he nearly dies. Ann goes to the church with Faro to pray for both Loomis and herself. While at the church, Faro finds a baby crow which has fallen from its nest, and Ann leaves it outside for its parents to find. Later she finds it gone, and is certain it has been returned to its nest. Ann looks on this as a good omen, and sure enough Loomis begins to get better, and Ann begins to think optimistically. Ann loves books and considers the possibility of going to Ogdentown to get some, using the suit; but this is clouded by the thought of what happened to Edward. Ann also dismantles the stove and brings it to the house. She is able to roast a chicken and bake a cake for her sixteenth birthday.

Chapters 16–20: Attacked and hunted

Ann's optimism is marred by Loomis's attitude. As he gets better he becomes more domineering. Then, one night, Loomis grabs her hand and makes what Ann calls a 'pass' at her. She is afraid and disturbed and realises that Loomis is trying to take control of her.

Loomis demands that she read and play the piano for him but this makes her feel tense. The next night he creeps into her room and attempts to rape her. She escapes and runs to the cave.

Ann realises that Faro is a threat to her, and Loomis makes a point of putting the dog on a leash and tying it up. She decides to go to talk to Loomis to work out a compromise. Ann keeps her hiding place at the cave secret. Loomis tries to find out where she is staying. She realises she can never trust him again. He does not even mention the attempted rape.

Ann still milks the cows and collects vegetables, ensuring that she gives Loomis exactly the same amounts as herself. Loomis, however, is training Faro to track, and he is learning how to drive the tractor. Ann begins to wish Loomis had never come to the valley, and she begins to think about escape.

Chapters 21–26: Leaving the valley

For about ten days the system Ann has worked out seems to be satisfactory. But Loomis is plotting. Ann finds Loomis has taken the tractor key and she goes to ask him for it. He does not give it to her, and again tries to ascertain her whereabouts and persuade her to return to the house. Ann refuses to tell him and leaves. A little later Loomis searches the store to see if she is staying there and puts padlocks on the doors.

Ann decides to go to the house to confront him. He shoots her in the ankle. Ann runs for her life. Loomis tracks her, using Faro, and Ann decides to shoot the dog to safeguard her own safety, but she cannot go through with it. Loomis gives up searching, but not before he has found Ann's cave and destroyed all her property.

Ann hides like a hunted animal for over a month. She decides she must steal the safe-suit and leave the valley.

One day she sees the door to the store has been left open but when she goes towards it Loomis shoots at her, and she realises she has walked into a trap. Ann flees, but Loomis trails after her with Faro on the leash. Ann fires above Loomis's head and scares him off. Faro has leapt into the contaminated Burden Creek and dies shortly afterwards.

This sparks Ann into action. She manages to take the cart, put on the suit, and head out of the valley, but she feels a need to speak to Loomis one last time.

Loomis comes after her. Ann is hidden, and as Loomis gets down from the tractor, Ann could easily shoot him, but does not. Loomis demands the safe-suit and pleads with her to stay, but Ann turns away and walks out of the valley, leaving it to him. Loomis yells after her that he has seen birds to the west. She acknowledges this, and walks on in hope.

DETAILED SUMMARIES

CHAPTERS 1–5: A STRANGER ARRIVES

CHAPTER 1

May 20th

Ann is afraid. She has seen a column of smoke rise into the air on three consecutive days, first behind Claypole Ridge (fifteen miles away), and gradually moving nearer. The last time she saw smoke it was a giant cloud, the result of the nuclear holocaust last year which left her alone on Burden Farm. She fears whoever it is that is approaching and her first thought is to go to the church and pray.

We learn that there is no one left alive in Ogdentown (ten miles further on from Claypole Ridge), something that Ann knows because her father, her brother Joseph and her cousin David had gone there after the war ended, and found only dead bodies.

May 21st

What is the significance of Ann's certainty that the approaching stranger is male?

The smoke is coming closer, and Ann realises the approaching stranger is deciding whether to take the east-west highway, which leads to Dean Town, or Country road 793, which leads over the ridge to Burden Valley. She wants him to follow the highway, to stay away, but she knows that if he gets to the top of the ridge he will see the green trees of the valley and come in her direction, since all else is dead.

Ann begins to explain why she is writing this document, which she began in February: she had started to forget when, and even whether, things had happened; in addition, the diary was 'like having someone to talk to' (p. 8), since she had thought she was the only person left in the world.

Is Ann's caution justified?

Ann tells of how at first she hated being alone. One by one, the radio stations had stopped transmitting, and the final broadcasts she had heard had disturbed her. The man had broken down and cried on air, and this has made her cautious: anyone who did arrive could be mad or mean or a murderer, so she has decided not to show herself immediately to anyone who arrives. Consequently, she has started to move her possessions to the cave.

May 22nd

The smoke has risen again from the same place as yesterday, and Ann knows that the person or persons have camped at the crossroads and are exploring east and west – she fears the next step will be to explore south, towards her valley.

Meanwhile, Ann tells us that on the day after the trip to Ogdentown her family, along with Mr and Mrs Klein, had travelled southwards towards the Amish community to see how they had fared; then they were to travel on to Baylor and Dean Town. No one returned, and Ann realises that the Amish have all perished, as has everyone in Dean Town. She has also climbed the trees on the hills which surround the valley, and beyond the valley there is no sign of life – sensibly she does not go out there.

COMMENT   The diary form of the novel is immediately apparent in the dates of the entries. This means that the story is told as a **first-person narrative** (see Literary Terms) and we see all the events through Ann's eyes.

The first two sentences are short and shocking, pulling us straight into Ann's predicament: 'I am afraid. Someone is coming' (p. 5). This is a technique Robert O'Brien uses to great effect throughout the novel.

Another comparable technique is the use of **flashbacks** (see Literary Terms). This is effective and, indeed, realistic when one considers how a diary is written and the needs of the story: the reader has to be made aware of the background to Ann's situation, but the author does not allow her to reveal everything at once, as this would be clumsy and unnatural. Instead, Ann gradually fills us in on what has happened, with a little piece of information every so often. The **exposition** (see Literary Terms), starting with the most important incident, is subtle and natural. It also maintains interest by keeping the reader guessing (e.g. it is not until the end of Chapter 2 that we find out for certain that the narrator is a girl).

The fact that Ann's first action in response to the approach of the stranger is to go to the church and pray

all morning tells us something about her spiritual
nature. We also begin to admire her courage and her
resilience as we realise what she has lived through. An
atmosphere of suspense develops as we wonder with
Ann who the stranger or strangers will be, and what
they are like.

GLOSSARY   **dogwood** a wild shrub with dark red branches, greenish-white
                flowers and purple berries, found in woods and hedgerow
            Amish a strict Mennonite sect, a Protestant group that
                originated in Switzerland, and settled in Pennsylvania in the
                east of the United States. Named after their leader, Jakob
                Amman, they are farmers who try to live and work simply,
                using horses instead of tractors and cars and avoiding the use
                of electricity
            panel truck a small delivery van

CHAPTER 2

May 23rd

*Notice how careful
Ann is.*

Ann has reluctantly taken steps to cover up evidence of
her existence, letting out the animals and digging up
the vegetable garden. We learn that she has been lucky
with the animals, except that one day David's dog Faro
ran off. From the cave, where she has now moved for
safety, she can see most of the valley; but she is sure the
stranger will not see the cave as it is well hidden by
trees.

Ann tells us how difficult it is to keep track of time,
and how she would like to know when it is June 15th,
her sixteenth birthday. She looks back on how she has
survived, how lucky it was that the store was there in
the valley, and how lucky it was that the war – which
only lasted a week – had taken place in the spring, so
she has the summer to get used to things and prepare
for the winter.

Ann sees the smoke again, and calculates from its
position that the stranger is on his way towards the
valley. She decides that tomorrow she will go near the

A STRANGER ARRIVES

Is Ann right to take a gun?

top of Burden Hill and climb a tree to watch, taking one of her guns with her.

Ann writes about her water supply. There is a drilled well near the house, but this is now useless because it worked with an electric pump; similarly, she cannot use the electric water heater or the shower, so she has to carry water from one of two streams. She relates how, just in time, she realised that the larger of the two streams, Burden Creek, was poisoned, since it flows from outside the valley – just before using it she noticed dead fish and a dead turtle. The other, smaller, stream rises from a spring up the hill and flows into a large pond which contains pure water and live fish, which have been an important source of food.

Why is Ann now concerned about her appearance?

Ann has also begun to worry about her appearance. She is wearing men's blue jeans from the store, a man's work shirt, and boys' tennis shoes. Her hair is cut off square around her neck. She wonders about wearing a dress, but decides to wear the one pair of real slacks she has left.

May 24th

Ann has climbed a tree and seen that the stranger is a single man who is dressed in an orange, plastic-looking suit which covers him entirely, with a glass mask for his eyes. He has an air-tank on his back and he is pulling a wagon behind him, covered in the same orange material. Ann has to decide what to do.

COMMENT   In this chapter the reader is impressed by the way she has survived alone, and by the cautious but common-sense way in which she prepares for the stranger's arrival. Ann's caution in taking the rifle with her is sensible, and brings into the novel an important **motif** (see Literary Terms). Guns are to play an important part in the story. They can be important to survival, and it is notable that Ann, although a good shot, does not like guns. We learn that she has practised on tins and bottles rather than living creatures, but in taking the gun with her we see how common sense overrules her sensitivity. The fact that she does not expect to use it is **ironic** (see Literary Terms) and is one of many examples of her innate goodness and optimism.

The stranger's arrival in the valley brings an end to Ann's 'comfortable' existence. She has to destroy the garden she has worked so hard to create, and feels the need to leave her family home and live in a cave. This creates a sense of foreboding: 'I feel as if it is the beginning of the end' (p. 18).

The theme of survival is apparent in the story of the two streams: water is essential for life, but one of the streams has been polluted by the outside world and brings about death. Things – and people? – from the outside bring danger to the valley.

Ann's awareness of her appearance – she feels the need to dress like a girl – and the fact that this is a man approaching raises the question of sexuality, which will become important later.

GLOSSARY   **Guernseys** a breed of dairy cattle
a cord of wood a measure of cut wood, 128 cubic feet
bucksaw a large, heavy saw

A STRANGER ARRIVES

CHAPTER 3

Still May 24th

It is night and the stranger has entered Ann's house, or perhaps camped outside it in a small tent, for Ann cannot see too clearly. Ann tells of the man's reaction when he saw the green of the valley and the living trees. Anxious to take off his mask, he used two Geiger counters to check for radiation. Then he removed his mask and cheered – the first voice Ann had heard for a very long time, except for her own when she had sung sometimes. Ann liked the sound of his voice and her first reaction had been to run down and reveal herself, but she resisted. Ann had noticed he looked thin and not very healthy, but also 'rather poetic' (p. 27).

Having taken a gun out of his wagon, he had walked around the house, looked in every window and called again before entering. Ann feared she had left some evidence of her presence behind. After coming back out of the house twenty minutes later, he had set up his tent, made a fire and cooked a meal.

Ann believes he is now asleep and works out that the orange plastic material of the suit, the tent and the wagon cover is for keeping out radiation. She is still afraid but also feels it is '*companionable* to know there is someone else in the valley' (p. 30).

May 25th

Ann fears the stranger has made a mistake, and recounts the lead-up to it. When she came out of the cave he was already awake. Having taken from his wagon a larger gun, he shot one of Ann's chickens. This shocks her, since this is not the accepted way to kill a chicken. Coming across the pond, he had seen the minnows. He checked the water with his Geiger counter, then drank some, realising it was pure. After fetching some provisions from the store, he suddenly fired into some bushes, presumably at a rabbit. He missed.

Could Ann have prevented the stranger's mistake?

He then made his mistake. He went swimming and had a bath, but in the wrong stream, the contaminated Burden Creek. He had removed his clothing and carelessly jumped in, not noticing the dead grass and weeds on the banks or the absence of fish. Ann does not know for certain what is wrong with the water, and therefore how bad a mistake he has made. She hopes it hasn't killed him.

COMMENT

The fact that Ann likes the sound of the man's voice, and comments on his wild and poetic appearance suggest the beginnings of an attraction to the stranger.

The stranger's use of the gun to kill the chicken and his reckless shot at the rabbit reveal a violence and a lack of restraint which contrast starkly with Ann's sensitivity.

Ann's thoughtful and common-sense approach to survival is highlighted by his careless leap into the poisoned water.

Ann still decides to wait and watch, despite her concern for his well-being.

GLOSSARY

Geiger counter an instrument used to measure radioactivity levels, named after Hans Geiger, a German physicist

carbine a light automatic rifle

bolt-action a rifle where the breechblock takes the form of a manually operated sliding rod

pump a rifle where a backward and forward movement of a lever ejects the empty case, cocks the rifle, and loads a new round

fescue a type of grass

CHAPTER 4

Still May 25th

Ann is in the cave at night. Strangely, Faro has returned. He is very thin and has lost half the hair from his left side. Faro is a mongrel who enjoyed hunting; hearing the gunshots probably brought him back. The man tries to befriend the dog by feeding it chicken, but then Faro picks up Ann's trail and runs towards the cave. Fortunately for Ann, the man is unable to follow the dog, but Ann realises that Faro may soon betray her presence. Ann then starts considering why that should be such a bad thing. Being alone for nearly a year; she had longed for someone to arrive, but now she considers the possibility that this may not be a good man. She continues to wait and watch to find out what he is like.

May 26th

According to her calendar, Ann believes it to be Sunday. Normally she would go to church and make it a day of rest. The man cooks breakfast quickly, and feeds Faro, who is still wary of him. The man goes into the store and comes out with new clothes on, making him look younger, 'thirty or thirty-two'. Walking towards the far end of the valley, the man finds the point where Burden Creek and the smaller stream join. Here, the difference between the smaller stream, full of fresh water life, and the dead Burden Creek is clear, though Ann is not sure if the man notices.

The stranger explores Ann's valley.

Ann tells us something of the geography of the valley and the fact that it was said to have its own weather due to its enclosed nature.

On his way back to the house, the man stops, sits down and is very sick. He collapses a further three times before reaching his tent and crawling inside. Ann hopes he will be better in the morning.

COMMENT

Faro's arrival can be compared to that of the stranger: it is a sign of hope, but also a potential danger.

We have evidence of Ann's natural possessiveness over 'her' valley: in the last chapter she was mildly annoyed at the man's shooting of one of her chickens, his entry into her house, and his building a fire with her wood. Now she speaks of his using her plates ('mine!') and her clothes ('*My* clothes').

CHAPTER 5

May 27th

Faro seems to be taking to the stranger and this makes Ann worried. Meanwhile, Ann knows the man is ill but not how seriously. He has remained in his tent: has he decided just to rest, or is he very ill, or even dying?

This morning Ann dreamt it was her father in the tent, ill, and that her whole family were in the house again. She had become used to the idea of being alone, probably forever, but now with the arrival of the man, she cannot bear this thought. Even though he is a stranger and she is afraid of him, she worries about his being ill, so she decides to go down to the tent, warily, with a gun.

May 28th

Who is Edward?

Ann is back in the house, in her own room. She had gone down to the tent and discovered the man lying there in his own vomit. As she touched his hand, the man said, 'Edward … Edward?' and also mentioned the word 'bullets' in his delirium. Ann is worried because she does not have the knowledge to take care of him. She cleans the man up, and brings him some soup.

He improves slightly and the next morning says he needs to know what made him ill. Ann explains that it was his bath in Burden Creek, and he realises his mistake in not testing the water. Using the Geiger counter, Ann tests the area by the water where he bathed. When he hears the result he realises he has radiation poisoning, about which he knows a great deal. Although he seems better, he explains the sickness comes in stages, and that soon he will become much worse again. He will have no resistance to germs, so Ann decides that she must try to prevent his catching an infection; she will also try to get him into the house, where it is drier and warmer. She realises she still does not know his name.

COMMENT

Dreams are important in this novel. The lonely world Ann has inhabited would be a severe trial for anyone, and she has dealt with this strongly in her waking life. She has shown tremendous self-discipline, but she cannot control her dreams, where she feels joyful at the idea that her family are back; this reveals her submerged grief.

Ann's natural goodness and compassion overcome her fear and caution as she decides to find out how ill the man really is.

Ann's bravery and common sense are revealed again in her reaction to the man's illness and her decision to nurse him. Her practical nature helps her to cope.

The man's fevered reference to 'Edward' gives us a tantalising hint of something that is troubling him. The reader feels the urge to read on and find out what this means.

GLOSSARY   **anaemia** deficiency of red blood cells
pneumonia acute inflammation of the lungs
dysentery an infection of the intestine

Identify the speaker.

5 'I don't know where I am'

1 'What did you find?'

4 'Bullets. It won't stop ...'

2 'There were dead birds all over the streets'

3 'Anybody here?'

Identify the person(s) 'to whom' this comment refers.

6 'I am afraid'

7 'Maybe he was beginning to be ill'

8 'He was cheering'

Check your answers on page 91.

 Consider these issues.

a What significance the diary format has in the telling of the story.

b What we know about Ann's life before the war and how it prepared her for solitude.

c What the reader has learnt about the man so far and what we feel we need to know.

d The way in which the man, like other things from outside the valley, presents a threat and a sense of danger.

e The **symbolism** (see Literary Terms) of guns, water, birds and radiation.

f Ann's mixed emotions over the arrival of the stranger.

CHAPTERS 6–10: NURSING THE SICK

CHAPTER 6

May 29th

Ann tells us that the man is called John R. Loomis, and that he seems much better. Loomis asks, somewhat suspiciously, if she is alone. Ann reveals she found out later he was a scientist, but his statements and questions suggest this. He tells his story and Ann tells hers. He says that he had seen no life until now on his ten week journey from Ithaca, in New York state.

Loomis has been sleeping in the tent because it is radiation-proof but now he realises the valley is safe and accepts Ann's offer to stay in the house. He goes on to tell Ann more of his background as an organic chemist working with the Nobel prizewinner, Professor Kylmer. In a secret laboratory built in the mountains they had discovered a way of making magnetic plastic, or 'polapoly' as they named it, which could stop, or at least deflect radiation. They developed a suit made of this substance, together with a portable device for filtering water and air. After three years of work they had

Consider the way in which the people in the Air Force fallout shelter died.

produced a single pilot model of each, and these were what Loomis had used on his journey – the suit and the wagon. But the war had broken out before these items could be mass-produced. When the bombing began, Loomis says he was alone in the laboratory, surviving because it was eighty feet underground and cut out of solid rock. He had waited three months to see if the outside radiation levels would drop, and then began to make excursions to the outside world, finding only death.

Why is Loomis so shocked when Ann mentions Edward?

Ann asks him about Edward. He seems shocked, but then tells her that Edward was a man who had worked in the laboratory with himself and Professor Kylmer. Loomis was unaware that he had mentioned his name.

COMMENT

Ann takes care to take a bath and improve her appearance. She is aware of Loomis as 'company'.

She is also aware of Loomis as a scientist: 'scientists won't just accept things – they always have to try to figure them out' (p. 62). This becomes important later.

Robert O'Brien allows Loomis to give scientific reasons why he has been able to survive, and the same is done for the valley: this increases the reader's belief in the narrative.

Loomis's reaction to Ann's knowledge of Edward creates more suspense at the end of the chapter.

GLOSSARY

Cornell a famous American university

Nobel prize a prestigious award given annually for work done in the fields of chemistry, physics, medicine, literature, and peace

the Pentagon the headquarters of the United States Defence Department in Arlington, Virginia, named after the building's shape

asphyxiation suffocation

CHAPTER 7

June 3rd

Ann has been keeping track of Loomis's temperature. She has suggested she give him some aspirin but he thinks they should save it. Ann has decided to 'cook better meals' now she has this companion to look after – she had often not bothered when she was by herself. She decides to dig over the garden again and plant some seeds, in the hope it is not too late, but realises she needs more space because there are now two mouths to feed. This proves difficult, and as she is toiling Loomis suggests she uses the tractor. Ann comments that she has no petrol – there are two pumps at the store but they work with electricity. Loomis tells her he could take off the electric motors and make them work by hand.

They watch the sun setting before returning to the
house, Loomis walking unaided. He sits in her father's
chair by the fireplace. Ann asks if Loomis would like a
book. He does not, but when she suggests that she play
the piano he is more enthusiastic. She plays from her
study books and from a hymn book. Loomis is compli-
mentary and tells Ann, 'This is the best evening I have
ever spent'. When Ann replies, 'Ever? You mean since
the war' Loomis becomes angry: 'I said "ever"' (p. 81).
She puts this reaction down to the fever, and he goes
to bed.

Playing the hymns has made Ann feel sad. She
remembers going to Sunday School with her family,
and a picture book she had called *The Bible Letter Book*.
The first page was 'A is for Adam', and the last page
was 'Z is for Zachariah'. Since Adam was the first man,
she had assumed for a long time that Zachariah must
be the last man.

*Zachariah is a
minor Jewish
Prophet in the Old
Testament.*

Ann wishes she were back in the cave again. She is
about to go, when she hears Loomis talking loudly in
his sleep. He is talking to Edward. He says that Mary
and Billy are dead. Then, 'Get away. I warn you. Get
away from –' (p. 84) followed by a groan, and silence.
Ann decides not to go to the cave, since Loomis might
need help.

COMMENT   The chapter contrasts Ann's artistic tendencies with Loomis's scientific frame of mind. Loomis's scientific background looks like it will prove useful, and indicates that, however practical Ann may be, her lack of technical knowledge would have been a disadvantage to her.

There are indications that Loomis and Ann could have a partnership and, indeed, a relationship, which could be mutually beneficial.

The religious side to Ann's character is emphasised again. Through the novel's title we are led to consider the differences between Ann and Loomis's situation – the last man and woman on earth? – and that of Adam and Eve – the first man and woman.

The harmony of the piano-playing scene is ruined by Loomis's angry outburst. If it was his best evening ever, what does that say about his existence up until now?

Loomis's nightmare creates more tension and suspicion.

GLOSSARY   **'Für Elise'** a piece for piano by Beethoven (1770–1827), a German composer

CHAPTER 8

June 3rd (continued)

Ann has had a dream, remembering her mother walking across a field in early June gathering cress and poke greens. Together with dandelion leaves these would make a salad, and Ann takes a basket to collect these items. Having collected the plants, Ann notices a crabapple tree in full bloom. The flowers make her mind drift to weddings and she decides that if she ever got married, it would have to be in May, or early June, with apple blossom in the church. She remembers her first real date, with a boy from junior high school. Then

Does Ann really think marriage to Loomis is likely?

her thoughts turn to the possibility of marriage to Loomis. She thinks about having children some day, but then she is overcome with a feeling of sadness for her mother and puts the thoughts out of her head. She cuts a branch of the apple blossom as a bouquet for Loomis's sickroom.

Loomis has gone to Burden Creek to test the water and has realised that Ann's results were correct – he has indeed taken a large dose of radiation. His thoughts turn to using the poisoned stream to create electricity by building a dam that could run a small generator. He could do this if he had an electric motor, and Ann remembers there are two or three in the barn. The electricity could power a light, a refrigerator and perhaps a freezer.

What could Loomis's enthusiasm for going fishing tell us about his background?

After breakfast, Ann says she is going fishing. Loomis has never fished before and wants to come with her. On the way to the pond, however, he collapses. He has anaemia and he is helped back to the house. After fishing alone, Ann dismantles the old wood-coal stove from the barn and pulls it out, but she will need help to get it on the cart and bring it to the house. She gets out the best china and they eat. Then Ann finds a set of books called *The Farm Mechanic* which Loomis reads.

COMMENT

Dreams play an important part in *Z for Zachariah*. Here, as later, a dream helps Ann. Loomis's dreams, by contrast, are nightmares which create cause for concern. Ann's optimistic nature is apparent as she looks forward to the possibility of marrying Loomis and bearing children.

Ann's naïvety and sense of what is traditional and appropriate come over in her decision that the wedding will have to be in church, with words from the *Book of Prayer*.

This chapter has an optimistic tone. Notice the **symbolism** (see Literary Terms) of the apple blossom and how it is used later in the novel (see Comment on p. 35 of these Notes).

GLOSSARY   **poke greens** edible wild plants
               junior high school similar to a British middle school, students
                  moving on at about fourteen years of age
               masonite a type of dark brown hardboard
               Thanksgiving an annual holiday, in thanksgiving to God, held on
                  the fourth Thursday in November in the USA

CHAPTER 9   Ann gets the tractor running, having been told by
               Loomis how to get the petrol pumps operating. Ann
June 3rd   plans her planting, showing her knowledge of farming.
(continued) As she drives the tractor she feels like singing, and she
Contrast Ann's recites a poem to herself. It is brought to mind by
excitement about thoughts of her responsibility to the planet. As Ann
starting the tractor ploughs she notices eleven crows in the sky, attracted by
to Loomis's lack of the noise of the tractor.
emotion.
               That night Loomis's temperature rises considerably.

COMMENT   Optimism again radiates throughout this chapter:
               notice how the sun comes out when Ann is ploughing,
               and the appearance of the crows, once classed as pests,
               but now **symbols** (see Literary Terms) of life and hope.
               Ann's love of singing and poetry again throws light on
               her optimistic nature. She has put out of her mind up
               to now the fact that the supplies in the store will not
               last forever. Contrast this with Loomis's practicality in
               saving the V-belt for future use.

GLOSSARY   **squash** a marrow-like vegetable
               hominy coarsely ground corn boiled with milk or water

CHAPTER 10

June 3rd   The fever has made Loomis afraid to be left alone. Ann
(Continued) wishes she were a trained nurse, and wishes she had
               warned Loomis about the water he bathed in. She does
               not tell him about her wishes with relation to marriage.
               When Ann goes to milk the cow Loomis sits up in bed

NURSING THE SICK

and calls for her; he has imagined things in his feverish state but he will not tell her what.

Consider Ann's reaction when Loomis points the gun at her.

She has to go to the brook for more water, and to the store for provisions. When she returns, Loomis staggers from the house and grabs the carbine rifle from his wagon. He shoots at the second floor of the house, then aims the gun at Ann. She remains calm and talks to him; he claims he had thought he had heard someone in the house. Ann takes the gun from his hands and returns it to the wagon. She puts Loomis back to bed and inspects the damage, which is minimal.

Still fevered, Loomis mentions Edward, and asks if he has gone. Ann tells him he has been dreaming again. He realises this and says that Edward is dead. Ann wonders why he wanted to kill his friend.

COMMENT

Notice how Loomis calls Ann by both forename and surname, 'Ann Burden', while Ann calls him 'Mr Loomis'. They still hardly know one another.

'Poor Ann Burden … You're going to wish I had never come' (p. 110) – here, Loomis is referring to his illness, but his words are packed with **irony** (see Literary Terms) in the light of what happens later.

Ann demonstrates her sensitivity and caring nature in looking after Loomis, and in her courage when he confronts her with the gun. Notice that this incident is mirrored at the end of the novel.

There is more destruction brought to the valley by Loomis, and the suspense grows when we learn that Edward is dead.

GLOSSARY   **steeped** soaked

Identify the speaker.

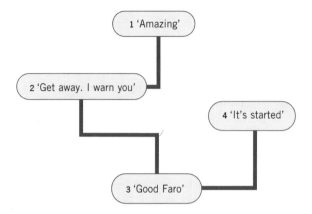

> 1 'Amazing'

> 2 'Get away. I warn you'

> 4 'It's started'

> 3 'Good Faro'

Identify the person(s) 'to whom' this comment refers.

> 5 'It turns out he is a real expert on the subject'

> 6 'I suppose they kept going too long'

Check your answers on page 91.

 Consider these issues.

a How well Ann copes with Loomis's illness.

b The differences shown in these chapters between Ann and Loomis.

c What Loomis's background may have been like, as a child and as a young man.

d Loomis as a danger to Ann and life in the valley.

e Ann's romantic, religious and artistic nature.

f The significance of the novel's title.

g The author's use of the **symbolism** (see Literary Terms) of nature.

CHAPTERS 11–15: LIVING WITH A MURDERER

CHAPTER 11

June 4th

Loomis's temperature has reached one hundred and six, the highest reading the thermometer can show. Ann tries her best to reduce this by rubbing him with alcohol. Loomis's nightmares continue, dreaming that Edward is there, in the room and threatening him. Ann is beginning to piece together the story, realising that Loomis and Edward 'were not friends at all, but enemies, at least at the end' (p. 121). When Ann brings Loomis breakfast he drifts in and out of his hallucination. He tries to get out of bed and Ann holds him down, with Loomis whispering, 'He'll steal the suit' (p. 122). Ann tells him the suit is in the wagon, but this incites Loomis to try to get out of bed again. Loomis is weak, and Ann can easily hold him down, but she is worried that if he falls he will injure himself and she will not be able to put him into bed again. So Ann decides to stay in the room with him, and when he is asleep, go out to feed Faro and bring in the suit. Ann is affected by Loomis's dreams, and half expects to see Edward herself.

Ann is only concerned with Loomis's well-being.

Afternoon

Ann manages to piece together the story of Edward and Loomis. The two scientists were together in the underground laboratory when the bombing began. Edward wanted to go and look for his wife, Mary, and son, Billy. In the laboratory was the one suit in the world which would allow him to venture out into the radioactive, polluted air. Loomis would not allow Edward to use the suit: everyone outside was dead, he argued; and what would happen if Edward did not return with the suit? Loomis had a gun. He swore at Edward and threatened him as Edward tried to leave with the suit.

Loomis collapses again on his bed, leaving Ann to wonder if he had really shot Edward. As Loomis sleeps again, Ann inspects the suit and her worst fears are confirmed: there are three patched bullet holes across the middle of the chest, and Ann knows that if Edward had been wearing the suit when they were fired he would certainly have been killed.

Night

Loomis sleeps peacefully, but Ann realises there is nothing more she can do for him. She takes a Bible and walks to the church to pray for him.

COMMENT

Notice the **hookline** (see Literary Terms) at the beginning of the chapter: 'This is a terrible day' (p. 120) creates more suspense and pulls the reader into the story once more.

Ann can see both sides of the argument between Loomis and Edward. She is very fair and can see how it would be pointless to search for a wife and child who are almost certainly dead. But she also identifies with Edward: 'Poor Edward … I know how he felt' (p. 125).

'One suit, and two people' – compare this with the situation now, with Ann and Loomis together in the valley.

We now suspect that Loomis is a murderer, capable of killing to gain what he wants; but despite what Ann has heard, she does not give up caring for him.

CHAPTER 12

June 5th　　Loomis has lived through the night, although at one point Ann was sure he had died. The strain is beginning to tell on her; she feels dizzy and ill, and goes to the church again. This time, she knows it is for her own benefit. She is fatalistic, realising that her presence will now make no difference to whether Loomis lives or dies. She is also worried about what she heard from Loomis about the events in the laboratory.

In the church Faro discovers a baby crow which had fallen from a nest built up in the roof. Ann picks it up and places it in the grass outside, and the crows fly down to it. She admits to being a little superstitious, and thinks of this as a good omen.

Evening　　Loomis's condition is unchanged. Ann decides to read to him, thinking first of the Bible, but then deciding on Gray's 'Elegy Written in a Country Churchyard'. She also considers playing the piano, as much for her benefit as his.

Ann again considers the rights and wrongs of Loomis's actions in the laboratory. In a way, she believes what he did was in self-defence: if Edward had gone, Loomis would have eventually run out of food, water or air and he would have died. Loomis might also have been thinking about saving the suit for humanity. But what if Edward was sensible or honest? What if Loomis wanted the suit for himself? She does not know enough about either Edward or Loomis.

June 6th　　Ann goes to church again and prays. Loomis has now lain motionless for more than thirty-two hours, but

Ann does not want to give up. The baby bird has gone, and Ann is sure it has been returned to its nest. On the way back to the house she picks wild roses and puts them in a vase in Loomis's room. The apple blossoms have wilted and fallen off. Loomis's respiration has decreased, although Ann does not know if this is a good thing or a bad thing. She plays the piano.

COMMENT   We can easily imagine the strain on Ann, with Loomis near death, and on top of that, the knowledge that this man, perhaps the only man left alive on earth, is probably a murderer.

Ann acknowledges the **symbolism** (see Literary Terms) of the bird, a sign of life and hope. She tells us that she once thought of birds as prayers, flying up to heaven.

Ann speaks of doing things for her own benefit: she feels comfort in prayer, poetry, and music.

The apple blossom, once the **symbol** (see Literary Terms) of her projected happy future with Loomis, has died; this future has now seemingly been put in jeopardy.

GLOSSARY   **cupola** a roof in the form of a dome
two-by-four planks of wood, two inches thick, four inches wide
'Elegy Written in a Country Churchyard' a famous poem written by Thomas Gray (1716–71) in 1750

CHAPTER 13

June 7th   Loomis is better. Ann changes his bed linen and pyjamas. It is a messy job and Ann realises she was not cut out to be a nurse. She had once considered it, but she had decided she wanted to be a teacher instead. She reflects that these and other plans are effectively over. One of her plans had been to buy books; we learn that she loves books. She wonders if Loomis could go to the library and bookstore in Ogdentown and bring back books. Would he be interested, seeing as he does not appear to be much of a reader? Would the books be safe or contaminated? Could Ann go herself, in the suit? These thoughts are suddenly clouded by thoughts of Edward.

June 8th

Loomis awakes. His temperature is down, but he is extremely thin. Ann thinks about food for him and wishes she had the stove. Using the tractor, she brings it to the house and, with a little difficulty, rebuilds it. She only needs some stovepipe and an elbow to connect it to the kitchen chimney. She is elated – having the stove there is 'like getting a Christmas present' (p. 146).

COMMENT

We see that Ann's plans for a career have always been influenced by her desire to help people.

Ann despairs for a moment, because her ambitions cannot be fulfilled, but the rest of the chapter has an atmosphere of hope and optimism. Loomis is recovering; she maintains a sense of purpose, to survive and improve the quality of their existence, by rebuilding the stove.

Books will also improve the quality of Ann's life, but there is still the shadow of Loomis's attitude to her plans, and the fear of his jealous possessiveness over the suit. Her desire is similar to Edward's desire – and Loomis killed Edward.

CHAPTER 14

June 15th

It is Ann's birthday. She is sixteen, and, with the stove now fully connected, she has roasted a chicken and baked a cake, which, despite her inexperience, has turned out perfectly. They are also celebrating Loomis's recovery, although he still cannot walk.

Ann starts to turn her thoughts to the future again: the garden needs attention and she needs to plant seeds.

Ann had intended to keep these problems to herself, but Loomis had enquired about the tractor and the planting. His tone was nervous and suspicious. Ann admits that the corn is not yet planted, that she had not dared tell Loomis when he was so ill. When she tells Loomis that she had gone to church – three times – he is angry and abrupt. She calms him by telling him that her family had planted corn before at this time, and even later, and it had fared well. But she is startled by his tone and attitude – Ann had always thought of the valley as her own, but now she realises Loomis would be living there too.

Why is Loomis so angry that Ann went to church?

Ann harrows the soil, and plants most of the corn. She starts to cook but then hears Loomis fall; he has tried to get out of bed. He refuses help and tells Ann not to watch as he awkwardly returns to bed. He asks for drawing instruments and paper.

COMMENT   Ann's diary entries are no longer written on a day-to-day basis. This indicates the pressure she is under and how busy she is. The story is again recounted by telling the reader the important facts, building up suspense, and following them by **flashbacks** (see Literary Terms) to the details of the events.

The chapter seems optimistic enough, but Loomis again taints the atmosphere with his aggressive insistence not to be helped and his reaction to her delay with the planting.

As it becomes obvious that Loomis will recover, it also becomes obvious that he sees the valley as his as well as Ann's. Ann's reaction to this reveals her sense of fairness and tolerance.

Ann's reference to this as 'one of the best of weeks' (p. 147) is perhaps **ironic** (see Literary Terms) in the light of Loomis's behaviour.

CHAPTER 15

June 22nd

Another week has passed and Loomis has gradually learned to walk again. He does this in private, but Ann is pleased at his progress.

Loomis is designing the water-powered generator, and finds the magazines inadequate. When he says he needs books, Ann brings up the idea of going to the library in Ogdentown. Ann touches on her desire to read works of literature but Loomis is not interested. When he dismisses the idea because he is unable to walk that far, Ann makes the mistake of saying that she could go, if he lent her the suit. His anger at this suggestion is apparent. Loomis then gives a logical reason for Ann's not going: it would be foolish to risk its loss for the sake of a few novels, and if something happened to Ann and she did not return, he would be stranded. Ann sees the sense of the argument, but still retains some hope.

Is Ann's suggestion totally unreasonable, as Loomis suggests?

Ann suggests putting a chair for Loomis on the front porch. He would like it on the back porch, where he can see her doing the planting. Ann says the corn is rising, but Loomis is not satisfied: he asks why she had not planted beets and wheat, for sugar and flour. Ann had thought about these, but before the tractor was working, and there was only so much she could do. Loomis calls her 'foolish and short-sighted' (p. 164) and talks about the valley as being the whole world, where they should be thinking about starting a colony which will last permanently. Ann had had these thoughts, but now she feels uneasy.

COMMENT   As Loomis becomes stronger, he becomes increasingly
            domineering, and Ann is beginning to feel threatened.
            He is making decisions and beginning to take control;
            Ann is conceding that he is right and good-naturedly
            allowing him to do this.

            The contrast between Ann and Loomis is never more
            evident than in his attitude to books. For him the only
            worthwhile books are 'practical' ones. Ann's quality of
            life would be much improved by literature and the
            world of the imagination.

            Loomis is patronising towards Ann. In calling her
            'foolish and short-sighted' (p. 164) he is being unfair
            and short-sighted himself when one considers what
            Ann has done for him, and what she has achieved on
            her own.

            Loomis is also disparaging about Ann's religious
            instincts – notice how he refers to 'your church'.

            Loomis talks about starting a colony. This obviously
            has implications: to survive on a long-term basis,
            Loomis and Ann must produce offspring, just as the
            cattle must also be used for breeding.

            Power and control are centred on the suit. When he
            tells Ann she must never touch it, Loomis's words are
            echoes of what she heard him say to Edward in
            Chapter 11.

TEST YOURSELF (Chapters 11–15)

A *Identify the speaker.*

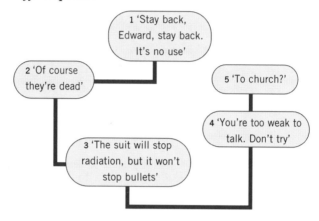

1 'Stay back, Edward, stay back. It's no use'

2 'Of course they're dead'

3 'The suit will stop radiation, but it won't stop bullets'

4 'You're too weak to talk. Don't try'

5 'To church?'

Identify the person(s) 'to whom' this comment refers.

6 'you're a thief and a liar'

7 'He may have been thinking not just of himself, but of human survival'

Check your answers on page 91.

B *Consider these issues.*

a Ann's fair-mindedness when confronted by the reality of what Loomis has done.

b The **symbolism** (see Literary Terms) of the bird which has fallen from the nest.

c The difference between Ann's attitude to books and that of Loomis.

d Loomis's scientific disposition compared with Ann's artistic, spiritual nature.

e How optimism is often built up, only to be clouded by subsequent events.

f Loomis's gradual improvement in health, accompanied by his gradual desire to become the dominant partner in the relationship.

CHAPTERS 16–20: ATTACKED AND HUNTED

CHAPTER 16

June 24th

Ann is growing more and more uneasy. She has planted wheat and beets, following Loomis's outburst. As she suggested, she has put a chair on the front porch, and one on the back porch. Despite the fact that the back porch is the less comfortable place to be, this is where Loomis insists he will sit. He watches while Ann works.

Ann later joins him on the front porch. She has realised that she knows nothing about him, does not understand him. She has worked out a theory that he has tried to blot out the past – the murder of Edward, the long walk through the dead countryside – because it was so horrible. She is sensible enough not to try to discuss Edward, but she tries to start up a conversation, hoping to gain a little more information about the times before that. She finds out that he is from a poor background in Nyack, New York, and that he was in the Navy for four years. Ann then asks him if he ever got married. At this, Loomis grabs Ann's hand and pulls her towards him. He says, 'No, I never got married. Why did you ask that?' (p. 171) and holds Ann's hand in both of his.

Is Ann any the wiser about Loomis's background?

Ann is startled, and then feels 'embarrassed, and awkward, and afraid' (p. 171) – embarrassed, strangely, because his hands are softer than hers; awkward because he has pulled her off balance on his chair; and afraid because when she tries to pull away he tightens his grip. He shows no gentleness and has no expression on his face. He will not relax his grip until she answers his question, but when he tightens his grip even more and pulls Ann even further off balance she falls forward and accidentally hits him in the face. She releases herself but Loomis tells her she should not have done so. Ann apologises and retires to the kitchen, as Loomis says, 'You held my hand once before' (p. 173).

In the kitchen Ann is shaking and she feels about to cry but stops herself. She tries to calm down, telling herself it was just a 'pass': it had happened to girls at school on dates. However, it is very different when there is nobody around – in Ann's case, perhaps nobody in the world! To comfort herself, Ann imagines that her family are coming back. She calms herself and continues with dinner.

Loomis returns to the bedroom and when Ann brings his food he acts as if nothing had happened, but they do not talk. Ann remembers when she did hold his hand: for several hours on the night he was most ill, but she realises this is not the same thing. She realises Loomis is taking charge, taking possession, and she feels uneasy.

COMMENT   Loomis is gradually taking control. Ann describes him as 'rather like an overseer' (p. 167), and he is now stronger than Ann. There are **ironic** (see Literary Terms) reversals of situation in this chapter. Ann once watched over Loomis, when he was ill; now he watches over her as if to check on her work. She once held his hand gently, nursing him; now he holds her hand aggressively, as if possessing her.

Ann tries to justify Loomis's secrecy when talking about his past, just as she has tried to see both sides of the story before.

We do not know for sure what Loomis's intentions are, because we see everything through Ann's eyes. Perhaps he does believe that Ann's reference to marriage indicates that she is sexually attracted to him, but we know of Loomis's cold attitude towards founding a colony.

Ann has shown great strength of character to keep her family from her conscious thoughts. Now she needs to think of them to deal with this situation.

GLOSSARY   **overseer** the person on a plantation who watched over the slaves to ensure they did their work
naval ordnance laboratory a laboratory where work on military equipment is carried out for the Navy
chemistry major a student whose main subject at university is chemistry

CHAPTER 17

June 30th

Note the use of flashback (see Literary Terms) once Ann has told us she is back in the cave.

Ann has returned to the cave, and recounts the events which have led to this drastic action. On the night of the 'pass' Ann could not sleep; the next day she felt 'everything had changed' but she tried to get on with her chores.

Although Ann is feeling strained and tense, Loomis acts as though nothing has happened. He watches her work again, making Ann feel under more pressure. At dinner, Loomis decides he will not eat in bed any more, but at the table. He tries to make conversation, and attempts to pay her compliments about the corn and the vegetable garden.

Loomis asks Ann to read to him again. She does so against her will, although she realises he is not even listening. She begins to feel nervous and afraid. She even feels he is trying to play some kind of trick on her. But she puts this thought from her mind and again tries to justify his behaviour.

COMMENT   Ann tells us how she feels better working in the open air. Her love of natural things contrasts with Loomis's unnatural behaviour.

Loomis uses Ann's love of reading to gain more power over her. She does not want to read, but feels compelled.

Ann tries to make herself believe that Loomis's request is reasonable enough, but her sensitivity makes her realise that there is something threatening in this.

Ann reads Gray's 'Elegy Written in a Country Churchyard' again, and also Jane Austen's *Pride and Prejudice*, in which two people at first dislike one another but later fall in love and marry – this could perhaps be seen as a reversal of what has happened in *Z for Zachariah*.

CHAPTER 18

*Still June
30th*

*Loomis is spoiling
everything that
Ann used to enjoy.*

Ann describes the next night, which was even worse. This time he has asked her to play the piano. As she plays, with her back to Loomis, she is wary of him. She worries he will creep up behind her. He taps his cane and she turns around, startled. He claims his can had slipped but she does not believe him, and she is trembling so much she has to stop. She thinks he is deliberately trying to unnerve her.

The next evening he does not ask her to read or play the piano, so she goes for a walk with Faro. At the church she hears the two crows and their young ones in the belfry. On her way back, she sees Loomis walking, unaided, to the wagon. He appears to be checking the safe-suit. After a short time, Ann returns to the house, goes to her bedroom, and, feeling uneasy, sits on the bed, having decided not to undress.

She falls asleep but awakes in the darkness to hear Faro growl and run out of the room. Then she realises why: Loomis is in the room with her. He thinks she is asleep, and he creeps forward until he is next to her. He begins to touch her. Breathing quickly and loudly, he tries to pin her to the bed. She tries to escape, and after a prolonged scuffle, she hits back with her elbow and catches him in the throat, enabling her to run out of the door.

COMMENT   Loomis uses subtle ways to put pressure on Ann. He asks her to do things which she normally enjoys, such as playing the piano. But he taunts her – the tapping of his stick is almost certainly not accidental, and he knows he has her worried.

When Ann makes the excuse that she is tired, Loomis replies, 'Tired so soon?' (p. 184) He is being sarcastic and sexually threatening, just as he was when he held her hand.

The fact that Loomis walks to the wagon without the use of the cane suggests that he may have been pretending to be weaker than he actually is.

When Ann goes for her walk there is a return to the peace nature engenders in her. The crows are still there, and the young one she rescued is still thriving. But this can be seen as the calm before the storm, a lull before the violence of Loomis's attempt to rape her.

Loomis now tries to possess her fully. The writing is powerful and full of horrific action. We are reminded of Ann's fears in Chapter 1 about the arrival of a stranger: 'suppose it was someone mean, or even cruel, and brutal? A murderer?' (p. 10) Loomis has turned out to be all these things.

GLOSSARY   **Clementi**   an Italian composer (1752–1832)

                sonatina   a short piece of music

                andante   piece of music to be played slowly

                Heller   a Hungarian composer (1815–1888)

ATTACKED AND HUNTED

> **whip-poor-wills** birds native to North America, named after
>   their cry
> **fireflies** flying insects which give off light from their tails

CHAPTER 19

June 30th   Ann continues to recount the fateful night, and
(continued)   tells us that she has never been so afraid. She runs
                down the road, unsure of whether Loomis is
                following her or not. She stops at the store and sits
                there for an hour or more, watching the road. When
                she has pulled her thoughts together she realises
                she cannot return to the house. Remembering that
                there are still blankets in the cave, Ann takes shirts
                and shoes from the store by candlelight, and goes to
                the cave.

The next morning, she observes the house, using the
binoculars which she had left in the cave several weeks
ago. Faro is the first to appear. The dog sniffs the
ground and begins to follow her trail. Luckily, Faro
goes towards the store, following the scent, and not
straight to the cave. Loomis cannot follow the dog's
movements from there, and Faro arrives at the cave ten
minutes later.

Ann makes a mistake: she should have fed Faro immediately, as she did every morning; she still has three tins of meat in the cave. But Faro returns to the house, looking for food, and Ann realises that the dog could betray her location to Loomis. Watching the house, Ann sees Loomis feed Faro, at the same time tying the dog to the porch rail with a long cord. Ann feels sorry for the dog as it unsuccessfully tries to escape.

Are Ann's hopes for a compromise realistic? She starts thinking about her responsibilities, such as looking after the animals and the garden, and wonders whether she can work out a compromise. Could she still do the outdoor chores? Should she bring Loomis supplies from the store? She will not go into the house to cook, but she feels she cannot let Loomis starve, 'no matter what he had done'. Ann is willing to compromise, but she is unsure if Loomis will be, so she decides to go and talk to Loomis. She could do this from a distance. She sleeps, eats, and later on decides to build a fire in a way Loomis will not be able to see it.

COMMENT The author effectively conveys to us Ann's fear with the details of her pounding heart and her dizziness. She jumps when the door of the store slams shut, and the cold wind and her shivering add to the atmosphere of fear, isolation and suspense. We identify with Ann and feel sympathy for her plight. Tension is further built up by the threat that Faro can be used to track her down.

The way Faro is tied up, and his reaction to this loss of freedom, causes Ann to sympathise with the dog, and she feels the need to release him. In many ways, it is also a parallel situation to the one in which Ann now finds herself.

Ann is still concerned about her 'duties' as she sees them. Her concern for Loomis, despite what he has done to her, underlines her innate goodness, as does her desire for compromise. She feels they can share the valley – though this is perhaps somewhat naïve – and she is sensible enough, and brave enough, to want to talk things through.

CHAPTER 20

July 1st

Ann has realised that Loomis is definitely going to use Faro to track her: he ties Faro on the electric cord leash, but only for fifty yards or so before he limps back to the house. Ann believes Loomis knows she is watching him, and that he is playing some kind of game with her. She assesses the resources she has in the cave: some food, the two guns and ammunition and some other essentials, but not a great deal. She realises she is vulnerable if she sleeps in the cave, so she sleeps instead on a small shelf, near where she has been building a wall to conceal the fire.

The next morning, she goes to the house, by an indirect route so Loomis will not know where she is coming from. She stops on the road in front of the garden and Loomis steps out onto the porch. Loomis tells her he had thought and hoped she would come back. She is stunned for a moment, but then realises she cannot trust him again, and she tells him she is not coming back. He asks why this is, and where she will stay. He acts as if he has forgotten what he has done, but Ann knows he is just pretending. She tells him that she is willing to tend to the crops, the seeds, the garden and the animals, as well as bring him water and food, if he leaves her alone. He asks where she will go at night, but Ann does not reveal where she is staying. Loomis agrees to this, saying that he hopes Ann will change her mind and 'act more like an adult and less like a schoolgirl' (p. 204).

Ann is not convinced when Loomis pretends he has forgotten what has happened.

After the conversation, Ann realises that Loomis is still plotting, that he has not really accepted her offer. She knows Faro must be tied up inside the house, in case she tried to release him and take him away. She has a vision of herself tied up like Faro, Loomis's prisoner. Ann puts the idea out of her mind and milks the cow, realising that its milk is drying up. She divides the milk fairly between herself and Loomis, and does the same with the eggs, vegetables, and groceries from the store. She is slightly optimistic that this system might work.

Notice how fairly Ann divides the food.

On her return to the cave, Ann completes work on her hidden fire, but then she sees Loomis, with Faro on the leash, tracking again. They get as far as the barn, where Loomis starts up the tractor and teaches himself how to drive it. Ann lights her fire and cooks dinner.

Why does Loomis teach himself to drive the tractor?

She wishes now that Loomis had never come to the valley; she does not wish him dead, just that he had perhaps found some other valley.

C OMMENT   The threat that Loomis will use Faro to track Ann down now becomes frighteningly real. The only thing stopping him now is his lack of strength, but the knowledge that this will return heightens the tension.

Loomis is still playing games with Ann. She likens it to a game of chess, a game she does not want to be involved in: 'Only Mr Loomis wanted to be in it, and only he could win it' (p. 199).

Compare the 'game of chess' here with the reference to chess on pp. 254–5 of the novel.

Ann is again concerned with the basic necessities for living, and shows her humanity and concern by still trying to be absolutely fair to Loomis, sharing out the provisions and hoping he will accept her compromise.

Ann knows now, however, that Loomis is not sorry for what he has done. He has tried to rape her and he pretends nothing has happened. She realises that he wants to treat her as a possession, to keep her as much a prisoner as Faro. He tries again and again to find out where she is staying.

In Chapter 1, Ann thought that 'there are worse things than being alone' (p. 10). Now she realises this is true, but she still does not coarsen her humanity by wishing Loomis dead. She begins to wonder if there are similar valleys, with people still alive.

GLOSSARY   **burlap** a coarse fabric used for sacking

Identify the speaker.

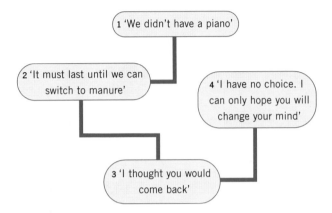

1 'We didn't have a piano'

2 'It must last until we can switch to manure'

4 'I have no choice. I can only hope you will change your mind'

3 'I thought you would come back'

Identify the person(s) 'to whom' this comment refers.

5 'there was nothing childlike about him'

6 'I will not change my mind'

Check your answers on page 91.

B *Consider these issues.*

a Ann's constant attempts to justify Loomis's behaviour and see some good in him.

b Ann's love of nature and that which is natural, in contrast to Loomis's unnatural actions.

c The way in which Loomis uses pastimes that Ann once enjoyed to threaten her.

d The power of the writing in the scenes leading up to, during, and just after the attempted rape.

e The similarities between Faro's position and Ann's.

CHAPTERS 21–26: LEAVING THE VALLEY

CHAPTER 21

August 4th
(I think)

We immediately learn that Ann has been shot by Loomis. She has not written for over a month because she was too ill and afraid. She has had to keep moving, and she is now hiding in thick woods high up in the south end of the valley. She shelters herself and her possessions in a hollow tree. She gives an account of the incidents which have occurred since July 1st.

For about ten days the compromise system seems to work. Ann does the chores and leaves food and provisions on the back porch for Loomis. Loomis, meanwhile, practises tracking with Faro, allowing the dog off the leash at times, and he also practises driving the tractor, on one occasion testing it to see how fast it can go.

On the morning of the tenth day (although Ann is not sure if this is accurate) Loomis changes his behaviour. He walks furtively towards the store, and then to the side of Burden Creek, where he hides in the trees and bushes. Ann realises that he is trying to find out where she is coming from, so she uses another route. She gathers eggs for Loomis. She realises she has forgotten to bring anything to carry eggs in for herself; she has also left behind her milk pail and her knife.

Ann makes a mistake.

Ann takes Loomis's water can towards the pond, and then, out of sight, she runs back to the cave for the knife and the pail. She feels confident she has escaped detection but she is wrong. She completes some chores and goes to use the tractor to put fertiliser on the wheat, but finds out that the ignition key is missing. At first she thinks Loomis has dropped it, but then she realises he has taken it deliberately. She goes to ask him for it.

Loomis is ingratiatingly polite, and invites her in for lunch. She refuses, and ignores his question about where she will cook her half of the chicken. He says he has taken the key for safekeeping. When she tells him she needs it, he replies that he will have to think about it, threatening her that if she continues 'this stupidity' there are things they are going to have to go without. He suggests he might fertilise the wheat himself. Then he mentions the knife and pail, and goes in.

Loomis controls the tractor.

Ann realises the error she has made – he has obviously watched her going for the knife and pail, and has deduced that wherever she is staying is only a few minutes from the pond. Ann realises Loomis has taken the key because he fears she will steal the tractor, just as he had feared she would take the safe-suit and Faro.

COMMENT

The first two sentences of Chapter 21 are the most powerful **hooklines** (see Literary Terms) of the novel. They prepare the reader with a sense of suspense leading up to the conclusion of the novel.

Ann's lifestyle seems to have deteriorated to that of a hunted victim, while Loomis lives in the house that was once hers and her family's – the references to Burden Hill and Burden Creek emphasise this; she has been totally dispossessed. She is working for Loomis as he regains his strength – notice how he now moves with no apparent effort. This serves to underline the **irony** (see Literary Terms) of her situation.

Ann feels the loss of her Bible.

Ann stops off at the church once or twice, but 'It seemed strained' (p. 212). She still prays, and still has a sense of hope and faith in God, but the normality of her life has been irreparably altered.

Look at what has changed since Ann picked the apple blossom in Chapter 8.

Ann passes the crabapple tree on her way to the farm, recalling those earlier days when she had thoughts of having apple blossom at her wedding. The blossom has gone, to be replaced by bitter crabapples, **symbolic** (see Literary Terms) of how her life has since become bitter.

Ann still maintains a remarkable sense of honesty and fairness in her division of the food, but this is in contrast to Loomis's unscrupulousness, and it puts her in more danger as he grows stronger and healthier. Similarly, Ann has used the tractor for their mutual benefit, but Loomis now uses it for his own ends.

CHAPTER 22

August 4th (continued)

Ann knows that unlike when Loomis shot at the house, this time he is acting deliberately.

Ann has walked to the store after going fishing when she hears the tractor engine, so she runs up the hill to hide in the woods. She then watches in amazement as Loomis drives the tractor, steering with his left hand; in his right hand he carries a rifle. He stops the tractor near the store and, taking the ignition key, walks warily around before going in.

Ann sees Loomis's face appear at the window of the Kleins' living quarters on the first floor – he obviously believes Ann has been staying there. In fact, Ann has only been in the apartment once before, looking for books, She remembers feeling guilty about this intrusion, even though the Kleins were dead.

Ann sees Loomis come out of the store, go back in again, and then start doing something with the door. After he has finished and returned to the house, Ann walks down to the store to find that he has padlocked both the front and the back doors. She realises that now she will have to ask permission to use the tractor and to enter the store; or, worse still, he might not allow her to have the keys at all.

COMMENT

Ann wonders why he has the gun with him – Does he think she has a gun? Will he shoot her? The reader knows that at some point he will, since Ann

Ann sees that Loomis's actions are governed partly by fear.

has already told us so. The structure of the novel in relation to time becomes complex here. Ann is recounting past events, and in the middle of the chapter she goes further back in time to tell the reader of the time she ventured into the Kleins' apartment.

Ann's feeling of guilt at entering the Kleins' residence contrasts with Loomis's lack of concern. He has already taken over her home.

There is a certain **black humour** (see Literary Terms) in the picture of Loomis riding the tractor, rifle in hand 'like an Indian on horseback in an old Western movie, attacking a wagon train' (p. 225). The same filmic quality can be seen in Ann's observation that Loomis seems to be 'storming' the store.

CHAPTER 23

August 4th (continued)

Ann tells how she began the next day in a more optimistic frame of mind. She has recognised Loomis's obsession for being in charge, and she rationalises that his locking of the store is just a result of this. He wants to ration the provisions. However, she sees the other alternative: he could be trying to starve her into submission.

Is Ann right to try to talk to Loomis?

Ann begins to plan again. She realises that she cannot survive indefinitely on her provisions in the cave, and she bravely decides to walk to the house and to talk to him. As she stands in front of the house, she suddenly finds she has been shot in the ankle. A second shot misses, and Ann runs for her life. He stops shooting and she finds refuge in the trees. She examines the wound and finds it is not serious. She realises that she has no bandages or disinfectant, and washes the wound with soap at the cave.

Ann wonders about Loomis's shooting. She gradually comes to the frightening conclusion that he was not aiming to kill her, but to disable her – starvation would force her to return, and then he would keep her prisoner, using the gun as a threat. Hearing the tractor, Ann runs up the hill to the bushes. Loomis stops at the store. He has Faro with him, and, with the dog on the leash, he begins to track her. He has the small rifle, and he is obviously concerned that Ann might shoot at him.

Why doesn't Ann shoot Faro.

Ann runs to the cave, knowing she cannot stay there any more, and takes what she can carry, including the small rifle and a box of shells. Moving higher up the hill into the woods, Ann realises the danger Faro now poses, and decides she must shoot the dog. She watches and waits. Loomis stops, and she has Faro in her sights, but Faro perceives her presence. He gives a bark of greeting and Ann cannot go through with it.

Loomis and the dog arrive at the cave. Ann smells, then sees, smoke. She hears the tractor, and knows Loomis is returning to the house. Ann goes back to the cave to find her possessions burnt. Loomis has taken the tins of food and the other gun. She is devastated, but her main cause for concern is that she had decided to kill Faro – she feels this makes her as much a murderer as Loomis. She leaves the reader with the statement that in the end she did kill Faro, but 'not with the gun' (p. 241).

COMMENT

Ann still tries to rationalise Loomis's behaviour. She at first cannot bring herself to believe that anyone could behave in such a callous manner. Her common sense takes over, however, but she still wants to talk and to compromise. Her innate sense of goodness and morality are shown throughout this chapter.

Robert O'Brien slowly works up towards the shooting incident, making it, when it comes, all the more shocking, especially when contrasted to Ann's generous intentions. Notice also how the author makes Ann recount the story in the present tense, making it more immediate and gripping.

Ann's despairing thought, 'why must he do it?' (p. 237) reveals her incomprehension of Loomis's behaviour.

Ann cannot bring herself to shoot Faro. Her sensitivity makes her believe that even the thought of killing the dog makes her a murderer like Loomis.

Ann has always shared the food and provisions. Now Loomis destroys everything he can, and takes the rest. **Symbolically** (see Literary Terms) he even destroys her last book. He has destroyed everything she holds dear.

The final paragraph of the chapter forces the reader to continue in order to discover why and how she eventually kills Faro. Note, though, that this technique is not entirely consistent with the diary since Faro does not die until August 6th.

GLOSSARY   **draw the bead** aim the rifle

CHAPTER 24

August 6th   Ann has been ill and feverish because of her wound but she is now feeling better. She feels more optimistic because she has made a plan: she has decided to steal the safe-suit and leave the valley. Loomis has not tried to track her again, although he could easily have done so. He perhaps did not know she was injured.

Is Ann's dream   Ann has had a dream about a class of schoolchildren
perhaps prophetic?   who cannot read and are waiting for a teacher. It has recurred night after night, and it has indicated to her that there is another place to live, where she is needed. She has come to the conclusion that Loomis is insane and that they cannot live in the same place. She will go

LEAVING THE VALLEY

south, towards other valleys, and look for the children in her dream.

Ann has seen and heard Loomis working. Ann has survived by fishing and foraging, even sneaking down to steal vegetables from the garden. Life has been hungry and monotonous, and Ann, who has been taught from childhood that hatred is wrong, admits to herself that she would like to hurt Loomis. It is the memory of her burnt book which brings these thoughts most strongly to Ann's mind. Stealing the safe-suit would be her revenge.

Is this the first time Ann has contemplated taking the suit?

She puts off her plan of action until one day when she sees that Loomis has left the door to the store open. She needs supplies for the journey so she takes her chance. She is fifty yards from the road when a shot rings out. It misses her and she flees back up to the trees. Loomis has laid a trap.

He comes after her with Faro on the leash and a gun under his arm. Ann runs to the hollow tree and gets her gun. She moves north, reaching the banks of Burden Creek. She crosses on stepping stones and sights her rifle behind a rock. Loomis and Faro are following, and Faro leaps into the water. Loomis jerks back and Ann fires a shot above his head. Loomis had not known Ann had the gun. She fires again and Loomis heads back towards the house. Faro is swimming in the contaminated water. She leads the dog to her camp where she tries to feed him but he is not interested. In the morning he is sick, and by nightfall he is dead.

Ann is now ready to start her plan.

COMMENT   Ann's dream is linked to her desire to help others. The reader is left to wonder whether it is merely a dream based on her previous expectations, or perhaps a premonition of something that is to come about.

Ann displays uncharacteristic procrastination in putting her plan into action. She is perhaps lulled by Loomis's seeming reluctance to continue tracking her, and also by the fact that she knows he will kill to protect the safe-suit.

Even the sounds of nature now frighten Ann instead of giving her comfort.

It is Loomis's action of burning her last book which raises her desire for revenge. He has tried to rape her and to keep her prisoner and he has shot her, but even in these circumstances her deeply moral upbringing prevents her from expressing out-and-out hatred.

CHAPTER 25

August 7th

Ann is now 'taking the offensive'.

Ann is at the top of Burden Hill, wearing the safe-suit. She has wisely taken the cart and supplies out of the valley towards Ogdentown, but she has decided that she must come back to speak to Loomis. Ann realises the danger in this but she has a gun. She knows, however, that she could not kill him. She compares her offensive against Loomis to games of chess she once played with her father. She tells us how she put her plan into action.

Ann takes the gun, food, water and clothing down into the valley before dawn. Hiding her supplies in the ravine, she approaches the house. She has written a note which she leaves under a stone on the front porch. It asks Loomis to meet her at the south end of the valley, and to leave his gun behind.

She hides and watches as Loomis comes out. He reads the note in the house, and after a while, leaving his gun on the porch, he makes his way to the meeting place. Ann runs to get the cart, loaded with equipment, and pulls it up the road, passing the house. She remembers her past life there, but also tries to think of her dream. She thinks of Faro, and a tear comes to her eye, but she also remembers Loomis when he was ill, and the sadness she felt when she thought he was going to die.

Ann knows he will be enraged, and that he will do anything to make her stay. She puts her supplies into the wagon, puts on the safe-suit, and rolls the cart down hill towards Ogdentown. She comes back with the notebook and the gun and waits for Loomis.

COMMENT   Although we know from what she tells us at the start of this diary entry that Ann has the suit, the tension is sustained right until the final chapter, as we do not know what the result of her final confrontation with Loomis will be. The last sentence of the chapter heightens the suspense. Ann fatalistically writes: 'I am glad to have told my story' (p. 262). His may be the last human voice she hears.

Ann's courage and sense of what is right have never been in question, but here, in perhaps her most courageous act, she determines she will speak to Loomis one last time. Even now, she knows she cannot kill him.

Ann has referred to her struggle against Loomis as a game of chess once before in Chapter 20. Then it was his game, now she is on the offensive.

Her feelings of sadness at leaving are reflected in her memories as she pulls the cart out of the valley. We are made aware of the gigantic and dangerous step she is taking.

CHAPTER 26

August 8th   The plan seems to be going awry. Loomis approaches on the tractor at top speed with the gun. Ann shouts to him to stop, and fires her gun in the air, but he ignores her and brings the tractor to a halt opposite her hiding place. He jumps down, looking for her. He has his back

to her but she cannot bring herself to shoot him. Ann
calls on Loomis to drop his gun, but he wheels around
and fires. She believes she is going to die after all her
efforts to survive. Her disappointment is so great that it
overcomes her fear, and she stands up to confront him.

Loomis does not shoot. When he sees the safe-suit he
yells that it is his, and tells Ann to take it off. She
refuses and he points the gun at her. Without thinking,
Ann reveals to Loomis that she knows he killed
Edward; she realises that telling him this probably
saved her life. Loomis turns away and, trembling, says
Edward tried to steal the suit, as Ann is doing now.
Ann explains that she has no choice. She will not be
hunted and she will not be held a prisoner.

*Loomis's
desperation is
revealed.*

Loomis pleads with her not to go, not to leave him
alone. Ann tells Loomis that if he kills her he will really
be alone. He has the valley. If she finds people she will
tell them about him and they may come to find him.
Her last words are that he did not even thank her for
looking after her when he was ill, and she reflects that
her last words are childish.

She turns her back on him and waits to be killed. But
the shot never comes, and she walks away. He shouts
after her, and she turns to see him standing on the edge

of the deadness, pointing westwards, indicating where he has seen birds circling. Ann raises her hand in acknowledgement and walks away.

Ann leaves the valley in hope.

Ann has walked all afternoon and nearly all night. She has slept a little, not knowing where she is, but the dream has returned. In it she has found the schoolroom and the children. On waking, the sun is high and there is a stream flowing west. She walks on, hopeful, looking for a trace of green.

COMMENT

Ann is not infallible. She has made mistakes in the past, and now we see Loomis thundering after her with the gun – she could easily have taken this with her. Even now she will not shoot Loomis. Instead she is ready to die herself.

Why does Loomis allow Ann to go?

We are left to speculate as to why Ann's words about Edward make Loomis cave in. It may be that they confront him with his guilt; or that he sees a recurrence of the very same scenario and he cannot let it happen again; or that he realises Ann has known about this but still cared for him; or a combination of these.

Loomis breaks down and reveals himself as the frightened, guilty, weak person he is or has become. The reader perhaps begins to feel some sympathy for him, particularly when he makes one final gesture of goodwill by pointing out the birds, the **symbols** (see Literary Terms) of hope, to the west.

Ann recognises that she does feel bitter. Loomis now has everything that was once hers, but even more, he has rejected any chance they had of sharing them and forging a future together. He has gone about everything the wrong way, whereas Ann remains moral and correct to the end.

Although we do not know what happens to Ann, the shining sun and the optimistic dream ensure that the story ends with a feeling of hope.

T<small>EST</small> YOURSELF (Chapters 24–26)

A *Identify the speaker.*

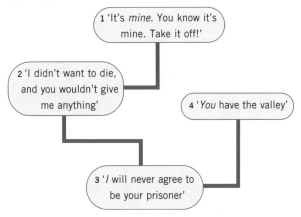

1 'It's *mine*. You know it's mine. Take it off!'

2 'I didn't want to die, and you wouldn't give me anything'

4 '*You* have the valley'

3 '*I* will never agree to be your prisoner'

Identify the person(s) 'to whom' this comment refers.

5 'a small and tidy woman'

6 'he missed his chance'

Check your answers on page 91.

B *Consider these issues.*

a Whether or not it is sensible of Ann to share the food and provisions so fairly with Loomis.

b The way in which Robert O'Brien uses time, moving backwards and forwards, and the way in which the diary form helps create suspense.

c Ann's inability to shoot the dog or Loomis.

d The use of dreams in the novel.

e To what extent the reader gains sympathy for Loomis as the novel draws to its close.

f The hope and optimism which is sensed at the end of the novel, and how it is brought about.

PART THREE

COMMENTARY

THEMES

The themes of *Z for Zachariah* are to do with the fundamental issues of what it is to be human. All human beings have, of course, good and bad within them. In this novel, due to the unique and desperate circumstances in which the characters find themselves, these opposites are highlighted. The fact that the two **protagonists** (see Literary Terms) are, as far as we and they know, the only two people left on earth, serves to throw their contrast into starker relief. The four themes discussed below are listed as opposites, but as in any good work of literature, the issues are complex and interlinked.

GOOD AND EVIL

The title of the novel brings the reader to consider good and evil, innocence and experience. Ann tells us that she possessed a picture book called *The Bible Letter Book*, in which the letters of the alphabet were illustrated by characters from the Bible. It began with 'A is for Adam' and ended with 'Z is for Zachariah', and since Adam was the first man, she had assumed for a long time that Zachariah was the last man. A clear parallel can be drawn: Adam and Eve were the first man and woman, just as Loomis and Ann are the last. The Bible states that Adam and Eve lived in the Garden of Eden, in which grew 'every tree that is pleasant to the sight, and good for food … And a river went out of Eden to water the garden' (Genesis 2:9–10). The valley in *Z for Zachariah* can be compared to the Garden of Eden, a place where food and good water is available; outside is wilderness. When Eve, and

Consider the parallels with the story of Genesis.

then Adam, eat the fruit of the one tree God has forbidden them to touch – the Tree of Knowledge – God is angry. Adam is banished from the Garden, because 'the man is become as one of us, to know good and evil' (Genesis 3:22). In *Z for Zachariah*, Ann, at first, is innocent to a large extent. Loomis's arrival brings about a change, he brings about a contamination of the valley's peace and harmony, and, in the end, Ann must leave: 'I went into the deadness' (p. 266).

At the beginning of the novel we find the earth has been all but destroyed by forces Ann was obviously powerless to control, the evil use of scientific progress in the form of nuclear war. Ann, however, has risen above this. She tells us that her first reaction to the sight of smoke from Loomis's campfire has been to go to the church and pray all morning. The last time she had seen smoke outside the valley it has been the smoke of the nuclear war, the smoke of destruction.

Ann fears that the approaching stranger may be evil: 'suppose he was crazy? Or suppose it was someone mean, or even cruel, and brutal? A murderer?' (p. 10). These words are proven to be prophetically **ironic** (see Literary Terms); but this is not to say that the rest of the story is a clear-cut case of Ann representing good and Loomis representing evil. Ann certainly displays no trace of what we might in any way term evil. The nearest she comes to displaying any of the negative characteristics common to humanity is when at the end of the novel, having been forced to endure the most terrible ordeals at Loomis's hands, she tells us that although she is not sure whether she has ever hated anybody, she wanted to hurt Loomis, to 'cause him grief' (p. 247). She plans revenge, which she achieves by taking the safe-suit. She has travelled from innocence to experience.

In taking the safe-suit, is it fair to describe Ann's actions as 'stealing'?

We could speak of Loomis's 'inhuman' behaviour, but it would be truer to say that whereas Ann represents many of the good and positive features of human beings, Loomis displays many of the evil and negative characteristics. This is due, in large part, to the solidity of Ann's Christian upbringing: as a child she was taught that hatred was wrong.

Ann's goodness is not a totally naïve goodness. She has grown up surrounded by good people, in a loving and caring environment, which she remembers fondly in times of danger; but she has been brought up with discipline – she tells us that Faro used to crawl under the porch when she or Joseph or David were scolded – and, of course, she has lived through the horror of nuclear war. So it is reasonable that Ann is wary of Loomis and that she conceals herself in the cave when he appears in the valley.

Why are Loomis's violent actions so shocking?

Perhaps the first indication that Loomis is a violent person is when he shoots one of Ann's chickens. Ann finds violence and destruction shocking, but she is always ready to forgive and make excuses for Loomis's behaviour.

Ann's ambitions have always been to help people – 'I liked most people' she tells us – but she knows, from what she heard on the radio during the war, that people can be 'desperate and selfish' (p. 41). When Loomis is ill Ann cares for him and prays for him, even when she knows that he has probably murdered Edward. Ann tries as hard as she can to justify Loomis's actions, arguing that he killed Edward in self-defence, and even attempting to persuade herself that Loomis had not just been considering his own survival, but that of the entire human race. This fairness, this selflessness, is even more in evidence when Ann, despite having been nearly raped by Loomis, shares out the food and provisions so meticulously between herself and her attacker. She tries even then to compromise and to communicate. She has opportunities to shoot Loomis, to kill him. In the circumstances, many people might have been tempted to do just that, but Ann's strong sense of morality, of what is wrong and what is right, prevents her from doing so. She will not even kill Faro when the dog becomes a threat.

Loomis's behaviour is in total contrast to this. He kills as soon as he enters the valley. As he recovers from illness he becomes more and more selfish. He wants Ann as a possession, not as a companion, and he cynically begins to treat her as a slave, showing no gratitude for the care she has taken of him.

Do you regard Loomis as evil?

We can perhaps justify, if not condone, some of Loomis's behaviour. He has lived through unique and terrible events, but then so has Ann. He finds it difficult to behave in a caring and humanitarian way, resulting in his appalling treatment of Ann, and his attempt to rape her. He taunts Ann, he has no respect for her religious beliefs or her rights to individuality and freedom. When Ann tries to compromise, Loomis shoots her. He then attempts to track her down like a hunted animal. But are these the actions of an evil man, or a man, as Ann recognises later in the novel, who is sad, lonely and frightened? Loomis displays traits which can be described as evil, but, in the end, he does not kill her when he has the chance. Instead, he points her to where he has seen signs of life, and he gains something of the Christian ideal of redemption.

LIFE AND DEATH

At the beginning of the novel, Ann believes that she is the only human being alive. There is life inside the valley, and only deadness outside. Loomis comes from outside the valley and brings death and destruction with him, just as Burden Creek comes from outside the valley and kills everything it touches.

Ann nurtures the plants and animals of the valley in order to create new life and, therefore, to continue nature's existence. The continuation of the human race depends, of course, on the arrival of a man, to promulgate the species. The arrival of Loomis should therefore be a cause of great hope and celebration. Ann has hopes of 'marrying' Loomis and having children; Loomis sees the importance of founding a 'colony'. The difference between these two concepts is important, as Ann's idea includes the belief that some sort of spiritual bonding is necessary, not just a physical union.

Ann has respect for all forms of life, demonstrated, for example, when she saves the baby crow. Her upbringing on the farm has made her practical enough to allow her to fish and to kill chickens for food, but she is unable to shoot Faro, even when it seems certain that the dog will lead Loomis to her hiding place. She has only shot at bottles and cans, whereas Loomis shoots a chicken as one of his first actions in the valley. Ann cannot bring herself to shoot Loomis; that would be against her moral code. Instead, she leaves the valley, in the hope that life exists elsewhere, and with the promise that if she can she will send people to help Loomis.

HOPE AND DESPAIR

In her days of loneliness, Ann had hoped that someone would come to the valley. However, when a sign of life does appear, she is afraid. Despite her reservations, Ann starts to entertain thoughts of marriage and children with Loomis, and at this point the future looks promising.

Optimism Ann is naturally optimistic, strengthened by her faith in God and her positive upbringing. Her hopes often become fact: Loomis recovers; the stove works again; the tractor can be used. Ann sees **symbols** (see Literary Terms) of hope in the natural world: the apple blossom is a symbol of her hope of marriage to Loomis, but later it withers and dies, representing the death of this ambition. Saving the baby crow gives her a sense of hope and optimism for the future.

Dreams

Ann's dreams, too, provide her with a sense of purpose. We believe with her that there may be, somewhere out there, in another valley, living human beings, a class of schoolchildren waiting for their teacher.

The final words of the novel are 'I am hopeful' (p. 267) and our hopes are not just for Ann, but for the continuation of the human race. We are also left with hope, in as much as Loomis has at last shown some of the positive characteristics of mankind, directing her towards life, towards the west, where the birds fly.

Art and science

Z for Zachariah may be classified as a science-fiction novel. Loomis is a scientist, but because of the **first-person narrative** (see Literary Terms) any scientific details are recounted through the words of Ann, who is not a scientist, although she is interested in science. Understanding is thus made easy, and any disbelief we may experience as to, for example, the possibility of a valley remaining uncontaminated by nuclear fallout, is made secondary by the drive of the narrative.

Would the situation make for as interesting a story if their partnership was successful?

Often in the story we are made to think 'if only ...'. If only Loomis's scientific knowledge and logical mind had been allowed to combine with Ann's practical farming knowledge, common sense and sensibility, this would surely have been a fortuitous, formidable and positive relationship. Ann is practical and able, skilled in the ways of farming, having helped and watched her father. She is also sensitive, spiritual and artistic. She believes in God and the power of prayer. She loves literature and music, which she uses in bringing Loomis back to health. Loomis, on the other hand, sneers at Ann's church-going, and sees it as a waste of time. He is seemingly insensitive to the beauty of nature. He is also oblivious to the need for literature, and believes that the only useful books are 'practical' ones. Science, of course, is practical. Loomis has worked on the development of the plastic which has resulted in the production of the safe-suit. Had it been produced earlier, the future of the human race might have been much more secure. Loomis is able to make the petrol pumps work again and he plans to build a dam in order to restore some electricity to the valley. His obsession with control, however, leads him to be insensitive, cruel, and unable to communicate in any caring and cooperative manner.

The fact that he at first truly enjoys Ann's reading and piano-playing shows that, perhaps unconsciously, he needs these things. When he burns the *Famous Short Stories of England and America*, Ann finally decides to leave the valley. The combination of Ann and Loomis's positive characteristics could have provided a firm base for the future of the human race, but the relationship founders on Loomis's self-centredness.

STRUCTURE

Z for Zachariah is written in the form of a diary, and the action of the novel is therefore recounted as a **first-person narrative** (see Literary Terms) by Ann Burden, everything being seen through her eyes and from her point of view. The diary entries start on May 20th of an unspecified year sometime in the future, and end on

August 8th in the same year. On one level, this is a very
false device: how can we be reading the diary of events
that will happen in the future, after some as yet to be
experienced nuclear war? On a practical level, this
reservation does not really arise. In reading the novel
the reader enters into what the poet and critic Samuel
Taylor Coleridge called 'the willing suspension of
disbelief'. We are pulled along by the strength of the
narrative, and any questioning of the total logic of the
piece is almost irrelevant. The reader forgets that this is
a very carefully constructed novel by Robert O'Brien –
we choose to believe it is a diary written by teenager
Ann Burden.

The diary form allows Ann not just to tell us what
happens on each particular day, but to recount what has
happened in the past. This is useful for the **exposition**
(see Literary Terms) at the beginning of the novel,
when we must learn the background of the nuclear war
and Ann's previous life with her family in the valley.

Flashbacks   Robert O'Brien's use of time is extremely clever.
Throughout the novel, **flashbacks** (see Literary Terms)
are used in subtle and effective ways. Ann frequently
refers back to times before the war with her family, and
she hears Loomis, both consciously and unconsciously,
describe what happened in his life before he entered the
valley. As well as these references to events prior to the
start of the diary, there are also flashbacks within the
timescale of the diary, when Ann has been unable or
unwilling to write for a day or more, and she has to tell
us what has happened since her last diary entry.

This leads us to the use of **hooklines** (see Literary
Terms), which the author uses throughout the novel in
order to keep the reader in suspense. The very first
sentence of the novel is an example: 'I am afraid' (p. 5).
Robert O'Brien continues this device with page-turning

regularity, for example: 'Now it is night. He is in my house' (p. 24); 'I am in terrible trouble. Mr Loomis *shot* me' (p 211). On these occasions the reader is drawn into the narrative, as Ann tells the reader what has happened in the lead-up to each event. We are in suspense as to what has occurred.

Suspense and tension

Suspense and tension are formidable qualities of the novel. We really want to know what happens to Ann. But seeing the events through Ann's eyes only serves to heighten the tension, as we can never be sure what Mr Loomis is thinking. We are with Ann all of the time, we side with her, and we also worry and fear with her.

The **first-person narrative** (see Literary Terms) creates uncertainty and ambiguity. If the story were told in the third person by an all-seeing narrator, the reader might know, for example, who the approaching stranger is and what Loomis's plans and motivations are. In many ways, it is more exciting and more 'real' when we do not know. For example, when Loomis drops his stick, we are no more knowledgeable than Ann as to whether it was done on purpose or if it was an accident.

Prophecies

Throughout the novel, linked to the idea of dreams and premonitions, Ann is aware of dangers which later become prophetically true. Will Loomis be mad, or bad, or cruel? He becomes so. Will Faro give Ann away? He nearly does. Might Loomis make her his slave? He tries to.

The first words of the novel are 'I am afraid', the last words are 'I am hopeful'. There is a sense of an almost religious journey about the progress of the novel; the Bible tells us the greatest sin is despair, and Ann never succumbs to this, despite all that happens to her.

ANN BURDEN

Ann Burden, at the beginning of the novel, is fifteen years of age, and she believes she is the only person left alive in the world. This is an extraordinary situation in which to find oneself at any age, and how she copes when a man appears in her valley and threatens her existence is the essence of the story.

Ann has lived through a nuclear war. Her parents and brother and cousin have all gone off, looking for life, and they have never returned. She has been alone for over a year, having heard grown men break down on the radio and having decided that outside the valley is just deadness. Many people might have given in to despair, fallen apart, and given up on life. But Ann Burden, as we come to find out, is an extraordinary human being, one who **symbolises** (see Literary Terms) the spirit and hope, the positive virtues of humanity. Far from giving up, she has used the farming knowledge, common sense and practicality with which her upbringing has provided her. She has created for herself a haven of life in the middle of the wilderness, living a dignified and hopeful existence.

When she spies a stranger approaching she does not immediately reveal her presence. She is careful, prudent and wise beyond her years. She knows men can be cruel as well as kind. She is sensible enough to be able to give up her almost cosy existence, dig up her vegetable garden and hide in the cave when the stranger enters the valley, so as to allow herself time to judge the motivations and character of the newcomer.

In appearance we know she is skinny, but 'not as skinny as I used to be' (p. 22). She keeps her hair cut off straight around the neck and she keeps it clean. She retains her dignity and dresses in a practical way, using the clothes available to her from the store.

Practical
Caring
Optimistic
Sensitive

Ann's behaviour does represent all the good and
decent traits of humankind, the characteristics which
perhaps set us apart from animals. Her upbringing
has ensured this. Ann has a spiritual and emotional
depth which is truly admirable. She prays, and visits
the church; she enjoys playing the piano, especially
hymns. When there was a future outside the valley she
had considered becoming a nurse or a teacher. She
genuinely cares for people and wants to help them.

She becomes a nurse in an unforeseen way when
Loomis becomes ill. She takes excellent care of him,
working out what to do with a combination of
experience and common sense. Despite starting to
suspect that Loomis is a murderer, she continues
to care for him. She retains the Christian values of
hope and forgiveness, and attempts to understand and
justify his actions. She always thinks things through
logically and methodically, whether it be the planting
of the crops, the husbandry of the animals, or the
reasons behind Loomis's shooting of Edward.

Ann has a deep respect for life. She is not against the
killing of animals for food, but when she contemplates
shooting Faro so as to secure her own safety, she cannot
pull the trigger – she considers herself to be a murderer
for even thinking about such an action. When she has
the chance to kill Loomis, she would rather die herself
than do so.

Ann finds optimism in nature. As she is ploughing, she
feels like singing. She recites poetry to herself, and
watches crows in the sky. She finds apple blossom and
dreams of a marriage to Loomis.

She dreams of having children, but all this comes to
nothing as Loomis's behaviour becomes more and more
tyrannical. Even when Loomis's desire for domination
becomes intolerable, even when he has attempted to
rape her and control her, Ann's morality does not come

into question. She still feels a responsibility towards his well-being, meticulously sharing the food and provisions.

Ann knows the value of communication. She tries to talk to Loomis, to compromise with him, and he shoots her. He tries to destroy, whereas she tries to create. Even when she knows she must leave the valley and takes the suit, she feels the need to speak to Loomis one last time.

Note the number of times Ann refers to 'Poor Mr Loomis' or 'Poor Faro'.

Despite all this, the reader never thinks Ann is too good to be true. She is strong, moral and sympathetic, but Robert O'Brien succeeds in making Ann Burden a rounded character. Her surname is perhaps **symbolic** (see Literary Terms): she has many burdens to bear, and she bears them stoically. She has incredible self-control, and whenever her thoughts turn to her dead family, she strains desperately to put them out of her mind. At the end of the novel she feels she wants to hurt Loomis and she wants revenge. We have to be reminded that she is still a child, and she recognises that her last words to him are childish: 'You didn't even thank me for taking care of you when you were ill' (p. 265).

It is Ann's dreams which finally lead her out of the valley – the thought that somewhere there is another valley, with children waiting to be taught. If she finds people, she will send them for Loomis, but she cannot live with him. Ann is able to believe in dreams, and the reader is able to believe that if she finds another valley, the continuation of the human race will be in good hands if she is part of its future.

JOHN R. LOOMIS

Loomis brings death and destruction to the valley, and Ann is right to be cautious of him as he approaches.

Selfish
Violent
Reckless
Scientific

Physically he is quite attractive to Ann. When he trims his hair and beard Ann comments that 'he looks almost handsome' (p. 42). His face is long and narrow, and he has quite a big nose. He is in his early thirties.

From the start Loomis behaves in a wary manner. At first he does not sleep in the house, but this caution is understandable. It is also understandable that he should make use of what the valley provides in the way of food and resources, although the reader perhaps shares Ann's feelings of slight indignation that he should shoot her chicken. It is his manner of killing the chicken, more than anything, which shocks Ann. It is over-violent, and almost desperate – characteristics we see in Loomis to a larger extent later on.

Ann's fears about the stranger are renewed by his indiscriminate shooting at something – a rabbit? – in the bushes, but then we feel concern for him when he takes his reckless leap into Burden Creek. Despite Loomis's supposition of his own superiority later in the novel, we are shown by this big mistake that Loomis can be wrong, he can be careless; he is not infallible.

We find out that Loomis is a scientist, and that he must have been well respected to be invited to work with a Nobel prizewinner. Loomis's scientific knowledge has helped in the development of the safe-suit, which could have proved to be the salvation of the human race had it been mass-produced. His technical knowledge allows him to get the petrol pumps working again, and he makes plans to generate electricity using water power. If Loomis's scientific skills had been used in cooperation with Ann, their alliance may well have been successful and happy. However, Ann begins to realise that there is something sinister in Loomis's background, and when we find out that he is a murderer we start to see that this man could never be a compatible companion for the sensitive and moral Ann.

Ann attempts to justify Loomis's murder of Edward.
There is some logic in her argument that he may have
been acting for the benefit of the world as a whole, but
in the light of Loomis's totally selfish behaviour
towards Ann later, this seems unlikely. As Loomis
becomes well again, he becomes overbearing and
domineering to the level of tyranny.

Just as the author lets us appreciate Ann as a rounded
individual, we cannot be allowed to look on Loomis as
merely the evil force which descends on the valley.
When Ann asks him if he wants her to play the piano,
he is extremely enthusiastic. When she has finished, he
tells her 'This is the best evening I have ever spent'
(p. 81). Loomis reveals his vulnerability when Ann asks
him if he means his best night since the war. He spoils
the atmosphere by responding angrily, 'You heard me
… I said "ever"' (p. 81). Loomis states that he comes
from a poor background, but it is evident that his
background has been spiritually, emotionally and
culturally deprived; he has not just been poor in
material terms.

Loomis attaches no importance to Ann's artistic and spiritual needs

Thus when Ann suggests using the suit to go to
Ogdentown for books, Loomis asserts that the suit
cannot be risked for such a trivial purpose. He cannot
see the importance of the arts, nor can he recognise
Ann's need for some spiritual dimension in her life. He
mocks her church-going and praying, and he has no
real respect for the natural world or any life other than
his own. To broaden the picture, he is representative of
the society which can allow itself to be destroyed by
nuclear weapons and nerve gas, a **symbol** (see Literary
Terms) of the contemporary man.

Loomis cannot cope with the awful predicament in
which he finds himself. He lacks Ann's inner resources.
However, it is difficult to make any excuse for his
attempt to rape Ann, or his later attempt to shoot her.

He refuses or is unable to see her goodness in caring for him when he was ill and bringing him provisions when she was living in the cave. Loomis tries to possess and rule Ann; when she hides in the cave he tries to hunt her down; and when this fails he tries to starve her into submission.

When Ann plays Loomis at his own game and takes the safe-suit, Loomis reveals himself to be 'frightened and bewildered' (p. 265). His penultimate words betray his desperation: 'Don't go … Don't leave me here alone' (p. 265). Loomis's final words, however, give the reader hope that he is heading towards some sort of salvation. He indicates the birds to the west, a gesture at odds with the selfishness he has displayed up until now. We do not know why he does this but perhaps some of Ann's goodness and selflessness has rubbed off on Loomis, just as he brought spiritual contamination to the valley.

FARO

Compare Loomis's treatment of Faro to his treatment of Ann.

Faro was Ann's cousin David's dog. He returns to the house soon after Loomis's arrival, having gone missing, presumably in search of David, when the rest of the family left the valley. When he comes back he is in a very bad condition, thin, and with half the hair gone from his left side.

At first Faro is wary of Loomis, just like Ann, but Loomis feeds him chicken to win his confidence. Then Faro picks up Ann's trail and follows it to the cave. Ann fears that the dog will give her away, a concern that later proves to be well founded.

Loomis keeps Faro prisoner, tied up with an electric cable that the dog cannot chew through. Then he uses Faro to track Ann and to try to find her hiding place in the cave. Faro has previously saved Ann from Loomis's attempted rape, by barking as Loomis approached the bed. And the dog has accompanied Ann around the farm and on her visits to the church. It is these attachments, together with Ann's respect for life, which prevent her from shooting Faro when the dog is a real source of danger to her.

Faro later dies by leaping into the contaminated stream, and this prompts Ann to put her plan for leaving the valley into action.

MINOR CHARACTERS – THE DEAD

Ann's family   Those people who have died are important to the background of the story. Ann's father and mother have provided her with the upbringing which allows her to be able to survive both physically and mentally in the desperate situations in which she finds herself. Obviously stoical and moral, they brought up Ann, her brother Joseph and her cousin David, who had moved in about five years before when his father had died, leaving him an orphan. Ann's parents taught her practical skills and imbued her with a strong sense of right and wrong, a love of the arts and nature, and common sense.

The Kleins   The Kleins, who ran the store, have left Ann an important source of food, provisions and clothing. Ann has only once ventured, guiltily, into their living quarters, in search of books. But she found none, only a sense of a clean and well-ordered household that perhaps too had suffered loss, judging from the photograph of a son or brother which was lying on the bed, probably the last thing they had looked at before venturing out of the valley to their own deaths.

Edward   Edward's situation has been a foretaste of Ann's. He too wanted the suit, he too faced Loomis's desire for control, and he too faced Loomis's gun; but Edward, unlike Ann, dies as a result of this.

Notice how the narrative style adapts itself to the action being described.

As the novel takes the form of the diary of a teenager, it would be unconvincing if it were written in a high literary style. Robert O'Brien does well to make Ann's journal completely believable, and the **hooklines** and **flashbacks** (see Literary Terms), far from seeming unnatural, seem totally realistic.

There is, therefore, no extensive use of metaphor or simile, but certain things and objects do take on a **symbolic** (see Literary Terms) meaning. Birds are an obvious example. Ann states that she has always thoughts that birds bring good luck, and she actually tells us on page 135 that she sees them as symbols of optimism. Thus when she finds the baby crow she sees it as a good omen; when the war began the birds disappeared; and at the end of the novel Loomis points out that he has seen birds to the west, indicating hope for Ann's journey. The crabapple tree and the apple blossom are also used symbolically. At first, Ann sees the crabapple tree in full bloom, another sign of hope which brings about thoughts of marriage. She takes some of the blossom into the house and places it in Loomis's bedroom, but later it dies, as do Ann's hopes of a future with Loomis. The apple blossom is sweet-smelling but its fruit is sour.

Ann's love of nature is reflected in her writing.

There is symbolism too in other aspects of nature, such as the contrast of the green of the valley with the wilderness outside, and the two streams, one bringing poison into the valley from outside, as Loomis in a sense does, the other emanating from within the valley, good and pure like Ann. Many objects take on a symbolic significance, for example the guns representing Loomis's violence.

Description in *Z for Zachariah* follows on from Ann's desire to explain. Overall, the style of the novel is matter-of-fact and in some ways understated, underlining Ann's common sense and practicality.

PART FOUR

STUDY SKILLS

HOW TO USE QUOTATIONS

One of the secrets of success in writing essays is the way you use quotations. There are five basic principles:

- Put inverted commas at the beginning and end of the quotation
- Write the quotation exactly as it appears in the original
- Do not use a quotation that repeats what you have just written
- Use the quotation so that it fits into your sentence
- Keep the quotation as short as possible

Quotations should be used to develop the line of thought in your essays. Your comment should not duplicate what is in your quotation. For example:

Ann thinks that by tapping his stick, Loomis is trying to frighten her: 'maybe he is trying to frighten me'.

Far more effective is to write:

When Loomis taps his stick, Ann thinks 'maybe he is trying to frighten me'.

The most sophisticated way of using the writer's words is to embed them into your sentence:

When Ann confronts Loomis for the final time, the reader realises, with her, that he has become 'frightened and bewildered'.

When you use quotations in this way, you are demonstrating the ability to use text as evidence to support your ideas - not simply including words from the original to prove you have read it.

Everyone writes differently. Work through the suggestions given here and adapt the advice to suit your own style and interests. This will improve your essay-writing skills and allow your personal voice to emerge.

The following points indicate in ascending order the skills of essay writing:

- Picking out one or two facts about the story and adding the odd detail
- Writing about the text by retelling the story
- Retelling the story and adding a quotation here and there
- Organising an answer which explains what is happening in the text and giving quotations to support what you write

....

- Writing in such a way as to show that you have thought about the intentions of the writer of the text and that you understand the techniques used
- Writing at some length, giving your viewpoint on the text and commenting by picking out details to support your views
- Looking at the text as a work of art, demonstrating clear critical judgement and explaining to the reader of your essay how the enjoyment of the text is assisted by literary devices, linguistic effects and psychological insights; showing how the text relates to the time when it was written

The dotted line above represents the division between lower and higher level grades. Higher-level performance begins when you start to consider your response as a reader of the text. The highest level is reached when you offer an enthusiastic personal response and show how this piece of literature is a product of its time.

Coursework essay

Set aside an hour or so at the start of your work to plan what you have to do.

- List all the points you feel are needed to cover the task. Collect page references of information and quotations that will support what you have to say. A helpful tool is the highlighter pen: this saves painstaking copying and enables you to target precisely what you want to use.

- Focus on what you consider to be the main points of the essay. Try to sum up your argument in a single sentence, which could be the closing sentence of your essay. Depending on the essay title, it could be a statement about a character: Ann's morality, practicality and fairness have helped her to survive, and these qualities give us hope for the survival of the human race; an opinion about setting: Burden Valley is like a Garden of Eden, set amidst the wilderness, but it is tainted by the outside world and so Ann must leave; or a judgement on a theme: An important theme of *Z for Zachariah* is the struggle between good and evil which goes on within all human beings, but it is too simplistic to say that Ann is totally good and Loomis totally evil.

- Make a short essay plan. Use the first paragraph to introduce the argument you wish to make. In the following paragraphs develop this argument with details, examples and other possible points of view. Sum up your argument in the last paragraph. Check you have answered the question.

- Write the essay, remembering all the time the central point you are making.

- On completion, go back over what you have written to eliminate careless errors and improve expression. Read it aloud to yourself, or, if you are feeling more confident, to a relative or friend.

If you can, try to type your essay using a word processor. This will allow you to correct and improve your writing without spoiling its appearance.

Examination essay   The essay written in an examination often carries more marks than the coursework essay even though it is written under considerable time pressure.

In the revision period build up notes on various aspects of the text you are using. Fortunately, in acquiring this set of York Notes on *Z for Zachariah*, you have made a prudent beginning! York Notes are set out to give you vital information and help you to construct your personal overview of the text.

Make notes with appropriate quotations about the key issues of the set text. Go into the examination knowing your text and having a clear set of opinions about it.

In the examination   In most English Literature examinations you can take in copies of your set books. This is an enormous advantage although it may lull you into a false sense of security. Beware! There is simply not enough time in an examination to read the book from scratch.

- Read the question paper carefully and remind yourself what you have to do
- Look at the questions on your set texts to select the one that most interests you and mentally work out the points you wish to stress
- Remind yourself of the time available and how you are going to use it
- Briefly map out a short plan in note form that will keep your writing on track and illustrate the key argument you want to make.
- Then set about writing it
- When you have finished, check through to eliminate errors

To summarise, these are keys to success
- **Know the text**
- **Have a clear understanding of and opinions on the storyline, characters, setting, themes and writer's concerns**
- **Select the right material**
- **Plan and write a clear response, continually bearing the question in mind**

A typical essay question on *Z for Zachariah* is followed by a sample essay plan in note form. This does not present the only answer to the question, so do not be afraid to include your own ideas, or exclude some of the following. Remember that quotations are essential to prove and illustrate the points you make.

Consider how the themes of life and death are relevant to an understanding of *Z for Zachariah*.

Introduction   Life and death are essential elements in the novel. The war has caused death. As far as Ann knows she is the only person left alive on earth – until Loomis appears. Ann's struggle for life has been successful up until Loomis's arrival. After he arrives it soon becomes a struggle not against the effects of the war, but against him.

Part 1   Ann by herself.
- Ann has coped exceptionally well in harrowing circumstances.
- She has survived but her family have died, as have the Kleins, the Amish, the people on the radio, probably everyone in the world. Although sad, Ann has coped mentally, through her toughness of spirit and practicality.
- The valley has survived, allowing Ann to eat fresh food, drink fresh water, and make use of the provisions in the store.

Part 2   Loomis arrives.
- Just as Burden Creek brings poison into the valley and destroys all it touches, Loomis comes from outside the valley and brings violence and death.
- He seems careless with life; uses his gun in a reckless manner. Then he is careless with his own life and comes near death because of his bath in the polluted stream.

- Ann respects all life and does what she can to preserve it (e.g. nursing Loomis, saving the baby crow, tending to crops and animals). When she considers killing Faro she brands herself a murderer because of the very thought.
- We find out that Loomis is a murderer; he puts his life before all others. He envisages the foundation of a 'colony' whereas Ann hoped for 'marriage'.
- He enslaves Faro and tries to enslave Ann. He attempts to rape Ann and shoots her. He tries to starve her into submission even when she has shared everything with him.
- Ann cannot bring herself to kill Loomis when she has the chance. Loomis points Ann towards signs of life, and Ann walks off through the wasteland.

Part 3   Spiritual life.

- Part of what divides us from the animals is our ability to appreciate the spiritual and aesthetic. Ann has this quality whereas Loomis appears not to – e.g. sneers at her love of church and prayer; uses Ann's love of music and reading to try to entrap her.
- Ann's dreams of life in some other valley give her the courage to leave the life of the valley and venture out into the deadness.
- Loomis's change of attitude at the end gives us hope of life in the future; but mainly we rely on Ann to be fundamental to the survival of humankind.

Conclusion   Despite the war and the deaths of all those close to her, Ann is able to survive. She possesses life-affirming qualities. Loomis presents many of the negative traits of human beings, but, at the end of the novel, through his contact with Ann he begins to show signs of positive behaviour.

When Ann leaves the valley, she walks westward looking for life, and this gives hope to the reader for the survival of the human race.

1 To what extent does the environment play a part in the story of *Z for Zachariah*?

2 The final words of the novel are 'I am hopeful'. What has Ann to be hopeful about?

3 How much do the backgrounds of Ann and Loomis play a part in their ability to cope with the unique circumstances in which they find themselves?

4 What is the significance of the title *Z for Zachariah*?

5 What do you think are the main differences between Ann Burden and John Loomis?

6 Imagine that Loomis kept a diary from the time Ann left the house following his attempt to rape her. Write his diary entries from this point to the time after Ann has left the valley.

7 Ann Burden has an artistic nature; John Loomis's career has been rooted in science. How could these differences have been helpful to them if they had been able to live together in harmony? Why do you think it goes wrong?

8 How does the diary format affect your view of the characters and events in the novel?

9 What part do dreams play in *Z for Zachariah*?

10 Write about violence in *Z for Zachariah*.

11 What part do animals and birds play in *Z for Zachariah*?

12 What is your opinion of Loomis?

PART FIVE

CULTURAL CONNECTIONS

BROADER PERSPECTIVES

As an example of the science-fiction genre, *Z for Zachariah* (1974) may be compared with works by H.G. Wells, such as *The War of the Worlds* (1898) or *The Time Machine*, (1895) and glimpses into what may happen to the human race in the future are contained in novels such as *Nineteen Eighty-four* (1949) by George Orwell and *Brave New World* (1932) by Aldous Huxley. Ray Bradbury's *Fahrenheit 451* (1953) is set in a future in which books have been banned and teams of 'firemen' are sent out to burn any books they find.

When the Wind Blows (1982), a cartoon book by Raymond Briggs, looks at the consequences of nuclear war. You may be able to watch the documentary-style television play *Threads* (1983) by Barry Hines, based on the idea of a world-wide nuclear conflict.

The idea of Ann and Loomis living in an isolated, self-sufficient environment is one which finds echoes in many other stories. A starting point is the story of Adam and Eve in the Book of Genesis in the Bible, but other links are with stories set on islands, where self-sufficiency is all-important. Daniel Defoe's *Robinson Crusoe* (1719), R.M. Ballantyne's *The Coral Island* (1857) and William Golding's *Lord of the Flies* (1954) could be compared in many ways with *Z for Zachariah*.

black humour a cynical humour used despairingly in unpleasant situations

exposition the explanatory part at the beginning of a novel or play, where background information has to be passed on to the reader

first-person narrative a story told from the point of view of an 'I' character, like Ann Burden

flashbacks a jump backwards in time to fill in details which have occurred previously – a device frequently used in films, and now common in novels and plays

hookline a line, often at the beginning of a book or chapter, which 'grabs' the reader and makes him or her anxious to read on and find out what happens

irony saying one thing and meaning another – often through understatement concealment or indirect statement

motif a literary device, such as a theme, image or symbol, which recurs frequently, either throughout a body of literature or within a single work

protagonist the principal character in a story or play

symbolism the use of an object or idea to represent something else by association. For example, birds in *Z for Zachariah* can be seen as symbols of hope

TEST ANSWERS

TEST YOURSELF (Chapters 1–5)

A 1 Ann's mother *(Chapter 1)*
2 Ann's father *(Chapter 1)*
3 Loomis *(Chapter 3)*
4 Loomis *(Chapter 5)*
5 Loomis *(Chapter 5)*
6 Ann *(Chapter 1)*
7 Ann's father *(Chapter 1)*
8 Loomis *(Chapter 3)*

TEST YOURSELF (Chapters 6–10)

A 1 Loomis *(Chapter 6)*
2 Loomis *(Chapter 7)*
3 Ann *(Chapter 8)*
4 Loomis *(Chapter 10)*
5 Loomis *(Chapter 6)*
6 Ann's parents *(Chapter 6)*

TEST YOURSELF (Chapters 11–15)

A 1 Loomis *(Chapter 11)*
2 Loomis *(Chapter 11)*

3 Loomis *(Chapter 11)*
4 Ann *(Chapter 14)*
5 Loomis *(Chapter 14)*
6 Edward *(Chapter 11)*
7 Loomis *(Chapter 12)*

TEST YOURSELF (Chapters 16–20)

A 1 Loomis *(Chapter 16)*
2 Loomis *(Chapter 17)*
3 Loomis *(Chapter 20)*
4 Loomis *(Chapter 20)*
5 Loomis *(Chapter 20)*
6 Ann *(Chapter 20)*

TEST YOURSELF (Chapters 21–26)

A 1 Loomis *(Chapter 26)*
2 Ann *(Chapter 26)*
3 Ann *(Chapter 26)*
4 Ann *(Chapter 26)*
5 Mrs Klein *(Chapter 22)*
6 Loomis *(Chapter 24)*

Notes

TITLES IN THE YORK NOTES SERIES

GCSE and equivalent levels (£3.50 each)

Maya Angelou
I Know Why the Caged Bird Sings

Jane Austen
Pride and Prejudice

Harold Brighouse
Hobson's Choice

Charlotte Brontë
Jane Eyre

Emily Brontë
Wuthering Heights

Charles Dickens
David Copperfield

Charles Dickens
Great Expectations

Charles Dickens
Hard Times

George Eliot
Silas Marner

William Golding
Lord of the Flies

Willis Hall
The Long and the Short and the Tall

Thomas Hardy
Far from the Madding Crowd

Thomas Hardy
The Mayor of Casterbridge

Thomas Hardy
Tess of the d'Urbervilles

L.P. Hartley
The Go-Between

Seamus Heaney
Selected Poems

Susan Hill
I'm the King of the Castle

Barry Hines
A Kestrel for a Knave

Louise Lawrence
Children of the Dust

Harper Lee
To Kill a Mockingbird

Laurie Lee
Cider with Rosie

Arthur Miller
A View from the Bridge

Arthur Miller
The Crucible

Robert O'Brien
Z for Zachariah

George Orwell
Animal Farm

J.B. Priestley
An Inspector Calls

Willy Russell
Educating Rita

Willy Russell
Our Day Out

J.D. Salinger
The Catcher in the Rye

William Shakespeare
Henry V

William Shakespeare
Julius Caesar

William Shakespeare
Macbeth

William Shakespeare
A Midsummer Night's Dream

William Shakespeare
The Merchant of Venice

William Shakespeare
Romeo and Juliet

William Shakespeare
The Tempest

William Shakespeare
Twelfth Night

George Bernard Shaw
Pygmalion

R.C. Sherriff
Journey's End

Rukshana Smith
Salt on the snow

John Steinbeck
Of Mice and Men

R.L. Stevenson
Dr Jekyll and Mr Hyde

Robert Swindells
Daz 4 Zoe

Mildred D. Taylor
Roll of Thunder, Hear My Cry

Mark Twain
The Adventures of Huckleberry Finn

James Watson
Talking in Whispers

A Choice of Poets

Nineteenth Century Short Stories

Poetry of the First World War

Six Women Poets

Advanced level (£3.99 each)

Margaret Atwood
The Handmaid's Tale

William Blake
Songs of Innocence and of Experience

Emily Brontë
Wuthering Heights

Geoffrey Chaucer
The Wife of Bath's Prologue and Tale

Joseph Conrad
Heart of Darkness

Charles Dickens
Great Expectations

F. Scott Fitzgerald
The Great Gatsby

Thomas Hardy
Tess of the d'Urbervilles

James Joyce
Dubliners

Arthur Miller
Death of a Salesman

William Shakespeare
Antony and Cleopatra

William Shakespeare
Hamlet

William Shakespeare
King Lear

William Shakespeare
The Merchant of Venice

William Shakespeare
Romeo and Juliet

William Shakespeare
The Tempest

Mary Shelley
Frankenstein

Alice Walker
The Color Purple

Tennessee Williams
A Streetcar Named Desire

Forthcoming Titles in the Series

Jane Austen
Emma

Jane Austen
Pride and Prejudice

Charlotte Brontë
Jane Eyre

Seamus Heaney
Selected Poems

William Shakespeare
Much Ado About Nothing

William Shakespeare
Othello

John Webster
The Duchess of Malfi